ESSENTIAL
FENG SHUI

SIMON BROWN

WARD LOCK

To my father Michael John Hilton Brown

A WARD LOCK BOOK

This edition first published in the United Kingdom by
Ward Lock
Wellington House
125 Strand
London WC2R 0BB

A Cassell imprint

First published 1999
Reprinted 2000,2002

Created and produced by
CARROLL & BROWN LIMITED
20 Lonsdale Road
London NW6 6RD

The material in this edition was first published in *Practical Feng Shui* 1997

British Library Catalogue-in-Publication Data
A catalogue record for this book is available from
the British Library

ISBN 0-7063-7854-7

Reproduced by Colourscan
Printed and bound in Great Britain by Bath Press Group

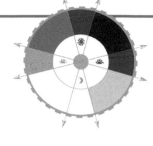

CONTENTS

FENG SHUI TODAY

Feng Shui originated in China over 4000 years ago and its practice has a long history throughout the East. Similar ideas have also existed in other parts of the world at one time or another. The notion that the 'spirit' or atmosphere of a place has an effect on your well-being is widely accepted, but in Feng Shui it has developed into a complex and integrated system of theory and practice embracing almost every aspect of people's lives.

The Chinese characters for 'Feng Shui' translate as 'wind and water'. Feng Shui is actually the art of designing your home to promote success in life, health, wealth and happiness.

The underlying premise of Feng Shui is that everything in your overall and immediate surroundings – even down to the smallest details of furnishing and decor – can either further your aims in life or work against you. By understanding the subtle currents of energy (known throughout this book as 'chi') that flow through your body and through everything in the universe, you can arrange your living and working environments to help you reach your goals.

POTENTIAL BENEFITS OF FENG SHUI

- Improved health
- More harmonious family relationships
- Better relaxation at home
- Better sleep
- More stimulating social life

- Greater opportunities for love and romance
- More active sex life
- Improved chances of becoming pregnant
- Feeling more in control
- Increased motivation

- Increased fame and respect
- Greater control over money matters
- Increased likelihood of selling a home

the PRINCIPLES of FENG SHUI

The concepts of chi energy, yin
and yang, the Five Elements and
the Eight Directions explain
how making changes to your
living space can transform your
life and fortunes.

chi energy

'Chi' is a subtle flow of electromagnetic energy which links all things in the universe. In the Far East the understanding and control of energy flows underlies traditional healing systems such as acupuncture and Shiatsu as well as martial arts like Tai Chi, Qi Kong and Aikido. The energy has several names. In China it is called Chi, in Japan it is known as Ki (also spelt Qi) and in India Prana. There are no specific words for it in the West, although expressions such as 'atmosphere', 'mood', 'life-force' or 'spirit' describe how it is perceived. In this book it is referred to as chi energy. Chi is central to Eastern astrology and Feng Shui.

Chi stays mainly within entities such as human bodies, plants or buildings, but some of it constantly flows out and some flows in from other sources. Your own personal chi energy is always mixing with the chi energy around you. In this way you are connected to the immediate environment, and ultimately to the whole universe, as ripples of chi energy from far away reach you and you send ripples back again. Exceptionally sensitive people may be able to pick up advance information from these distant sources in the form of premonitions, visions or telepathy.

WIND AND WATER

The flow of chi energy from one entity to another is the basis of Feng Shui. The chi energy you take in from your environment influences your moods, emotions, physical energy and, over time, your health. Chi energy is carried through the environment by wind, water, the sun's energy, light and sound. It moves in a similar way to these natural phenomena except that, unlike some of them, it is able to flow through solid matter. It flows in and out of buildings mainly through the doors and windows, but some chi can enter and leave through the walls. It moves like water ebbing and flowing with the tides, and like wind moving around the Earth. The basic aim of Feng Shui is to enable you to position yourself where this natural flow of chi energy helps you to realise your goals and your dreams in life.

Heaven and Earth's forces
Chi energy radiating from the planets moves towards the Earth – Heaven's force. Earth radiates chi energy that moves away from it – Earth's force.

UNIVERSAL CHI

Chi energy flows not only throughout our planet, but through the entire solar system and galaxy. Our own planet, Earth, radiates chi energy that flows out and away from the planet. This appears to us as chi energy moving upwards and is called Earth's force. At the same time, the planets surrounding Earth radiate chi energy which travels towards and into the Earth. This appears to us to move downwards and is known as Heaven's force. So the movement of chi energy on the surface of the Earth, and therefore in our homes and in our own bodies, is influenced by the Earth itself and the surrounding planets. As the position of the Earth, Sun and planets changes, so does the movement of chi energy, which in turn affects our own flow of chi energy.

As Heaven's chi reaches Earth its movement is altered by the landscape (hills, mountains, rivers), vegetation (trees, crops, grasses, bushes) and the ground itself (rocks, clay, soil, chalk). As Earth's force and Heaven's force mix across the surface of the planet, various unique flows of chi energy begin to develop. The same is true of buildings in a city. Low flat dwellings, skyscrapers, pointed roofs, domes and tree-lined avenues all determine how chi energy flows across the surface, and roads, railways, offices, factories, homes, entertainment centres, churches, graveyards and hospitals all have an influence on the nature of that energy.

CHI IN BUILDINGS

Buildings alter the flow of chi energy. Their shape, openings and the materials they are made of define the way chi energy flows through them. It moves most easily through doors and to a lesser extent through windows, so the orientation of a building to the sun and the planets will determine the kind of chi energy that enters it. This changes as the planets move through the sky, so there is a new pattern of chi energy each year, month, day and hour. Features of the immediate surroundings, such as water or roads, further determine the kind of chi energy that flows back and forth through the doors of the building. In an ideal situation chi energy flows harmoniously through the whole of a building. The design and interior decoration should enhance the kind of chi energy that furthers the aims and desires of the occupants and should exclude or minimize features that hinder them.

UNFAVOURABLE CHI ENERGIES

Some situations produce unhelpful types of chi, causing problems for a building's occupants, and even physical or mental ill-health.

NEGATIVE CHI Certain building or decorating materials have a negative effect on chi energy: synthetic fibres, synthetic building materials, artificial lighting and air conditioning all add their own artificial chi energy, which negatively influences the chi energy of the occupants, and could lead to mental and physical exhaustion.

STAGNANT CHI Slow-moving and stagnant chi energy is produced by dark corners, cluttered rooms and dampness. They can lead to a slowing down of your own chi energy, which may cause serious health problems and a loss of direction in your life.

FAST-FLOWING CHI Chi energy moving quickly in a straight line can destabilize the flow through an entire building, so long corridors, straight paths or several features in a straight line should be avoided. Fast-moving chi energy directed towards you could push away some of your own chi energy, making you feel insecure and under attack. (See also Cutting Chi below.)

Furniture
Sharp corners on furniture can cause cutting chi. Avoid them in bedrooms and near seating areas.

Neighbouring buildings
If the corner of a building points at your home, it can cause cutting chi. Plant bushes to shield the front door.

CUTTING CHI

If chi energy passes a sharp corner it begins to spin and swirl, forming eddies and whirlpools like a fast-flowing stream passing a sharp bend. This is called cutting chi and can occur inside or outside buildings. It can make your own chi energy swirl, leading to disorientation and confusion and, in time, ill-health. Plants and fabrics can be used to 'soften' sharp edges.

PERSONAL CHI

Along the centre of the body are seven concentrations of energy called chakras (see right), which are similar to large organs where blood concentrates. Spreading out from the chakras are 14 paths of chi energy known as meridians. These flow along your arms, legs, torso and head. Like blood vessels and capillaries, they take chi energy to smaller and smaller channels until each cell is nourished by both blood and chi energy.

While blood carries oxygen and nutrients, chi energy carries thoughts, emotions and your dreams in life. It also carries some of the chi energy from the environment. Therefore, what you think and where you think it, will have a direct influence on the cells in your body.

Chi energy operates as a two-way process whereby the way you think influences your chi energy, and your chi energy influences the way you think; so your environment will influence your chi energy and that change will alter the way you think and feel.

Like trees planted in the best soil for their needs, we also thrive if we are planted in an environment that has the most appropriate chi energy. By moving from one building to another, one city to another, or one country to another, you have the opportunity to change your own chi energy and therefore the way you think and feel. If the chi energy of the place where you live matches the chi energy you require for happiness, then it will have a very positive influence on your life. Unfortunately, it is also possible that your home may work against you, and the chi energy of some places could negatively affect your well-being.

Many factors affect the chi energy that comes into your body – among these are food, weather and the people you are with. In Feng Shui terms, the primary influence is the chi energy of the environment. This includes your home, your place of work and the surrounding landscape. A building itself has an influence. Being in a large ornate building such as a museum or cathedral can be inspiring, exciting and stimulating, whereas a small cosy place such as a cottage or bar is more relaxing and intimate. A building's location also helps shape the kind of chi that enters your body, as different landscapes have different kinds of chi.

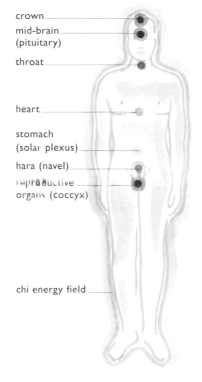

crown
mid-brain (pituitary)
throat
heart
stomach (solar plexus)
hara (navel)
reproductive organs (coccyx)

chi energy field

The chakras
Chi flows through the human body by means of channels called meridians which act rather like blood vessels. They radiate from seven key points in the body where energy concentrates, called chakras. Typically, chi extends at least 10cm and up to 1 metre outside your skin.

yin and yang

The concept of yin and yang offers a comprehensive way of looking at the world and how it affects you. It makes it possible to adjust your relationship with people and your surroundings so that you can place yourself in favourable rather than unfavourable situations. Ultimately, you will be able to use your knowledge of yin and yang to get more out of your life with less effort.

At the time of a full moon, for example, people become more yang, which means they are more active, want to go out more and are generally more sociable. Conversely, at the time of a new moon they become more yin – more peaceful, spiritual, relaxed and inward-looking. So if you want to organize a party, the days before or during the full moon are the best times. People will be more outgoing and more in the mood for a get-together. At the new moon you risk fewer people turning up and those who do will be quieter.

basic principles

EVERYTHING IS EITHER MORE YIN OR MORE YANG

Yin and yang are relative terms used to compare everything in the universe. Things are more yin or more yang depending on what they are compared with. For example, resting is more yin than working, but more yang than sleeping. Yin and yang can describe physical things or non-physical things. You need to be clear about how the terms are applied in particular cases. For example, a flame is more yang than a stone in terms of a process: the flame produces heat and light. But the structure of stone is more yang than flame: more solid and harder.

EVERYTHING SEEKS A STATE OF BALANCE

Although everything is either more yin or more yang, as an entity it seeks some kind of balance. Individually nothing is in perfect balance, nor can it be as everything is either more yin or more yang. Something that is more yin can reach a more balanced state with something that is more yang. Often we drift either side of the middle path. For a while we become more yin and then make changes that make us more yang, and vice versa.

Similar principles can be applied to your home, diet, exercise, work and leisure activities. They all have aspects that are more yin or more yang, and you can encourage them to work for you or against you depending on your needs at the time.

GLOBAL YIN AND YANG

The position of the sun and moon, and the seasons make you feel more yin or yang, and you instinctively adjust your lifestyle to keep a balance.

Yin and yang in time
The environment is most yang at midday, in high summer and at full moon. It is most yin at midnight, in midwinter and at the new moon.

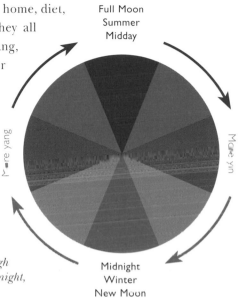

Full Moon
Summer
Midday

More yang

More yin

Midnight
Winter
New Moon

YIN AND YANG ATTRACT EACH OTHER

Things that are more yin attract other things that are more yang, rather like the poles of a magnet. As you become more yin you attract things that are more yang into your life and vice versa. A simple example is that by eating something more yang, such as dry salty snacks, you begin to crave liquids, which are more yin. An extreme of yin or yang will attracts its extreme opposite. For example, someone who becomes very yang — angry or aggressive — may end up in a very yin state — confined in hospital or prison (because of an accident or crime).

NOTHING IS WHOLLY YIN OR WHOLLY YANG

Everything has some yin and some yang. Nothing is entirely one thing or the other, though everything will be more one thing or another. It is better to think of yin and yang in terms of varying shades of grey, rather than black and white. Even the most ruthless criminal will have a tender spot just as the gentlest person will have known frustration and anger. There is always something positive in a negative situation just as there is something negative in a positive situation.

EVERYTHING CHANGES

The relationships between things that are more yin and things that are more yang are constantly changing. Everything is always moving from being more yang to being more yin or more yin to more yang. For example a person might be more yang — irritable, frustrated and pushy — but in the process of becoming more yin — relaxed, peaceful and calm. In the long term the direction you are going is more important than where you are now.

YIN AND YANG IN THE HOME

The sun's movement through the sky alters the flow of chi energy through your home. As the sun rises through the sky from morning to midday, the east, south-east and south of your home will become energized by more yang chi energy. In the southern hemisphere this will be the east, north-east and north of your home. After midday as the sun descends in the sky, the west, north-west and north of your home are energized by more yin chi energy. In the southern hemisphere this will be the west, south-west and south.

To check these directions, take a compass and stand in the centre of your home. Move around until you have a consistent compass reading. The needle of your compass will be pointing north. Alternatively, watch the sun move through the sky. Wait until it reaches the highest point. If you are in the northern hemisphere the sun is now south of your home; in the southern hemisphere it will be to the north.

The sunny side of your home is better for activities that require you to be more yang. The shady side is better for those that require you to be more yin. If you are already too yin or too yang, spend more time in a place that has the opposite type of chi energy in order to become more balanced. For example, if you get angry quickly and have difficulty relaxing you could be too yang and should spend more time in the yin side of your home. If you move your bedroom to a yin part of the building you will be taking in more peaceful yin chi energy as you sleep and this will counter your more yang tendencies when you get angry.

On the other hand, if you feel tired, depressed and tearful you could be too yin. Work or do things in the sunny side of your home to take in more yang chi energy. The effect of yin and yang on the different parts of your home will also influence how you allocate the various rooms there.

Yin and yang shapes
Tall thin and long narrow buildings are more yin, low squat buildings in compact shapes such as squares, circles and octagons are more yang.

PERSONAL YIN AND YANG

People can be more yin or more yang. More yin people tend to be relaxed, physically supple, sensitive, creative and imaginative. However, if they are too yin, they can be lethargic, slow and prone to depression. Conversely, more yang people tend to be alert, quick, more active, and more able to concentrate and pay attention to detail. If they are too yang they can become tense and irritable, angry or physically stiff and tight.

ARE YOU TOO YIN OR TOO YANG?

One way to assess this is to compare yourself to other people. When you are too yin, other people will seem more aggressive, irritable and impatient with you. They will want you to hurry, while you want to relax and take things easy. When you are too yang, you will find other people slow, indecisive and quiet. You may find yourself becoming irritable and angry with them. Some people are always more yin than most people, some are always more yang, and others will be more in the middle.

With an understanding of yin and yang you can adjust these natural tendencies to your advantage by tailoring your diet (macrobiotics is specially designed for this) and lifestyle. If you find it difficult to concentrate, for example, and your work is suffering, decide first if you are too yin or too yang. Concentration is a more yang activity, so a lack of it suggests you are too yin. The solution would be to avoid more yin foods such as alcohol, sugar and coffee, and include some mineral-rich yang foods, such as root vegetables, fish and natural soya sauce.

Yin and yang food
Eating the right kinds of food can help balance your personal levels of yin and yang. The foods above range from the most yang (salt and meat) at the top to the most yin (liquids and sugars) at the bottom.

yin and yang in your home

The shapes, materials and colours of objects you put in your home make the chi energy there more yin or more yang. This provides you with ways to alter the chi energy of your home to suit your needs.

SHAPES

Rounded shapes are generally considered to be more yin than straight-sided shapes – a long thin curved table is more yin than a rectangular table. A circle is the exception because, although it is rounded, it is also the most compact shape and is therefore more yang. Objects that are compact with straight or angular lines are also more yang in shape.

COLOURS

Colours have a great influence on yin and yang by reflecting different frequencies of light back into the room. People react to colours in a very personal way, but in general red, orange and bright yellow make us feel more yang, greens and blues more yin. Pastel shades of any colour are more yin than stronger brighter shades of that colour. The larger the area covered by a particular colour the greater its influence will be. Even small touches of strong bright colours, such as scarlet or purple, however, can be effective.

MORE YANG
SHAPES
Circular
Octagonal
Square
Broad rectangle
Broad oval
Long thin rectangle
Thin and wavy
MORE YIN
SHAPES

MORE YANG
COLOURS
Red
Orange
Yellow
Green
Blue
MORE YIN
COLOURS

MORE YANG
FLOORS
Marble
Stone
Hardwoods
Softwoods
Cork tiles
Rush matting
Rugs
Carpets
MORE YIN
FLOORS

Yin and yang objects
*Colour can make things more yin
(blues, greens) or more yang (reds,
oranges, yellows).*

A painting which includes a patch of brilliant red can change the chi energy of an entire room.

MATERIALS

What things are made of – especially the type of material and finish of their surfaces – encourages either a quicker more yang flow of chi energy or a slower more yin flow. Generally, hard and shiny, reflective surfaces such as glass, polished marble or stainless steel speed up the flow of chi energy, whereas soft, matt or textured surfaces such as natural wood and fabric slow it down.

MORE YANG WINDOW TREATMENTS	MORE YANG FURNISHINGS	MORE YANG MATERIALS
Shutters	Stone sculptures	Glass
Metal slatted blinds	Mirrors	Marble
Wooden slatted blinds	Varnished paintings	Granite
Paper blinds	Metal furniture	Polished stone
Cloth blinds	Hardwood furniture	Unpolished stone
Short curtains	Softwood furniture	Shiny metal
Unlined long curtains	Paper screens	Dull metal
Full draped curtains	Upholstered furniture	Polished hardwoods
MORE YIN WINDOW TREATMENTS	Tapestries	Natural hardwoods
	Large cushions	Polished softwoods
	MORE YIN FURNISHINGS	Natural softwoods
		Wicker
		Fabric
		MORE YIN MATERIALS

five elements

The Five Elements are associated with five directions that are related to the movement of the sun. In the morning the east of your home soaks up the upward chi, known as tree energy. As the day progresses, the sun moves from east to south so that the south of your home radiates with fire energy. Later, the sun starts to set and brings more settled soil chi energy into the south-west and centre of your home. As the sun sets, the west of your home takes in inward-moving metal chi energy. During the night, the north of your home benefits from flowing water chi energy.

These five energies are taken into your home most intensively at the relevant times of day and remain there until recharged again the following day. So the east of your home, for example, will always be charged to some extent with tree energy regardless of the time of day.

The Five Elements are also found in your home in their pure form. Tree energy is there in the form of wood, paper and tall plants; fire in the form of stoves, fireplaces and lighting; soil in the form of china, clay

five-element chi energies

The concept of the Five Elements is a refinement of the principle of yin and yang. Instead of two types of chi energy, there are five: tree, fire, soil, metal and water.

Tree *Imagine walking down a tree-lined path in the early morning in spring as the sun starts to rise. The overriding feeling is of energy moving up, like the branches of a tree reaching up into the sky. The tree is coming into leaf.*

Fire *It is the middle of a hot summer's day. Nature is in full bloom. The tree is in full leaf. Bright light and colourful flowers fill the picture. The energy seems to expand in every direction, radiating like the heat of a glowing fire.*

and plaster; metal in the form of iron, silver, stainless steel and other metals; water in the form of fountains, sinks, bathrooms and aquariums.

SHAPES, COLOURS AND MATERIALS

The Five Elements are associated with shapes, colours and materials (see chart on page 18) and, in this way, can be introduced into your home and applied to the building itself. Wallpaper with vertical stripes, for example, will bring more uplifting tree chi energy, making the ceiling appear higher and the room taller. Strong colours like red and black will be effective even when they cover a relatively small surface area, such as a vase of red flowers. Similarly, the material your furniture is made of – wood or metal, for example – will adjust the atmosphere.

These effects will be especially intense if you combine colours with particular patterns or materials. For example, green wallpaper with vertical stripes would represent tree energy and so on. This ability to manipulate the existing chi energy using the Five Elements is the basis of many Feng Shui remedies.

Soil *Think of an afternoon in early autumn. The leaves have changed colour and are beginning to fall. The sun is getting lower in the sky. The overall feeling is of energy moving down into the ground.*

Metal *It is evening in late autumn. As the red sun sinks below the horizon the feeling is of energy gathering in, and nature storing up its energy ready for the winter. Energy is moving inwards and becoming solid.*

Water *Imagine a damp, frosty night in midwinter. All is still on the surface, but powerful changes are taking place below the soil and there are strong currents of water beneath the ice. Water is calm on the surface but flowing beneath.*

FIVE ELEMENT	SHAPES/COLOURS		MATERIALS	MEANING
TREE East/South-east	rectangular tall thin vertical	green	wood wicker rush bamboo paper	life growth vitality activity
FIRE South	pointed star serrated triangular pyramid diamond zigzag	red	(plastic is the material associated with fire chi energy, but is not recommended for use in the home because of its negative effects on chi energy – see also page 78)	passion warmth excitement expression
SOIL South-west/Centre/ North-east	squat low flat wide check horizontal	yellow brown	plaster china clay ceramic brick natural fibres softer stone (e.g. limestone)	comfort security steadiness caution
METAL West/North-west	round domed arched oval circular spherical	white gold silver	stainless steel brass silver bronze copper iron gold	richness solidity leadership organization
WATER North	irregular curved chaotic wavy amorphous	black	glass	depth power flexibility tranquillity

FIVE-ELEMENT RELATIONSHIPS

Two flows of chi energy govern the relationships between the Five Elements: the support cycle and the destructive or control cycle. These can be compared to the annual agricultural cycle as each of the Five Elements relates to a particular season: water to winter, tree to spring, fire to summer, soil to early autumn, metal to late autumn.

WATER Winter is when the ground is prepared and seeds are planted. If spring is fine, the seeds grow. But if there are late frosts, new shoots are destroyed. Water supports tree, but if tree is deficient, water destroys fire. Think of water feeding a tree, but extinguishing fire.

TREE If spring goes well, the fields are full of crops in summer. But if summer is poor due to lack of sun or heavy rains, the crops rot in the ground in the early autumn. Tree supports fire, as wood is fuel but, if fire is deficient, tree destroys soil.

FIRE After a good summer the crops ripen in early autumn. If the weather is cold and cloudy in early autumn, the crops will not ripen in time for the late autumn harvest. Fire supports soil just as ash enriches the earth but, if soil is deficient, fire can destroy metal.

SOIL Plenty of sun in early autumn means a good harvest. But early frosts or heavy rain in late autumn destroys the harvest and there are no new seeds to plant in the winter. Soil supports metal just as minerals in the soil form metal ores, but if metal is deficient, soil will destroy water.

METAL If the crop has set seed in the late autumn and conditions in winter are good, the seed can be planted for the following spring. But harsh winter conditions may destroy the seed before it can to sprout. Metal supports water, but if water is deficient metal will destroy tree.

5 ELEMENT	SUPPORTS	DESTROYS	DRAINS
WATER	tree	fire (if tree is weak)	metal
TREE	fire	soil (if fire is weak)	water
FIRE	soil	metal (if soil is weak)	tree
SOIL	metal	water (if metal is weak)	fire
METAL	water	tree (if water is weak)	soil

USING THE FIVE ELEMENTS

The Five Elements and the relationships between them provide a model for understanding the universe and the interaction of the different types of chi energy. They can be used to manipulate the flow of chi in your home and are the basis of many Feng Shui remedies and solutions. Depending on what you are trying to achieve or what problem you are trying to solve, you can enhance one type of Five Element chi energy, calm another or maintain a balance by introducing objects associated with the relevant elements (see below) into the appropriate space.

Five-Element chi energies can be introduced into a space in pure form – actual plants, fire, soil, metal or water – or in the form of representative objects. The most powerful objects are those which combine the shape, colour and material of an element (for example, round, silver, metal balls for metal energy, or a low, brown, terracotta trough filled with brown earth for soil energy).

introducing five-element objects

Water
Use clean fresh water itself, glass objects or things that are black or irregular in shape. Those above include glass dishes and pebbles, black wavy stems and fabric.

Tree
Use actual plants, wood or paper and tall, thin green objects. Those above include a green pot, a tall green vase, tall lamp with paper shade and green frame.

Suppose you have a room in the south of your home, and you wish to increase the chi energy there to feel more expressive. The south is linked with fire chi energy. Fire is supported by tree energy. So you can boost the chi energy of the south by building up fire energy itself or by adding supportive tree energy. Fire energy is linked with pointed shapes, the colour red, lights and fire itself, so to boost it introduce candles, red star-patterned wallpaper and bright lights into the room.

Tree chi energy is linked with tall thin rectangular shapes, the colour green and materials wood and paper. Trees and tall plants are the element itself so tall plants, green vertical-striped wallpaper, wooden floors and a paper screen all increase tree chi energy in the room.

To reduce the chi energy in a southern room you would need to bolster the Five-Element chi energy that is draining to fire, namely soil. Low clay sculptures, the colour yellow, and low spreading plants growing in plenty of soil would bring more soil chi energy into the room.

Fire
Use fire itself and red or pointed objects. Those above include an oil lamp, star-shaped candle holders, a red star, red flowers in a red vase and red fabric.

Soil
Use soil or clay itself and yellow or brown or low rectangular objects. Those above include a clay trough, yellow flowers, a square plate, frame and checked fabric.

Metal
Use metal itself and round, silver, gold or white objects. Those above include a round metal frame, a round metal pot, a round wire tray and silvery balls.

eight directions

The principle of the Eight Directions takes yin and yang and the Five Elements a step further by identifying eight different kinds of chi energy. These eight different kinds of chi energy are each associated with the eight directions of the compass. Each direction is also linked with a trigram from the *I Ching* (see below), a Five Element, a symbol of the natural world, a colour, a time of day and a season. Together these all produce a detailed picture of the type of chi energy found in that particular direction.

TRIGRAMS The author of an ancient Chinese philosophical text called the *I Ching* devised the trigrams. Each trigram consists of three broken or solid lines (representing yin and yang respectively), symbolizing a particular combination of energies. For example, the trigram for water is a solid line at the centre with a broken line above and below. The lines represent an energy that is outwardly flexible and quiet (yin) but with deep strength inside (yang).

FIVE ELEMENTS Each direction and the centre is linked to at least one of the Five Elements (see pages 16–21). The north and south each have their own Five Element, the other directions all share a Five Element.

SYMBOLS Where two directions share a Five Element, they each have a different symbol. For example, the east and south-east share Five Element tree, so they each have a different symbol: thunder in the east and wind in the south-east.

COLOUR Each direction and the centre has a colour associated with it. The colours of the east, south-east and centre are the same as those linked with the Five Elements; the rest are different.

TIME OF DAY This is determined by the time when the sun is in the relevant direction. The chi energy there is strongest at that time, so the chi energy in the south of your home is strongest at midday.

SEASON Each direction is linked with a season and this is when the chi energy there will be strongest. For example, chi energy in the south of your home is strongest in midsummer.

CHI OF THE CENTRE This ninth type of chi energy holds the greatest power, implying greater possibilities, but also greater risks. It is changeable with two extremes: productive and destructive. It is linked with the Five Element soil, the number five and the colour yellow.

the eight types of chi energy

A distinctive type of energy is found in different sectors of a home, room or landscape. These sectors are defined by their direction from the centre of the home, room or landscape, which is determined by an ordinary compass (see pages 26–30). A room in the north of your home, for example, could hold the chi energy of the north, but different parts of that room also hold elements of chi energies of the other directions. Eight Directions chi energies include yin and yang, the Five Elements, and the other associations defined opposite. The diagram below summarizes the general picture and the chart overleaf describes the implications for each type of chi energy in detail.

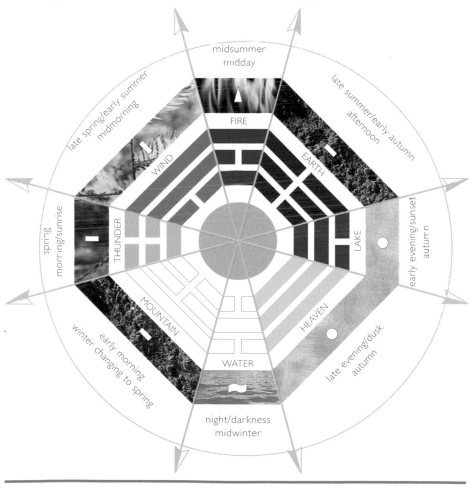

midsummer
midday

FIRE

late spring/early summer
midmorning

late summer/early autumn
afternoon

WIND

EARTH

spring
morning/sunrise

THUNDER

LAKE

early evening/sunset
autumn

MOUNTAIN

HEAVEN

winter
winter changing to spring
early morning

late evening/dusk
autumn

WATER

night/darkness
midwinter

DIRECTION	CHI ENERGY
NORTH ⬚⬚ **Trigram** yin/yang/yin ⬚⬚ **Five Element** water **Symbol** water **Colour** off-white **Time of day** night/darkness **Season** midwinter	North represents conception – life beginning – when the child begins to develop its individual characteristics in its mother's womb, almost independent of the outside world. On the surface all seems quiet, but inside powerful changes are taking place. The chi energy is quiet and most active at night and in midwinter. It relates to sex, spirituality and isolation. Water chi energy also implies depth and movement with flexibility. It can change direction easily, but this is done in a less disruptive way than with other types of chi energy. Off-white has an almost translucent quality most easily produced with a gloss finish.
NORTH-EAST **Trigram** yang/yin/yin **Five Element** soil **Symbol** mountain **Colour** brilliant white **Time of day** early morning **Season** winter changing to spring	This is when the child learns to interact with the world. It develops individuality, competitiveness directed at survival and preparing for the next phase, along with strength and stubbornness. The north-east is part of a north-east/south-west axis where both directions and the centre have the same Five Element – soil. Energy can move very quickly because it does not have to transform into another element – making these directions unstable. North-east chi is strong, piercing and quick to change direction. It is most active just before dawn and towards the end of winter. The mountain symbolizes a rocky harshness.
EAST **Trigram** yin/yin/yang **Five Element** tree **Symbol** thunder **Colour** green **Time** morning/sunrise **Season** spring	In this phase the child is ready to embark on a career. It is a time of ambition and new beginnings. The chi energy is active and focussed – and most intense at sunrise. The trigram has a solid yang line beneath two broken yin lines, allowing the yang energy to move forcefully up through the yin lines before retreating to a more tranquil state. The tree provides an upward thrusting energy, and the image of sunrise adds the idea that it is the beginning of a new day. Thunder provides great power, aggression and the urge to go out and make things happen. This energy is also linked with ambition and realising dreams.
SOUTH-EAST **Trigram** yang/yang/yin **Five Element** tree **Symbol** wind **Colour** dark green/blue **Time of day** mid-morning **Season** late spring/early summer	This phase of maturity and harmonious progress is when long-term relationships are formed, including engagements and marriage. The chi energy here is busy and active, but less sharp than that of the east. It is strongest in mid-morning and early summer when the sun is rising in the sky. The trigram has a yin line sitting beneath two yang lines. Gentleness at the heart is protected by great activity on the surface. The symbol of wind brings persistence and power to this chi energy, but is less aggressive and dramatic than thunder. Dark green symbolizes growth and vitality, but a more established kind than the east.

DIRECTION	CHI ENERGY

SOUTH
Trigram yang/yin/yang
Five Element fire
Symbol fire
Colour purple
Time of day midday
Season midsummer

This phase represents the prime of life when hard work has paid off and the benefits of success can at last be enjoyed. The chi energy of the south is fiery, passionate and brilliant, and is most active at midday and in midsummer when the sun is at its highest point. If the chi energy in this part of a home is moving well, fame and social success could be the result. The trigram is a yin line sandwiched between two yang lines. The chi energy is active and dynamic on the surface, but flexible and flowing on the inside. It is also linked with intelligence and beauty. The colour purple instils enthusiasm and heat.

SOUTH-WEST
Trigram yin/yin/yin
Five Element soil
Symbol earth
Colour black
Time of day afternoon
Season late summer/early autumn

This chi energy is symbolized by the more settled state of middle age – a state usually associated with spending more time at home – and family harmony is the dominant theme. This chi energy is most active in the afternoon and late summer as the sun sinks in the sky, providing an atmosphere that is conducive to consolidation and methodical progress. The trigram has three yin lines, implying a more receptive, yielding, motherly energy. The symbol of the earth carries the idea of supporting and nourishing life. Black, like the colour of rich, dark soil, enhances the atmosphere of nurturing and supportiveness.

WEST
Trigram yin/yang/yang
Five element metal
Symbol lake
Colour red
Time of day sunset
Season autumn

This is the time of late middle age approaching retirement and is associated with relaxing and enjoying the fruits of your labours. Most active at sunset and in autumn, the chi energy of the west is linked with financial income and the harvest. The trigram has a yin line over two yang lines. The calm of the surface is supported by strength below, which creates a playful movement of chi energy. The lake brings a deeper, more reflective quality, and metal energy is associated with material wealth and style. Red is like the fiery glow of a brilliant sunset and enhances feelings of romance and contentment.

NORTH-WEST
Trigram yang/yang/yang
Five Element metal
Symbol heaven
Colour silver white
Time of day dusk
Season late autumn/winter

This is the final phase in the cycle of life. By this time the accumulation of experience has led to wisdom, and the possibility of helping others and being a mentor through the earlier stages. The chi energy of the north-west is linked with leadership, organization and planning ahead, and is most active at dusk and in late autumn or winter. The three yang lines of the trigram bring a powerful, fatherly chi energy. The symbol of heaven adds dignity, wisdom and an image of superiority. The association of the colour silvery white with the hair of an elderly person reinforces the impression of dignity, respect and wisdom.

tools of feng shui

To apply the principles of Feng Shui to your home you first need to assess the pattern of chi energies there. This involves finding out which parts of your home fall in which directions, and therefore which parts are characterized by the different types of chi energy. In order to do this you must have a detailed and accurate floor plan of your home on which to align a grid of the Eight Directions. If one is already available, make sure all details relevant to Feng Shui considerations are marked on it (see right). If not you will need to draw one up yourself.

"Your home" in this context refers to the space you own, rent or occupy. It could be a house or apartment. If it is an apartment, the plan should cover only those areas of the building that are yours, for your sole use. Later, you can assess the apartment within the whole building.

equipment

1 cm graph paper

compass

tracing paper

acetate

stiff card

lightweight paper

pair of compasses

protractor of 360 degrees

steel tape measure

long pin

scissors

paper glue

rubber

ruler

acetate pen

craft knife

coloured p or pencils

ordinary pencil

THE FENG SHUI FLOOR PLAN

If your home has more than one floor, make a separate plan for each one. Draw them to scale using graph paper to make the job easier (see below). Include all the internal walls, all doors, windows, staircases, fireplaces, and mark likely problem features such as protruding corners, sloping roofs or overhead beams. Fixed features that are important in Feng Shui terms, namely, fireplaces, sinks, fixed cookers, baths, showers and lavatories, should also be marked. Finally, indicate the likely positions of movable items such as beds, chairs, sofas and dining tables.

The next step is to find the centre of your home (see page 28) and of all the main rooms (especially where they are used for more than one function such as kitchen/dining rooms). Finally, align the plan with the grid of the Eight Directions (see page 29). This will enable you to assess the balance of chi energies in your home at a glance.

drawing a floor plan

MEASURING THE ROOMS

Using a long retractable steel measure, note the length and width of each floor of your home, then of each room, and of staircases and corridors. Measure into alcoves and bay windows if appropriate.

Convert the measurements to a convenient scale, eg, 1 metre = 1 cm. So if your room measures 5.2 × 3.5 metres, the rectangle on the plan would have to measure 5.2 × 3.5 cm.

Transfer the measurements to the plan in the appropriate positions. In scale, add to the plan all windows, doors, fitted store cupboards, wardrobes and kitchen units. Indicate on the plan the way the doors open.

Adding relevant features
Mark on the plan all details relevant in Feng Shui terms (see above). Mark the fixed features in one colour, the movable ones in another, and the problem features in a third colour.

finding the centre

To determine the directions on your floor plan, first find the centre of each floor and of each of the main rooms. The easiest shapes to handle are simple squares and rectangles. Irregular shapes are rather more complicated. There is a mathematical method for finding the centre of irregular shapes, but the easiest way is to find the balancing point of the shape using a long pin.

Finding the centre of squares and rectangles
Draw lines between opposing corners. The centre of the shape is the point where they intersect.

Finding the centre of irregular shapes
Trace the shape of the floor or room, transfer or paste it on to stiff card and cut it out. Hold the card horizontally and try balancing it on the point of a long pin. Move the pin until you find the balancing point. This is the centre of the shape. Transfer it to the floor plan.

Finding the centre of L-shapes
The balancing point of an L-shape may be outside the shape itself. Glue a piece of lightweight paper over the area between the wings of the building where the centre is likely to be. You can balance the pin on this paper without it affecting the centre of the shape.

aligning the grid of the eight directions

The grid of the Eight Directions is shown on page 30. It includes a marker for magnetic north. Scan the grid into your computer or photocopy it onto transparent film or draw it onto tracing paper using a protractor and ruler. Next align the grid with the floor plan using a compass.

GETTING A CONSISTENT COMPASS READING

Many objects distort compass readings: things made of iron or steel, electrical appliances, concealed metal beams, water tanks, water or gas pipes. Walk around your home holding the compass steady until the reading is consistent in several parts of a room. If this is not possible indoors try doing it outside. Use the room or space where the reading is consistent to find north on your plan.

Finding magnetic north on the floor plan
Place the plan on a flat surface so that the walls on the plan align with the same walls in the area you are in. Place the compass on the plan so that its centre is over that of the plan. Turn the compass so the needle lines up with the marker line. Mark the plan at this point and draw a line to the centre.

Aligning the grid of the eight directions
Place the transparent grid over the floor plan aligning the centres on both. Push a pin through the centres. Rotate the grid until the line pointing north on the grid aligns with magnetic north on the floor plan underneath. You can now read off the directions in your home through the transparent grid.

the grid of the eight directions

The grid below is used to determine the directions, and therefore the pattern of chi energy in a home (see pages 28–29). Different Feng Shui schools draw up the grid in different ways. I use the system that divides it into four segments of 30 degrees and four of 60 degrees, which synchronizes the Eight Directions with the 12 animals of Chinese astrology.

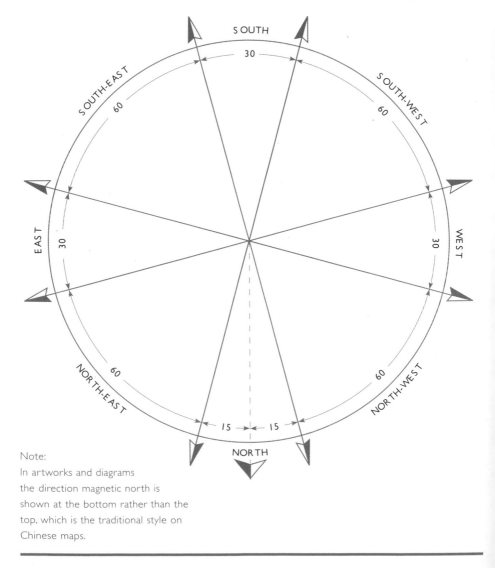

Note:
In artworks and diagrams the direction magnetic north is shown at the bottom rather than the top, which is the traditional style on Chinese maps.

the ROOMS in your HOME

If you place rooms in favourable locations and
choose your furnishings and decor
according to Feng Shui principles,
it can make you happier and more
comfortable in your home,
and generally further your aims in life.

simple feng shui remedies

If the chi energy in a room is not satisfactory for the activities that take place there, it may be impractical to implement any radical solutions such as redecorating or relocating rooms. In such cases there may be some very simple remedies that can be used instead. First, check the room's location. If the direction is not favourable for its function, decide whether the chi energy there needs to be enhanced or calmed. If the chi energy is favourable, simply help to strengthen that beneficial balance.

DIRECTION	ENHANCE CHI	STRENGTHEN CHI	CALM CHI
NORTH	Round silver or iron pot filled with red flowers or a red flowering plant.	Grow ivy or water lilies with white plants. Curved glass statue or crystal.	Tall plants.
NORTH-EAST	Candles. clay container.	White flowers in a low white china bowl.	Sea salt in small round ramekin dish.
EAST	Water feature.	Tall plants.	Candles.
SOUTH-EAST	Water feature.	Tall plants.	Candles.
SOUTH	Tall plants.	Candles. Lights.	Charcoal in a low clay container.
SOUTH-WEST	Candles. Bright lights.	Yellow flowers in a clay container.	Sea salt in a small round ramekin dish.
WEST	Yellow or gold fabrics and colours. Yellow flowers.	Red flowers in a round metal pot. Coins on a red cloth.	Grow ivy or water lilies. Curved glass statue.
NORTH-WEST	Yellow fabrics or flowers.	White flowers in a round silver pot. Clock.	Grow ivy or water lilies. Curved glass statue.
CENTRE	Keep empty.	Keep empty.	Sea salt.

the living room

The living room is central to family life and supports probably the widest range of activities of any room in the home. It is where you entertain your guests, host parties and hold important family celebrations. It is also, often, the place where you relax after a day's work and maybe read a book, watch television or listen to music.

A bright sunny room will help to create a lively uplifting place where you and your family will enjoy spending time together. The sunlight charges up the chi energy and helps to stimulate the flow of energy through the room. South-east is bright and lively. South is favourable for holding parties and large social events. South-west will help create a settled cosy atmosphere. West is good for entertaining and the pursuit of pleasure generally; it also has a romantic character.

Usually the living room is the largest room, and plenty of space is essential to its success. Chi energy can stagnate in overcrowded, claustrophobic rooms. If your potential living room is too small, open out two or more adjoining rooms. It is easier to keep chi energy flowing gently through one large room than through several small ones. Use mirrors where necessary, to adjust the overall proportions of the room and create an illusion of space (see page 90). Long thin rooms and L-shaped rooms can both be improved in this way.

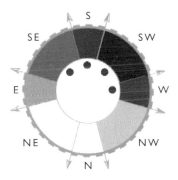

Recommended directions for a living room
South-east, south, south-west and west of the centre of your home.

LIVING/DINING ROOMS

Often, particularly in small apartments, it is practical to combine the living room and dining room. Generally, entertaining and eating are compatible functions, and you can usually create an atmosphere that works for both. Sometimes, the living and dining area also incorporates the kitchen. The main drawback here is that the kitchen part must be kept especially clean and tidy at all times. If not, it has a negative impact on chi energy which can easily spread to the rest of the room. (See pages 40–44 and 55–58 for considerations affecting dining rooms and kitchens.)

an ideal living room

The south-east, a favourable location, is characterized by lively, uplifting Five-Element tree energy. Use decor and furnishings to enhance the living room's spaciousness and to make it feel relaxing and comfortable. At the same time, try to promote sociability and family harmony. To allow chi energy to circulate freely, keep large pieces of furniture to a minimum and do not overuse heavy fabrics and upholstery. Remember to balance the need for comfort against the risk of chi energy stagnating.

THINGS TO AVOID

SPIKY PLANTS Plants with sharp-pointed leaves produce cutting chi, so plants like palms and yuccas should not be placed next to chairs and sofas where people are likely to sit, but ideally in the corners of the room.

CLUTTER To prevent chi energy stagnating, keep living rooms free of household clutter and too many decorative objects. Make sure the centre of the room is relatively empty.

CLOSED CURTAINS To allow energizing sunlight freely into the living room, try to keep curtains wide open during the day, exposing the entire window.

OVER-FURNISHING Chi energy needs space to move so keep furniture to a minimum.

PROTRUDING CORNERS If exposed these can cause cutting chi, so screen them with bushy plants or drape them with fabric.

❶ LIGHTING *The vertical beam of uplighters and the shape of standing lamps supports upward-moving tree energy.*

❷ TELEVISION *Electronic equipment has a negative effect on chi energy. Position the television away from the seating area.*

❸ PLANTS *Use plants to minimize the negative effects of the television. Tall palms strengthen tree chi energy, making the living room more social and exciting. In smaller living rooms, round-leaved bushy plants would be more appropriate.*

❹ SOFAS AND CHAIRS *Arrange seating to promote sociability and family harmony (see pages 38–9). Sofas and chairs placed north-west facing south-east and west facing east are the most favourable positions in this room, resulting in good communication. To promote relaxation, choose living room seating which is more yin – soft and rounded. Rounded shapes also prevent cutting chi. Green and cream are harmonious in the south-east — the more yin pale green helps create a spacious feeling.*

❺ FLOOR COVERING *The stripped wooden floor supports tree energy and generally maintains the harmonious flow of chi energy in the room. The pure wool rug provides comfort while avoiding the risks of stagnation that a fitted carpet would present.*

❻ WINDOW TREATMENT *Fabrics help slow chi energy, which is relaxing and appropriate to a living room. But curtains should not be too full as this risks stagnation.*

❼ WALL COVERING *Vertical stripes support this energy helping to create an impression of height and space. Patterned walls are more yin, ideal in a living room where relaxation and comfort are important goals.*

❽ PAINTINGS *Cheerful subjects such as a brilliant sunrise have positive psychological effects.*

❾ ACCESSORIES *Choose colours for accessories such as cushions to fine-tune chi energy. Purple calms tree energy.*

CHOOSING THE DECOR

In a south-east living room colours and patterns should aim to maintain the favourable lively chi energy. Dark green is a harmonious colour, but paler, more yin shades are also used to promote relaxation and give the room a light, spacious feel. To calm the chi energy here, use more pale purple; to build it up use more cream and off-white. Shades of blue could be used instead of, or in addition to, green. Vertical patterns such as stripes in green and cream support tree energy. Irregular patterns would be enhancing, pointed ones calming.

DECOR FOR OTHER
FAVOURABLE LOCATIONS

THE SOUTH The fiery chi energy here is warm and sociable, ideal for parties but, perhaps, a little too passionate for everyday relaxation. I recommend that you strengthen the ambient chi energy, but also add calming touches. Softer shades of purple with pale yellow accents will do this.

THE SOUTH-WEST The main feeling here is settled and domestic which is ideal for a cosy relaxed family living room, but it might need sharpening up for social occasions. You could strengthen the ambient chi energy but add enhancing touches. Earth colours such as yellow and brown are harmonious, and use purple here and there, perhaps, in a pattern on wallpaper or furnishing fabric. Check patterns will strengthen the soil energy here; pointed patterns or shapes, which represent fire chi energy, will enhance it.

THE WEST This is a playful, pleasurable location, which favours most of the activities likely to take place in a living room, so an appropriate strategy might simply be to strengthen this natural ambience. Use soft rusty reds and pinks, with occasional touches of grey and white. Rounded patterns – circles, ovals, stylized flowers, waves or scallops – will add to the favourable metal chi energy of the west. Circular cushions in harmonious colours, or round silver or gold plates hung on the walls would have the same effect.

SOUTH Pale purple strengthens chi here and yellow calms it.

SOUTH-WEST Checked patterns in shades of yellow and brown will strengthen soil energy.

WEST Warm maroons and soft pinks maintain metal energy, as do curvy patterns and motifs. Brass and copper, soft metals, are more yin than iron or bronze, hard metals.

THE FIREPLACE

A real fire provides Five-Element fire chi energy in its pure form, which enhances passion, excitement, spontaneity and brightness. Because of this, it is important, if possible, to position the fireplace in a location where it harmonizes with the Five-Element chi energy in that direction. The more yang

REMEDIES FOR UNFAVOURABLE LOCATIONS

THE NORTH Boost the overly quiet chi energy here by using brighter reds and maroons and by adding metal energy.

THE NORTH-EAST Calm the unsettling chi energy here using sombre reds and more yin surfaces – matt textures, carpets and tapestries.

THE NORTH-WEST Boost the over-serious chi energy here by using yellow fabrics, and by adding soil energy and soft metals such as copper or brass.

THE EAST Calm the over-active chi energy here by using yin pastel greens and yin materials like bamboo.

warmth of a fire is best suited to the northern part of a building where the usual energy is colder and more yin. On the northern side of the home, the Five-Element chi energy that is most in harmony with fire energy is the soil energy of the north-east. Therefore north-east from the centre of a building or room is the most suitable position.

Of the other positions, east, south-east and south-west are also harmonious in terms of the Five Elements. But being on the more yang sunny side of the home, they are less helpful in other respects. Avoid placing a fire in the south of the building as this could concentrate too much fire energy in one place and increase the risk of a fire.

Where the fireplace is in a favourable position, you can reflect more fire chi energy back into the room by hanging a mirror above it. Fire chi energy also can be introduced in the other forms – lighted candles, lanterns, oil lamps and bright lights, for example. Place them in dark corners where the chi energy is passive. If lights and lamps are impractical, shapes, colours and patterns associated with fire chi energy can be used in the interior decoration. Sharp, pointed or jagged shapes – stars, zigzags, triangles, pyramids – and hot yang colours such as yellows, oranges, reds and purples used in furnishing fabrics or wall coverings will add welcome fire-energy warmth to the room.

Since fire energy is supported by tree energy, tall plants will also help. You can also use a pointed fire-shaped plant, such as a yucca, or purple or red flowers.

ARRANGING SEATING AREAS

A living room is likely to be used by several people at a time, so the seating should be arranged to enhance a good sociable atmosphere. Often, if there is an uncomfortable atmosphere in the room, it can be attributed to an unsuccessful arrangement of the chairs and sofas. One general guideline is to have several items of seating (rather than one sofa, for example), and position them so that they all face the centre of the room. This also provides a variety of positions and directions appropriate to the varying needs and desires of your family and friends, and it should be possible for most people to find a direction that suits them. Ideally, wherever you are seated, most of the room will be in front of you. This is particularly important for parents of a household.

Positions and directions are most practical when you sit with your back against the wall facing the direction from which you want to benefit. For instance, if facing north is recommended, sit in the south facing the north. As well as rooms, apply this to your home as a whole.

Ideally, arrange seating so that it forms a balanced shape, such as a circle, square or octagon. If necessary, use items like side tables and plants to complete the shapes. Avoid placing chairs or sofas with their

For family harmony
Place a sofa in the north-west facing south-east, with two chairs in front and opposite each other, in the north-east facing south-west and in the south-west facing north-east, and one chair in the south-east facing north-west.
Closing the circle of seating in this way makes it particularly harmonious.

N
▼

backs to windows or doors. Your back to a door is the least secure position, especially if people are constantly entering or leaving the room. If possible, place sofas with their backs to the wall. Make sure, too, that people sitting in chairs are not exposed to cutting chi. For this reason, do not place chairs in front of protruding corners or near sharp-cornered furniture such as coffee tables and sideboards – a solid object such as a sideboard would have a stronger effect than a narrow table top. Use bushy plants to absorb cutting chi directed at chairs and sofas, and avoid sitting below a heavy beam.

Avoiding cutting chi
Trail a bushy, round-leaved plant over the sharp corner of a shelf or side table, or cover it with a cloth to prevent cutting chi.

N
▼

For being productive
Place two sofas opposite each other in the east facing west and the west facing east; and a chair in the north-facing south. This is a dynamic arrangement, good for meetings and getting things done.

For lively conversation
Place two sofas as described left, but place the chair in the north-west facing south-east. This is a more harmonious arrangement where the chair is in balance between the chi energies of the sofas, but is also a lively arrangement good for a social gathering.

the dining room

Given today's hectic lifestyles, the evening meal may be the only time of day a family can all be together. However small your home, it is important to set a side a special area, even if it cannot be an entire room, where you can sit and eat around a table. A successful dining room or dining area creates a pleasant atmosphere where everyone can relax, enjoy their food and take time to digest it properly. It helps, too, if the room is conducive to conversation and family harmony. The food is the focal point; the surroundings have a supporting role.

FOOD AND CHI ENERGY

The food we eat is a major influence on our health. In Chinese medicine food is often an integral part of the treatment. Different foods have their own flow of chi energy. When you eat you take in not only the physical nutrients but also the chi energy of the food, which is a vital ingredient in the healing process.

The chi energy of food is easily influenced by the ambient chi energy, so it is essential that the chi energy in a dining room be conducive to good health. Nowadays we all recognise the importance of healthy eating, but we do not always get maximum benefit from our food, not simply because of what we eat, but how we eat it. It is much more healthy to sit down while eating, for example, than to eat on the run. This helps the stomach adopt a shape that is more conducive to proper digestion. Relax and take your time while eating. When you are tense and rushed, you secrete more acids in your stomach, which can lead to indigestion. It also helps to keep conversations at the table positive and enjoyable.

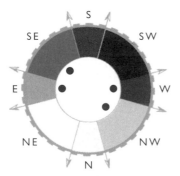

Recommended directions for a dining room
East, south-east, west and north-west of the centre of your home are all good directions.

FAVOURABLE LOCATIONS

East has a more lively atmosphere, and is a particularly good location for breakfasts because the sun shines on the eastern side of your home in the morning. The energy in the south-east favours conversation, and

the west contains the chi energy that is best for pleasure, romance and entertainment. It is a particularly
good location for the evening meal as the setting
sun naturally energizes this part of your home.
The north-west is best for more formal or more
serious occasions. Eating north-east from the
centre of your home exposes you to a sharp, piercing chi energy that is quick-changing and direct.
This is not the ideal atmosphere for a relaxing meal.

EAST *A green and white
leaf-patterned fabric maintains tree energy here.
Bright greens and blues
are harmonious.*

USING COLOUR AND PATTERN

Check the direction of the dining room from the centre of
your home. Use background colours and patterns that strengthen
the chi energy of favourable directions, adding calming or
enhancing features to fine-tune, depending on the ambience
you aim to create. If it is a room used throughout the day,
use bright colours. Darker shades work best in a dining
room used mostly in the evenings.

    The east is already vibrant and bright, and grassy
greens can strengthen this. A leaf-patterned wallpaper
or fabric with small touches of calming purple is
ideal. In the gentler south-east use more sombre
shades of green and blue. An irregular colour-washed
finish is enhancing.

SOUTH-EAST *Dark
blues and greens main-
tain the energy here.
Irregular-patterned wall-
paper enhances chi energy.*

    Warm pinks or even a dramatic rusty red on the walls
in a western dining room is ideal for evening meals.
To calm chi, colour-wash, rag-roll or sponge on
paint. Soften it further with satin-finish
cream paint on the woodwork. The
north-west has dignity so plain
painted walls in grey and
white with touches of red
and silver in accessories,
and starched white
table linen can
enhance this in a
formal dining room.

WEST *Strong dark reds
work well in a dining
room in this location.*

NORTH-WEST *The
dignified chi energy here is
maintained by grey and
white. Silver accessories
add to metal energy.*

matching tables with occasions

The yin and yang characteristics of materials and shapes make certain table tops more suited to some occasions than others.

Formal dinner parties
A more yin rectangle stretches energy and is more relaxing than a square top. Mahogany is more yang than softwoods, adding formality.

Family meals
An oval top spreads chi energy and is therefore more yin than a round top. A pine surface is also more yin and so particularly relaxing.

Business lunches
A square top is more yang and stimulating than a rectangular one. A hard marble top is also dynamic.

Romantic suppers
A round table is more yang and therefore more active than an oval one. A glass top adds excitement.

CHOOSING FURNISHINGS

The main aim in a dining area is to maintain the cleanliness required for handling food while promoting the relaxing atmosphere needed for good digestion and a convivial sociable ambience.

FURNITURE   Easy-to-clean surfaces are essential. Wood is ideal since it does not speed up chi energy. Different woods affect chi energy differently (see above). To avoid poor digestion and discomfort, ensure sharp-cornered furniture is not directed at your guests.

LIGHTING   Keep it flexible. Low lighting during dinner creates a romantic atmosphere, but at other times the rooom will require bright lighting. Lights which have dimmer switches will provide both these options. Candles add fire energy, which helps to produce a warm and vibrant atmosphere at the dining table.

WINDOW TREATMENTS Fabric roller blinds are preferable to curtains since they prevent stagnation of chi energy.

FLOOR COVERINGS Natural wood floors have a neutral effect on chi energy and are easy to clean. Rugs and carpets risk stagnation.

PAINTINGS Choose images that provide a sympathetic backdrop to relaxed eating. Still lifes of food, convivial scenes or restful landscapes are all suitable. An attractive bowl of real fruit on a sideboard has a similar effect.

ACCESSORIES A mirror on the wall or sideboard, reflecting the table, enhances the healthy chi energy produced by the food.

THE DINING TABLE

A round or square table is more yang and carries a dynamic kind of chi energy. An oval or rectangular table induces a more gentle energy, which is better for relaxed dining. Light softwoods, such as pine and elm, are more yin. Polished dark hardwoods, such as oak, mahogany and teak, are more yang. Hard surfaces, such as marble and glass, speed up the flow of chi energy across the table and make for a more stimulating, more exciting but also less relaxed atmosphere, which sometimes may be desirable. A linen table cloth will soften the atmosphere.

The combination of surface with shape allows you to influence the ambience of your dining area. You can combine more yin shapes (rectangles and ovals) with more yang materials and surfaces (marble, granite and glass), and more yang shapes (squares and circles) with more yin materials (light woods), or put yin materials and shapes together and yang materials and shapes together. All these combinations will create subtly different effects (see above left).

ENHANCING A MOOD WITH COLOUR

Relaxation	Stimulation	Vitality	Communication	Passion

	Security	Romance	Formality	Warmth

table settings

Your choice of table linen, dishes and accessories has a powerful influence on the ambience around the dining table. Using the concepts of yin and yang (see page 10) you can design quite different settings, which affect the movement of chi energy across the table in a variety of ways.

The shape of the table and the material it is made of is also important (see page 42). Even minor details, such as a particular plant, a touch of strong bright colour in a table napkin or the shape of a place mat, all have subtle effects that contribute to the over- all atmosphere in the dining room.

Choosing appropriate settings for different occasions can make all the difference to the success of a meal, whether it be a formal social event or a casual everyday family affair.

Yin table setting
Soft yin surfaces and gentle colours create a more passive flow of chi energy. This results in a calmer, more relaxed ambience that is suit- able for informal lunches or suppers and for easy-going everyday family meals.

Yang table setting
The exciting and stimulating chi energy that this creates is better suited to formal occasions. With the right touches, however, it can take on a romantic note. Yang settings are sparse and ordered with clean lines, strong colours and hard surfaces.

the bedroom

On average we spend six to nine hours out of every twenty-four in bed. Therefore the location and design of the bedroom and the positioning of the bed provide a superb opportunity to align yourself with the natural flow of energy in a way that helps you in other areas of your life.

A good night's sleep is essential for health, so it is also important to have a bedroom that calms you at the end of a busy day, and helps you to sleep well. It should also be a place where you wake up feeling refreshed, full of vitality and enthusiasm to make the most of a new day.

The bedroom has a significant influence on adult relationships, as it is where sex and physical intimacy take place. Privacy is also an important consideration. If possible, it is better not to use your bedroom for activities that require a different atmosphere, such as work. In the end, both will suffer.

FAVOURABLE LOCATIONS

Ideally, your bedroom should be exposed to sunlight at dawn which helps to increase your energy in the morning. If you have a choice of rooms, choose one where the atmosphere is calmest. The ideal direction for your bed is determined by what you are trying to achieve.

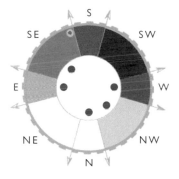

Recommended directions for an adult's bedroom

North, east, south-east, west and north-west of the centre of your home.

The north-west is ideal for parents. The chi energy here is more mature and can lead to greater responsibility, respect from others and improved ability to organize your life. The north has a quieter, more peaceful chi energy. This is particularly helpful for anyone who has difficulty sleeping. West is particularly favourable for romance, pleasure and contentment – desirable qualities in a bedroom shared by a couple. If your sex life has become dull, moving your bedroom to the north or west may bring increased or more satisfying sexual activity.

Generally, younger people benefit from a bedroom in the east or south-east of the home since they are building up their lives and the chi energy there favours making a good start.

an ideal bedroom

The chi energy of the west favours romance and contentment, making it an ideal location for a master bedroom. This position fulfils the requirements of promoting relaxation, restful sleep and the intimacy needed for romance.

Your bedroom should also contain lively, uplifting and cheerful elements to make it a pleasant place in which to wake up and begin the day. There is a playful aspect to the chi energy of the west which will produce this effect.

THINGS TO AVOID

SHARP CORNERS   Avoid spiky plants and rectangular or square furniture near the bed especially if it is directed at the bed.

MIRRORS   These reflect your own chi back at you while you sleep and impede the process of getting rid of old emotions. Cover or turn them to the wall at night.

HARD SHINY SURFACES

Glass, metal and marble all speed up chi energy and could prevent you from getting a good night's sleep.

EN SUITE BATHROOMS   These are not desirable because bathrooms introduce a heavier, damper atmosphere into bedrooms, and may drain them of healthy chi. Keep the door to an en suite bathroom closed, or screen the entrance with a curtain.

1 LIGHTING *Soft yin lighting is restful and intimate. Lampshades diffuse the harshness of electric light. Candles provide a more natural romantic glow and, if placed in the northeast, support soil energy.*

2 PLANTS *Round-leaved plants are soothing and, in the west or northwest of the room, help to maintain metal energy.*

3 STORAGE *Keep clothes and possessions tucked away in cupboards and wardrobes. Cupboards in alcoves or across entire walls reduce cutting chi.*

4 BED *A wood-framed bed has a neutral effect on chi energy. A headboard*

protects your head from fast flowing energy, though if your bed is against a wall this is less important. Place your bed in a favourable direction (see page 50). You should ideally be able to see the door and windows from your bed.

5 BED LINEN *Use bed linen made of pure cotton, linen or silk. Pink shades and circular patterns support western chi energy. Do not leave beds unmade.*

6 FURNITURE *Bedroom furniture should have round edges. Sharp corners should not face the bed. Cutting chi directed at you while you sleep will disturb your chi energy and could affect your health.*

7 FLOOR COVERING *Soft yin materials slow chi energy and create a relaxing atmosphere. Fitted carpets are ideal in this room.*

8 WINDOW TREATMENT *Full draped or ruched curtains slow the flow of chi energy through windows at night and so promote restful sleep.*

9 WALL COVERING *Pastel colours are more yin and calming. Pink is harmonious in the west.*

10 PAINTINGS *Avoid reflective yang surfaces. Tapestries or pictures without glass are helpful. Placing pictures, candles and table lamps in pairs symbolizes intimacy.*

CHOOSING THE DECOR

In a western room the decor should support the metal chi energy there, which is favourable for a bedroom. Strengthen it using pinks, white and grey, and increase it with touches of red, silver and gold. More red increases the romantic ambience, and more yin pastel shades, or off-white or cream, creates peace and tranquillity. Rounded patterns on fabrics and wall-paper also maintain metal energy. Irregular patterns produced by sponging and colour-washing are calming if you have trouble sleeping.

DECOR FOR OTHER FAVOURABLE LOCATIONS

THE NORTH This chi energy fosters introspection and spirituality, favouring older people and those suffering from insomnia. However, it's not so good for young people. Depending on your situation, strengthen the naturally cool chi energy using cream and off-white, or enhance it with warmer pinks and reds.

THE NORTH-WEST This natural ambience is responsible and serious, but again, too sombre for younger people. To strengthen it use grey, white and pink. Check patterns which incorporate some yellow, brown or black add soil energy to support the metal energy here.

EAST AND SOUTH-EAST Both these locations are better for younger people since they are generally stimulating and lively, especially in the mornings where they are exposed to the rising sun. Use more yin middle or pastel shades of green or blue and irregular patterns to calm the atmosphere for sleeping.

THE BED

The right bed can revitalize your energy, influence aspects of your everyday life and, indeed, shape your destiny.

Wood is the most favourable material for the bed frame because, unlike metal, it does not alter the local magnetic field. Wood also has a more subtle influence on the movement of chi energy. Bed frames made of brass and cast iron speed up chi energy, which is not generally conducive to restful sleep. Water beds are not recommended as they produce a damp, heavy atmosphere, which can lead to feelings of stagnation.

NORTH *Warm pink, burgundy or red increases vitality in an otherwise quiet and reflective bedroom in this direction.*

NORTH-WEST *Grey, white and pink strengthen the natural sombre energy in this location.*

EAST AND SOUTH-EAST *Blues and greens help to strengthen active tree energy in both these locations.*

REMEDIES FOR UNFAVOURABLE LOCATIONS

THE NORTH-EAST   Calm the sharp, piercing chi energy here by using pale yellows or rusty colours rather than bright shades of red and pink. Add calming metal energy with more yin curved, rather than more yang circular, patterns or objects.

THE SOUTH   Calm the excessively passionate fire energy in this location by using pale yin shades of purple and the soil colours yellow and black. Soft matt textures, such as those on carpets,

tapestries and upholstered furniture, will also help. Add soil energy by using check patterns, low spreading plants in unglazed terracotta pots or unglazed clay sculptures.

THE SOUTH-WEST   Stimulate the settled chi energy here using bright yellows and browns with touches of rich purple. Adding metal energy in its more yin forms – bronze and copper – will provide more stability.

Keep the space beneath your bed empty to avoid chi energy stagnating under you while you sleep. If you store things under your bed, clear it out and clean there regularly.

Choose a mattress made of natural materials. Cotton, wool, straw and hair are preferable to foam and other synthetics, which carry a static charge that can make you feel drained of physical and emotional energy. Pocket-sprung mattresses contain metal springs which affect the local magnetic field and cause the movement of chi energy to become chaotic. This can make you feel confused and disorientated.

Futons are ideal beds in Feng Shui terms. They are made of four to eight layers of thick cotton wadding bound by a strong cotton cover. In Japan they are placed on the floor on bamboo tatami mats, but in the West most people use wooden bases to raise them off the floor so that they can be aired properly.

Since they are used next to your skin, it is even more important that sheets, pillowcases, blankets and duvet covers are made of pure cotton, linen, silk or wool. Cotton and linen are preferable because they 'breathe' better than silk. Avoid synthetic fabrics. Quilts and duvets, likewise, should contain only natural down or cotton filling. Keep bed linen and bedcovers raised well above the floor, so that air can circulate freely under the bed. All bedding should be regularly washed and also well aired, preferably outside.

directions for your bed

The choice of rooms may be limited, but the position of your bed is often more flexible. The direction you sleep in affects your whole life as well as how well you sleep. Ideally, place your bed along an axis that passes through the centre of your home, and so that your head will point in a helpful direction.

	Head pointing **North**	This quiet direction can help with insomnia, but can also make your whole life too quiet. It is beneficial for elderly people, enhancing feelings of peace, tranquillity and spirituality, as well as for babies who wake often.
	Head pointing **North-East**	This direction is too sharp and piercing for good sleep. It can make you feel on edge and increase violent nightmares. It may improve your motivation but it is inadvisable to sleep like this over a long period.
	Head pointing **East**	This is ideal for young people, making them feel that everything is ahead of them and that anything can happen. Good for career-building, ambition and getting things done, it is also ideal for growth and for making life busier.
	Head pointing **South-East**	Good communication and increased creativity are the benefits you can expect from sleeping in this direction. It encourages growth and a more active life, but in a more subtle way than the east.
	Head pointing **South**	Its high energy and hot fiery nature means this direction is not conducive to sound sleep. It can also lead to heated arguments with the possible risk of separation. Although passion enhancing, use it only in the short term.
	Head pointing **South-West**	This is a settled position which implies more peaceful relationships, but it can make you too cautious. It also means you sleep with your feet pointing north-east and the north-east/south-west axis can make your life unstable.
	Head pointing **West**	This provides good sleep and general contentment, and may even improve income and romance. However, contentment can lead to laziness and low motivation so the west is more suitable for those in established careers.
	Head pointing **North-West**	This direction is associated with leadership and feeling in control. It promotes longer, deeper sleep and is suited to older people with the experience to exercise authority wisely. Recommended for parents.

the children's room

This often has to function as a bedroom and playroom, so the challenge is to make it fun during the day and peaceful at night. Balancing these two considerations will affect your choice of location, the direction in which you place the bed or beds, the furnishing and decor. For many parents the ideal children's bedroom is one where they sleep soundly the whole night through, but the chi energy in the room must also be supportive of activity, stimulation and other needs of growing children.

Sometimes two or more children may have to share a room and this can lead to friction. If you place all the beds in the same direction, it can make relations between the children more harmonious.

FAVOURABLE LOCATIONS

Ideally, your children's bedroom should be exposed to energizing sunlight at dawn. This would be the case in the east and south-east of your home. The west, which receives sun in the evening, is also favourable, especially for children who tend to be hyperactive.

The east contains the youthful uplifting chi energy associated with growth and development. This chi energy is also stimulating and active and represents the rising sun, which symbolizes the future. It has the feeling of the beginning of a new day, just as a child is at the beginning of a new life. Achieving restful sleep could be a problem, however, as eastern chi energy may be too active, and you may need to take steps to calm it (see pages 52–53).

Bedrooms in the south-east can also promote growth and lively activity. But the chi energy here is gentler than in the east, and could encourage a more harmonious development in life. It is also a more soothing place for sleeping.

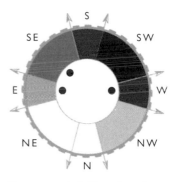

Recommended directions for a child's bedroom
East, south-east, and west of the centre of your home.

The west carries a more settled chi energy and would be the best location for a peaceful night's sleep. The chi energy here is playful, but does not convey the same benefits as the other directions in terms of a child's harmonious growth and development.

a child's ideal bedroom

The chi energy of the east is ideal for a growing child, being bright, positive, forward-looking and active. It also encourages imaginative play and healthy mental development.

At the same time, good rest is vital for a child, so the liveliness of the east may need to be moderated. Balance the need for stimulation with a peaceful environment that promotes good sleep.

BIG FURNITURE
Children need space, and bulky furniture can make the bedroom feel obstructive and confining.

CLUTTER It is easy for children's rooms to become littered with their possessions, ultimately becoming confusing and frustrating. Encourage children to keep their rooms tidy and to get rid of outgrown items.

ELECTRICAL EQUIPMENT
To reduce unnecessary electrical radiation, do not have TVs, video machines and personal computers in children's bedrooms.

THINGS TO AVOID

OPEN DOORS Keep the bedroom door closed at night and draw the curtains. This calms the flow of energy and helps children fall asleep more easily.

BEDHEADS BELOW WINDOWS
Do not place bedheads under windows as the chi energy here is more active and may prevent a good night's sleep.

❶ LIGHTING *Uplights that reflect off the ceiling support tree energy. To avoid trailing flexes, use wall lights instead of lamps.*

❷ STORAGE *Lots of units help clear the room for play. Place them within reach so children can put away their own toys. Floor boxes are ideal.*

❸ BEDS *Bunk beds save space and allow children to sleep in the same direction – helpful if they squabble. If your baby is not sleeping, place the cot so that the baby's head is pointing north. Beds should be cosy and inviting so use plump pillows and fluffy duvets in natural fibres. Blue is a particularly harmonious colour in this direction.*

❹ FURNITURE *Rounded stools and tables prevent cutting chi. When they sit at the table in the east of the room children face east, intensifying active chi energy. Bright colours are stimulating.*

❺ FLOOR COVERING *Natural wood supports tree energy, reduces stagnation and is easy to clean.*

❻ WINDOWS *Fabric blinds slow chi energy through the windows without causing stagnation. When rolled up, they expose the window completely, maximizing the room's exposure to favourable chi.*

❼ WALLS *Soft shades of blue are calming. Star patterns adds fire energy.*

❽ PAINTINGS *Fabric wall-hangings are good as they slow chi energy. Choose positive images to suit your children's needs. Bright colours like red, yellow and orange, are more yang and stimulating. Soft colours, like blues and greens, are more yin and soothing.*

❾ MOBILE *Mobiles can be arousing or relaxing. A shiny metal mobile in the west of the room is more yang whereas a soft fabric mobile in pastel colours is more yin and peaceful. Do not hang mobiles directly over a child's bed.*

❿ TOYS *Wooden toys are strong and durable, yet warm and pleasing to touch. Put toys away at night to calm chi energy.*

CHOOSING THE DECOR

Maintain the favourable active tree chi energy by using harmonious blue as a background colour but in softer, more yin shades to introduce calm. Elsewhere in the room, bright greens, yellows and blues in smaller quantities will also be harmonious, yet stimulating. Plain walls and bed covers are more yang and help to reduce any impression of clutter. Yellow is harmonious in any direction. Star motifs introduce fire energy and are calming to the tree energy of the east. For greater calm, use soft yin pastel shades and bring in more pale purple.

REMEDIES FOR UNFAVOURABLE LOCATIONS

THE NORTH   Boost the quiet chi energy of this direction by using bright red colours, shiny metal mobiles and metal wind chimes.

THE NORTH-EAST   Calm this sharp chi energy with more yin soil and metal energies: rusty pinks, pale yellow and generous use of fabrics and other soft matt surfaces. Place a cloth mobile in a harmonious colour in the north-east of the room.

THE SOUTH   Calm this hyperactive chi energy by adding yin soil energy. Remedies as suggested for the north-east are good, but use pale yellow and buff rather than pink. Place a terracotta bowl containing charcoal under the bed.

THE SOUTH-WEST   Boost this over-mature chi by adding more yang fire and metal energies: purples, reds and pinks in zigzag or circular patterns.

THE NORTH-WEST   Calm the over-solemn chi energy found here by adding water chi energy: creamy colours and irregularly patterned walls.

DECOR FOR OTHER FAVOURABLE LOCATIONS

THE SOUTH-EAST   This location shares many characteristics with the east, but is gentler and therefore unnecessary to introduce so many calming devices in this direction. Strengthening the natural ambience should be sufficient. Use stronger shades of the harmonious colours – greens and blues – while keeping them bright and cheerful, rather than sombre. Patterns with a vertical motif are also appropriate here.

THE WEST   This has a settled, contented ambience which could well suit an anxious or overactive child, or when children are going through a squabbling phase. But if you need to introduce a more stimulating, energizing quality to the room, use yang shades of red and pink, together with touches of bright yellow. Check patterns will also help.

SOUTH-EAST
Vertically striped patterns of harmonious green and blue will maintain the buoyant energy of a room in this location.

WEST *The metal energy of this direction can be enhanced with yang shades of red, pink and bright yellow in check patterns.*

the kitchen

Food has special significance in the Far East because it is widely used for healing. Practitioners of Japanese and Chinese medicine believe that a healthy well-balanced diet leads to good health and longevity. Air, water and food provide not only life-sustaining nutrients, but each also has its own flow of chi energy. There is relatively little we can do about the air we breathe, but we have more choice about drinking water and a much greater choice over the food we eat and how it's prepared. How we exercise those choices has a direct influence on our health and well-being.

Food preparation is influenced by the surrounding chi energy, so having kitchens in a favourable location is vital. Since kitchens combine the incompatible elements of fire and water, the location must be one where these elements can be harmonized, and particular consideration must be given to positioning the stove and sink (see page 58).

FAVOURABLE LOCATIONS

The most suitable positions are to the east and south-east of the centre of your home, where the energy is bright, uplifting and supportive to growth, activity and development. Also, the Five-Element tree energy of the east and south-east is compatible with both water and fire. The resulting harmonious flow of energy through the kitchen benefits the movement of chi energy throughout the home. The early morning sun warms and energizes the east and south-east sides of the home, making them particularly good locations for kitchens that double as breakfast rooms.

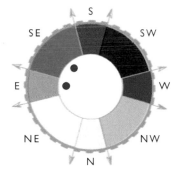

Recommended directions for your kitchen
East and south-east of the centre of your home.

Certain locations should be avoided if possible. The cold and quick-changing north-eastern energy is not the best atmosphere for creating healthy well-balanced meals. The quiet and still northern energy does not have sufficient vitality to promote good health. The south is also undesirable as it is in the position of Five-Element fire energy. Too much fire energy in one place can produce unbalanced meals and increase the risk of house fires.

USING COLOUR AND PATTERN

Enhance the favourable chi energy in an eastern or south-eastern kitchen by using off-white or cream as the main colours, with bright green in the east and dark greens and blues in the south-east used as accents. The chi energy in these locations will be boosted by irregular patterns, whether in decorative paint finishes on walls and woodwork, or in a wallpaper or fabric with a figurative motif. An all-over leaf pattern maintains tree energy here; or choose a culinary theme such as vegetables or fruits. Watery subjects in harmonious blues are also appropriate because Five-Element water energy is supportive to tree energy.

CHOOSING FURNISHINGS

Kitchens should be bright, clean and dry, as this will have a positive influence on the chi energy of your food before you eat it.

PLANTS   Place healthy leafy plants between the stove and sink to harmonize fire and water.

LIGHTING   Natural light is ideal; complement it with spotlights directed at the corners. Encourage sunlight to enter the room to help create an uplifting atmosphere. Sunlight also helps keep a kitchen dry, and therefore the chi energy fresh and clean.

FOOD AND FLOWERS   Displays of fresh foods and flowers promote a healthy flow of chi energy.

FURNITURE   Wood is the ideal surface for food preparation. Stainless steel and shiny ceramic tiles create a more yang, fast-moving atmosphere, but this may become a problem if you tend to spend a large amount of time in the kitchen. Laminates and vinyl tiles tend to block chi energy. Fit cupboards, shelves and worktops with rounded corners and edges to avoid cutting chi.

MATERIALS *Shiny ceramic tiles help keep chi energy moving and prevent stagnation. Cork flooring is more yin, enabling you to spend lots of time comfortably in the kitchen.*

COLOURS *Blues and greens maintain tree energy in the east and south-east. Touches of purple are enhancing and yellow is harmonious in all directions.*

MOTIFS *Images of fruit and vegetables in harmonious colours are sympathetic in a kitchen.*

FLOORS Natural wood flooring is recommended, because it is practical, warm and easy to clean. Cork tiles are the most yin wooden flooring you can have in a kitchen.

STORAGE Do not allow the kitchen to become cluttered with appliances, gadgets and utensils. These can cause stagnation, resulting in harmful influences on food preparation. Have well-arranged storage space and keep surfaces clean and tidy. Wash down open shelves and clear out cupboards regularly.

THE STOVE

In Feng Shui terms, the stove represents the creation of life because the food prepared on it contributes to the creation of life in your body. It is the most important appliance in the kitchen and should be as large as space permits. If your stove is positioned against a wall, hang a mirror on the wall above it. This will visually double its size, thus enhancing the life-creating image. You will also be able to see what is happening behind you when you are cooking.

Stoves with a natural flame are preferable to electric ones. Gas is ideal, but wood- or coal-burning stoves are good alternatives. A natural flame stove, like a real fire, also adds to the comfortable atmosphere of the room. Avoid electric stoves where possible as these give off electromagnetic fields which can negatively affect the chi energy of your food, and consequently your health. Microwaves are also not recommended. Work surfaces must be easy to clean and stainless steel is the best choice for a stove top.

A stove on an island in the kitchen will allow you to face into the room while you are cooking and to see the windows and doors. It also gives you a greater choice of positions within the kitchen so that you can face the direction most favourable to you. Facing into the room also makes for a more sociable setting as you can see and talk to your friends and family while you are cooking for them.

Adding metal and soil energies
The effects of kitchens located in unfavourable positions (see page 58) can be eased by adding soil energy or metal energy. Displaying clay pots or stainless steel pans is an appropriate means of doing this.

positioning the stove and sink

The stove and sink represent fire and water Five-element energy so should not be placed next to each other. Try to ensure that the stove and sink are in locations where Five-Element chi energy is compatible (see below). If possible, keep refrigerators and washing machines away from the stove.

DIRECTION/EFFECTS	SOLUTION
NORTH Unfavourable. The chi energy here is too quiet to promote health and vitality.	Add more metal chi energy. Stainless steel surfaces, saucepans and other objects that are round or made of metal will help. Red, white and silver are helpful colours. Add plants.
NORTH-EAST Unfavourable. This direction is on an unstable axis, making it too unpredictable and disorientating.	To stabilize chi energy, place small china bowls filled with sea salt in the south-west and north-east corners. Add metal chi energy.
EAST Favourable. Fire and water mix harmoniously with eastern tree chi energy, so this location is beneficial for both stove and sink. The chi energy here helps prevent possible stagnation in damp areas.	
SOUTH-EAST Favourable. The tree chi energy here is harmonious with fire and water chi energies. Although not as active as in the east, it is enough to avoid stagnation.	
SOUTH Unfavourable. The fire chi energy here makes this unfavourable for stoves as too much fire energy would be concentrated in one place, increasing the risk of accidental fires.	Add more soil energy: low, flat things made of clay or charcoal in a low clay pot next to the stove. Black and yellow are helpful colours. Place plants near the sink.
SOUTH-WEST Unfavourable. This direction is on an unstable axis, making it too unpredictable and disorientating.	To stabilize chi energy, place small china bowls filled with sea salt in the south-west and north-east corners. Add metal chi energy.
WEST Unfavourable. In this direction metal energy clashes with the fire energy of the stove, and is drained by the water energy of the sink.	Add more soil energy (charcoal in a low clay pot) near the stove, and metal energy (white flowers in a metal pot) next to the sink.
NORTH-WEST Unfavourable. In this direction metal energy clashes with the fire energy of the stove, and is drained by the water energy of the sink.	Add more soil energy (charcoal in a low clay pot) near the stove, and metal energy (white flowers in a metal pot) next to the sink.

the bathroom

Water is the main element in the bathroom. Rooms with a lot of water tend to have damp, wet surfaces and more humid atmospheres than other rooms. This can lead to a heavier flow of chi energy, which makes the room prone to stagnation. The situation is particularly risky when there is little or no exposure to sunlight and fresh air, so internal bathrooms without windows are the least desirable.

Bathrooms are often tucked away in small spaces in a home, but large bathrooms are preferable since it is easier to avoid a harmful build-up of stagnant chi energy if there is plenty of space. En suite bathrooms, linked to bedrooms, are undesirable in Feng Shui terms.

FAVOURABLE LOCATIONS

The activities which take place in bathrooms all involve Five-Element water chi energy in its pure form, so you need to allocate them carefully. Another consideration is the draining effect of the bath, shower and toilet. These functions make it difficult to allocate bathrooms in positions that are helpful to the flow of chi energy in the home generally. If they are in unfavourable locations, they can have a harmful draining effect on chi energy in the rest of your home. If you have a choice in the matter, it is best not to allocate your bathroom opposite the main door of your house, near staircases or near the dining room or kitchen.

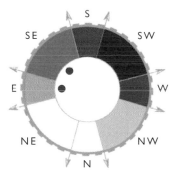

Recommended directions for a bathroom
East and south-east of the centre of your home.

Water is supportive to the Five-Element tree chi energy of the east and south-east and, as long as there are plenty of windows, this is also often a sunny part of the house, which helps to keep the room dry. The dryness and the exposure to sunlight are also both helpful in preventing stagnation.

The least desirable location is in the north-east of your home, which should be avoided if at all possible. Other locations all risk varying consequences for your physical and mental health. Use Five-Element solutions to mitigate the negative effects (see page 62).

USING COLOUR AND PATTERN

Enhance the vibrant chi energy in favourable east and south-east locations by using mainly cream and off-white in the paintwork and bathroom fittings. Use bright green in the east and dark blues and greens in the south-east in accessories such as towels, bath mats and blinds. Plain finishes on the walls are more yang, which is helpful here, but irregular patterns support water energy and would be enhancing. Employ them in moisture-resistant paint finishes, rather than fabrics or wallpaper. More yang materials (see below) are also beneficial. Colour and pattern can also be used to mitigate the effects of unfavourable bathroom locations. See page 62 for specific solutions.

COLOURS *Green and blue used in bathroom accessories support tree energy in the east and south-east.*

CHOOSING FURNISHINGS

The main objectives in a bathroom are to keep the room bright, dry and fresh and to counteract the tendency for chi energy to stagnate in humid conditions. Good ventilation dispels humidity and helps to prevent stagnation. Open the window and let in plenty of fresh air every day. This is preferable to using electric extractor fans.

MATERIALS *Hard, smooth and reflective materials used on floors, walls and other surfaces speed up the flow of chi energy, which helps to reduce the risk of stagnation in humid bathrooms.*

LIGHTING   Natural light is best. A bright sunny room creates a lively dry atmosphere and sunlight charges up chi energy and helps stimulate its flow. If natural light is limited, keep the room well lit, especially the corners.

WINDOW TREATMENTS   Slatted blinds are a good compromise between the needs of privacy and those of light. Avoid thick curtains. Keep blinds or curtains open as much as possible.

PLANTS   Plenty of leafy plants make the room feel fresh and alive and minimize the risk of chi energy stagnating in corners. Plants also help to absorb the extra humidity in steamy bathrooms, and generally grow well there for that reason.

FURNITURE Keep furniture and bric-a-brac to a minimum. Too many objects in the bathroom create a damper, more stagnant atmosphere. In particular, avoid overuse of fabrics. Surfaces should be easy to keep clean and dry. Hard shiny surfaces such as chrome, glazed ceramic tiles, polished marble and glass are more yang and stimulate the flow of chi energy, thereby counteracting stagnation.

MIRRORS Mirrors speed up the flow of chi energy, which is a positive feature in a bathroom where you are striving to avoid stagnation. Since bathrooms are often small, mirrors can also give a feeling of space. But do not have mirrors facing each other (see page 90).

THE TOILET

The toilet should be as inconspicuous as possible. To minimize its draining and flushing effect on the chi energy of the rest of the home, position it well away from the bathroom door if possible. If the bathroom is large enough, site it so that it cannot be seen from the door, and make sure it is not reflected in any mirrors. Ideally, place the toilet in the east or south-east of the room, concealed behind a half wall, screen or curtain. Keep the toilet lid closed as much as possible, but especially while it is being flushed. Keep the bathroom door closed, especially if it is an en suite bathroom.

THE BATHROOM FLOOR

Natural wooden flooring is neutral in its effect on the flow of chi energy, and helps to support tree energy, which is particularly advantageous in bathrooms in the east, south-east and south. Avoid synthetic materials such as carpets, rugs and linoleum. Marble, granite, glass and other hard, smooth, more yang surfaces speed up the flow of chi energy, especially if they are shiny and reflective, creating a much more exciting, stimulating environment and one that helps avoid stagnation.

Stone and ceramic tiles have similar properties to marble, but if the floor is uneven they tend to scatter the energy. This can be an advantage in locations to the north, where there is a particularly high risk of energy stagnating throughout the entire room, and such floors are especially desirable if the bathroom has little exposure to natural light.

solutions for bathrooms

Counteract the detrimental effect of unfavourable locations by harmonizing the bathroom's water chi energy with Five-Element chi energy in the relevant location. Determine the direction of the bathroom, then consult the chart below. Eight Direction colours (see page 74) are also helpful.

DIRECTION/EFFECTS	SOLUTION
NORTH Unfavourable. The bathroom's water energy added to water energy of the north is overwhelming. The chi energy here is quiet and still, risking stagnation. This can deplete your vitality and make you too introverted.	Grow tall plants to introduce tree energy and drain water energy. They will also absorb humidity and produce oxygen.
NORTH-EAST Unfavourable. This least desirable location can cause unpredictable life changes and possible ill-health.	Place sea salt in a white china bowl in the north-east area.
EAST Favourable. Water chi energy is harmonious with the tree chi energy found in this direction. However, the downward movement of a toilet being flushed and bath water being drained is contrary to a tree's upward movement.	Increase the upward tree energy by growing tall plants in the bathroom. Wooden floors and fittings will also help.
SOUTH-EAST Favourable. The effects of a bathroom in this direction are similar to those of a bathroom in the east, where water draining away may limit the upward tree movement.	Increase the upward tree energy by growing tall plants in the bathroom. Wooden floors and fittings will also help.
SOUTH Unfavourable. Water chi energy destroys the fire chi energy here. This can lead to lack of passion, fewer opportunities to achieve recognition, and vulnerability to law suits.	Harmonize water and fire by growing tall plants and have wooden and green accessories.
SOUTH-WEST Unfavourable. This chi energy is unstable and the soil energy of the south-west is destructive to water chi energy. If unchecked this location can compromise your health.	Boost metal energy by placing a small bowl of sea salt in the bathroom along with iron pots.
WEST Unfavourable. The metal chi energy of this direction is drained by water energy, which could cause a draining effect on your ability to increase your income.	Boost metal chi energy by growing red-flowering plants in iron pots.
NORTH-WEST Unfavourable. Water energy drains metal chi energy, maybe leading to feeling disorganized and out of control.	Build up metal chi energy by growing white-flowering plants.

the home office

Working from home has many advantages. Not only are you able to set the pace of what you do and the way you do it, but you also have a greater measure of control over your working environment. You can choose where you sit, the kind of lighting that suits you, the shape of your desk and so on. This gives you the opportunity to design your office to enhance your productivity and effectiveness, so that you can achieve the success you are seeking. Everything in the room should be working for you, not against you.

One of the challenges with a modern home office, studio or work-room is to balance electrical radiation from the various pieces of electronic equipment with more natural chi energy. The positioning of your desk and chair in relation to computers, printers, telephones, fax machines and copiers, as well as their direction in the room are vitally important (see pages 65 and 68).

FAVOURABLE LOCATIONS

Each has particular advantages which could be helpful, depending on the type of business you are engaged in, or the stage of your career.

The east has the chi energy to help you become busier, more active, more focussed and better able to put your good ideas into practice. This is the best position if you are starting a new business or embarking on a new career. The chi energy in the south-east is similar but gentler, which is more helpful for communication and the harmonious development and growth of your business.

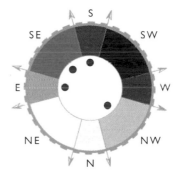

Recommended directions for a home office

East, south-east, south and north-west of the centre of your home.

The fiery chi energy in the south will help you attract attention for your business, and is more likely to lead to widespread acclaim and recognition for your work. If success is related to you being in the public eye, this is the place for your office.

The north-west is ideal for leadership, organization and for inspiring and maintaining the respect of others – qualities that would be helpful if you are working with, or perhaps directing, a team of people.

EAST AND SOUTH-EAST *Vertical stripes support helpful forward-looking chi energy here. Blue and green are also supportive colours.*

SOUTH *The colour purple maintains the fire chi energy here, which helps you achieve success and greater public recognition for your work.*

NORTH-WEST *This metal energy that is conducive to organization is enhanced by soil energy, so greys and whites with bits of yellow are helpful.*

CHOOSING FURNISHINGS

The ideal atmosphere in an office is stimulating, but not stressful. Because you may work there for long periods at a time, choose furnishings that tend to be more yang, but balance them with restful more yin elements.

FURNITURE   The desk is the most important item (see opposite). The desk chair should keep you alert while working, but not strain you physically or mentally. Much office furniture – filing cabinets, shelving systems – has sharp corners. Where it is impossible to find rounded alternatives, soften the edges with plants.

LIGHTING   Natural is better than artificial so choose a room with large windows. Avoid fluorescent lighting.

PLANTS   Plenty of leafy plants in the room balance electrical radiation. A peace lily is particularly helpful.

STORAGE   Work generates a great deal of paraphernalia – papers, files, books and so on. Have plenty of storage so that you can keep papers neat and well-organized, and avoid the stagnating chi associated with clutter. Cupboards are preferable to open bookshelves.

USING COLOUR AND PATTERN

Check the direction of your office from the centre of your home. Aim to main the chi energy of favourable directions, adding enhancing or calming touches. Use paler yin shades and more subtle patterns to reduce the stress in an over-active office. Where the chi energy is too unstimulating for productive work, use brighter, stronger colours.

In the east the chi energy is busy and active; vertical stripes in bright and dark greens maintain this helpful ambience. The gentler south-east direction can take enhancing colours; match blues or greens with cream and off-white on more yang plain walls. The chi energy in the hotter south will be maintained with middle shades of purple; soften it slightly with black and white touches. The north-west of your home is a more serious direction and is particularly appropriate to a more formal, businesslike working atmosphere; try grey, white and maroon with touches of yellow. Check patterns are also suitable here, because they add soil energy which supports the metal energy of the north-west.

THE DESK

Your desk and its accessories (see page 66–67) both influence how productively you work. A large desk helps you to feel dignified and powerful. It also conveys the impression that you have room to expand. A small cramped desk can make you feel constrained, and that you have nowhere further to go. A round or oval desk is usually preferable to a square or rectangular one. It is more relaxing to work at for long periods of time, and avoids the risk of cutting chi from sharp corners.

A wooden desk promotes a natural flow of chi energy, making you feel more at ease in your room. More yin softwoods like pine give a relaxed casual feel; darker hardwoods like teak and mahogany add formality. Glass is a stimulating surface for a desk, but is not as suitable as wood for lengthy working sessions.

Ideally, you should situate your desk in a beneficial location, facing a helpful direction, looking into the room, and being able to see the doors and windows easily. Avoid sitting next to electrical equipment, which can lead to reduced concentration and ill-health. Try to minimize your exposure to synthetic materials that emit toxic fumes.

In some cases your own needs may not be the only consideration. If several people use your home office and work as a team, arrange the chairs to enhance harmony between them. Generally, it is best to place the desks so that the people sitting in them face the centre of the room.

If your work involves having business meetings at home, arrange the chairs in your home office so that your visitors feel positive about working with you. If your office is large enough, set up a special area for meetings. Each direction has specific characteristics which promote certain qualities in the people sitting in those positions. You can use this knowledge to seat people appropriately, depending on their own personal and professional characteristics, and on what you are hoping to achieve from your meeting.

the desk top

The chi energy of your working environment is affected not only by your desk itself (see page 65), but also by the way you arrange the tools of your trade on the top. Favourable positioning can make the difference between a productive, creative and inspiring atmosphere that helps you achieve your goals, and one that is frustrating and demotivating.

To make your desktop work for you, first determine the directions on it: place it in your chosen location in the room, then find the centre, establish magnetic north and place a grid of the Eight Directions over it. Place objects in sectors where they harmonize with the energy of that direction (see right). Clutter obstructs the harmonious flow of chi energy so keep papers and paraphernalia neatly organized in convenient drawers and filing cabinets.

NORTH-EAST:MOTIVATION
Put objects here that will encourage you to work harder. They could be material, such as a financial forecast or the prospect of making a good profit.

NORTH:TRANQUILLITY
Plants, especially peace lilies can help minimize the disturbing effects of electrical radiation from office equipment. They also bring their own living energy into the working situation.

 N

**NORTH-WEST:
ORGANIZATION** *Keep your diary, forward planner or organizer in this position.*

EAST: FUTURE DREAMS

*This is the place for a
reminder of what you can
achieve with hard work, such
as the car you've always
wanted.*

SOUTH-EAST: COMMUNICATION

*This is the right
position for your mail
tray, the telephone and
fax if you have one.*

SOUTH: PUBLIC RECOGNITION

*Keep things such as
awards, prizes or
other public accolades
in this direction*

SOUTH-WEST: FAMILY HARMONY

*Photographs or other
mementoes of your
family are
appropriate here.*

WEST: FINANCE *This is the place for cheque
books, cashboxes and anything else to do with
money. If your chair is situated in the west, you
will be facing east, a favorable direction for
building up a career quickly.*

positioning your desk and chair

There are 64 possible positions for a desk and chair, each with a different mix of chi energies. The positions described below are some of the most advantageous. The position immerses you in the underlying flow of chi in the room. But the direction you face sitting at the desk has the greatest influence.

Sitting **N-W** Facing South-East	This is best for a chief executive or top manager. North-west enhances leadership, organization, responsibility, dignity and trustworthiness. Facing south-east is helpful for expansion, creativity and communication.
Sitting **N-E** Facing East	The motivating chi energy of the north-east combines with the active chi energy of the east, which is useful for someone lacking drive, or looking for a new direction. It is particularly suitable for people dealing in real estate.
Sitting **E** Facing East	Here the chi energy of the east is even more intense, favouring quick starts and fast growth. This is excellent for anyone starting a career or business, particularly in the computer or electronics industry.
Sitting **E** Facing South-East	This is similar to sitting east facing east, but less intense. Its qualities are conducive to communication, creativity and harmonious development. Media or travel business employees are likely to find this supportive.
Sitting **E** Facing South	This is helpful for putting ideas into practice, getting public recognition and promoting, so is suitable for PR, sales or advertising employees. However, it is not a good position if you feel restless and have difficulty concentrating.
Sitting **S-E** Facing East	This is similar to sitting east facing south-east, only the importance of the directions is reversed. The desk determines the underlying chi energy but the direction you face has greater influence, so east is dominant.
Sitting **S-E** Facing South	This combination of energies is ideal for people working in PR, marketing or communication. It is also good for lawyers. The chi energy is very active, so is not advisable for someone who becomes easily stressed or excited.
Sitting **W** Facing East	West chi energy relates to income, contentment and pleasure. Facing east helps you to become more ambitious, active and better able to put your ideas into practice. This is particularly helpful for people working in finance.

DESIGN ELEMENTS in FENG SHUI

Choose the objects you put in your home

carefully so that they encourage helpful

rather than unhelpful chi energy. Colours,

shapes, materials, plants, water and light,

among other things, all have implications

which can work for you or against you.

manipulating chi

No matter what it is, every object you place in your home influences the flow of chi energy. Some objects have powerful effects and others much weaker or neutral ones. Even the empty spaces, or lack of them, between objects or in rooms and hallways can help smooth the path of chi energy through your home or obstruct it. The more active design elements that help you to manipulate chi energy include water, lights, mirrors, plants, fresh flowers, crystals, candles, sounds and sea salt. Things such as furniture, carpets, curtains and cupboards are less potent. However, although relatively passive, your furniture sometimes defines where you will be in your home – your location and the direction you face. Its main function, therefore, should be to enable you to spend most of your time in the most favourable positions.

Generally, it is the shapes, colours and materials of furnishings and decorative objects that affect the flow of chi energy. The shape of an object physically alters the way chi energy flows around it, and how chi energy flows into and out of it. The colour determines the light frequencies reflected into the room, which will then influence the chi energy in that room. The materials that objects are made of also convey very different kinds of chi energy.

FENG SHUI GUIDELINES FOR CHOOSING FURNITURE

ONE	TWO	THREE	FOUR
FIVE ELEMENTS AND EIGHT DIRECTIONS Look at the Five Elements chart (page 18) and the Eight Directions colour wheel (page 74) to check that furniture will bring the type of chi energy you want in your life.	**HARMONIOUS COLOURS, SHAPES AND MATERIAL** Check the colours, patterns, shapes and materials charts on pages 73, 77 and 78 to ensure your piece will harmonize with its intended location in your home.	**YIN AND YANG** Consult the charts on pages 14 and 15 to decide which furniture will make the chi energy in your home more active and yang or passive and yin.	**POSITIONING** Place furniture and decorative objects where they will balance out the chi energies. Put more yang items in passive areas, more yin ones in active areas.

feng shui in practice

Positioning a large plant

You want to find the best location for a yucca. The plant is tall with long, tapering upward-pointing leaves. It is more yang and ideal for stimulating chi energy.

Solutions Because of the pointed leaves it will need plenty of space and should not be too close to seating or sleeping areas (to avoid cutting chi). A corner of a room where the chi energy might stagnate would be appropriate. The radiating shape represents fire chi energy. Green adds an element of tree energy, but the fiery appearance tends to override the colour in this case. Therefore, the yucca would be harmonious in a corner in the north-east, east, south-east, south or south-west of your home.

Choosing a living room sofa

You have decided to place a sofa in the west of your living room and you want one that will increase that area's romantic chi energy.

Solutions The shape of the west is round, the colour red and the material metal. A sofa that has rounded arms, a round back and metal feet or castors will increase the chi energy of the west. Red will also increase it. Complementary colours are white, yellow, black and grey. As red is a strong colour it need only be part of a pattern on the upholstery or on the cushions.

Finding an ideal bed

You need to buy a suitable bed to place in the south-east of your home so that the top of your head points east. The natural prevailing chi energy here is tree energy.

Solutions Materials, colours and shapes harmonious with the south-east are glass and wood; cream, green, blue and purple; irregular, tall and pointed. The ideal bed would therefore be raised off the ground (tall), with a natural wooden frame, and either painted in an appropriate colour or made up with cream, green, blue or purple bed linen.

Positioning a lamp

You have seen a free-standing lamp on a tall, thin, black metal frame, which you would like to buy, and you are wondering where to put it. Light itself is active and yang, and represents fire chi energy. The tall, thin shape produces tree chi energy, the material metal chi energy and the colour soil energy. The most active ingredient is yang fire chi energy.

Solutions The ideal location is a dark corner where the chi energy is more passive. In the north-east, east, south-east, south or south-west sector of your home or room, the light will harmonize with Five-Element fire energy. So a dark corner in any of those locations would be a suitable place for it – but especially in the north-east and south-west where soil and metal energies are in harmony.

using colour

Colours influence the light frequencies present in your home and will change your chi energy, whether they are used to paint walls, woodwork and furniture, or in soft furnishings such as curtains and upholstery, or in decorative objects. Even small amounts of a strong colour can have an effect. Colours can be related to yin and yang, the Five Elements and the Eight Directions (see pages 14, 18 and 22). Many Feng Shui practitioners use the Five Element colours, but I have found their relationship with the Eight Directions to be the most significant. Together with the centre, this gives you a palette of nine basic colours.

The outer ring of the colour wheel (page 74) shows the colours associated with the Eight Directions. These are the most strengthening colours for each direction. They maintain chi energy, which is a desirable aim if the chi energy there is favourable. Other colours can be used to enhance or calm chi energy in a particular direction. The chart opposite summarizes these relationships.

CHOOSING COLOURS

Colours can be used in two ways: as backgrounds over large areas and as accent colours in small areas. Background colours tend to be softer, paler shades, though this does not have to be the case, and accent colours tend to be stronger and more vivid, though again not necessarily. In Feng Shui terms, both uses can be effective if they are the right colours. The stronger the colour, the less you need for it to be effective. A small red cushion on a chair to the west of the centre of the room will be enough to enhance the chi energy associated with romance, contentment and income. To have the same effect, a soft pink would need to be used over a larger area such as a wall, large sofa or carpet.

The colours specified in the harmonious colours chart and shown in the colour wheel represent a range of colours rather than a single hue. Different shades and tones of these same colours share their harmonious qualities but carry a variety of nuances. For example, brighter shades are more yang than paler shades. Personal preference also has a part to play; if a colour has unpleasant associations for you, it would not be wise to use it whatever the charts advise. So, when choosing actual colours for a specific function, do not interpret the charts too rigidly.

harmonious colours

Ascertain the direction of the room you want to decorate, then choose a colour. Those in bold type are the most important. Yellow is harmonious in any direction.

DIRECTION	ENHANCE	STRENGTHEN	CALM
NORTH	red to pink white to grey	**off-white to cream**	pale green dark green to blue
NORTH-EAST	purple	brilliant white **yellow to brown** black	red to pink white to grey
EAST	off-white to cream	**bright green** dark green to blue	pale purple
SOUTH-EAST	off-white to cream	**dark green to blue** bright green	pale purple
SOUTH	bright green dark green to blue	**purple**	brilliant white pale yellow to brown. black
SOUTH-WEST	purple	black yellow to brown brilliant white	red to pink white to grey
WEST	brilliant white yellow to brown black	**red to pink** white to grey	off-white to cream
NORTH-WEST	brilliant white yellow to brown black	**white to grey** red to pink	off-white to cream

colour wheel

Each of the Eight Directions (pages 22–25) and its characteristic chi energy is associated with a particular colour, shown on the outer section of the wheel below. Using that colour in that direction in furnishings or decor will maintain the chi energy there. The inside ring shows the colours associated with the Five Elements which can be used as alternatives to the Eight Directions colours.

Different shades can produce subtle changes in the chi energy of an area. The swatches opposite show a variety of accent and background colours and their potential effects in certain rooms.

SOUTH

SOUTH-EAST

SOUTH-WEST

Black absorbs all the light

EAST

WEST

White reflects all the light back into the room

NORTH-EAST

NORTH-WEST

NORTH

ACCENT COLOURS

Emerald green This best represents the tree energy of the south-east. Warmer yellowy tones give it a lively excitement that is also comforting.

Turquoise Closest to tree chi energy of the south-east, this is more yin and creates a relaxing atmosphere that is still vibrant and uplifting.

Deep blue Linked with the tree energy of the south-east, this strong blue would suit a sunny room. It helps to create a harmonious atmosphere.

Violet Very close to fire chi energy of the south, this hot fiery purple brings passion to a room. Good for sociability.

Peach pink The colour of sunset and closest to western metal energy, this enhances playfulness and romance – good for evening dining.

Orange This hot sunny colour is closest to the metal and soil chi energies of the west and centre. Creates a bright atmosphere in dark areas.

Chocolate Close to the metal and soil chi energies of the west and south-west, this enhances stability. Good in sunny rooms.

Mid grey Closest to the metal energy of the north-west, this enhances feelings of dignity and authority and creates a more formal atmosphere.

BACKGROUND COLOURS

Citron A sunny colour but with a lightly sharp edge, this is close to the soil energy of the centre. It evokes envigorating freshness and warmth.

Lime green Closest to eastern tree energy, this symbolizes new growth and produces a bright optimistic atmosphere. Good for young people.

Eau de nil Closest to south-eastern tree chi energy, this mix of watery blue and green is yin and peaceful. Good for creativity and relaxation.

Powder blue This soft pastel blue creates a more yin gentler flow of the normally uplifting tree energy. Soothing in bathrooms and kitchens.

Lavender Close to southern fire chi energy, but too pale to evoke passion, this has a more yin, mildly stimulating aura. Good for socializing.

Sugar pink Closest to the metal energy of the west, pink enhances a youthful, playful atmosphere.

Pale apricot This is closest to the soil energy of the centre, with a hint of western metal energy. Good for bedrooms.

Biscuit A quiet, light brown shade which enhances feelings of stability and security, this colour is closest to the soil energy of the centre.

using pattern

Patterned wallpaper, carpets, curtains and soft furnishings influence the nature and movement of chi energy in each room. The effect of different patterns is determined by the association of the shapes in them with yin and yang and the Five Elements. Similarly, the shapes in paintings, sculptures and other decorative objects will also have an influence (see page 80). If the pattern or shape is combined with its associated colour – for example, pointed patterns in purple, or circular patterns in red – the effects will be stronger.

PATTERNED WALLS

Walls are generally painted or papered. Plain painted walls are more yang than patterned walls. Irregular patterns produced by decorative paint effects such as sponging, colour-washing, rag-rolling and stippling are associated with Five-Element water energy, and create a more peaceful relaxing atmosphere. The use of creams, blues and greens would accentuate the calming effect.

Pattern is usually added to walls in the form of wallpaper, but stencilling, stamping and mural painting can do this too. Sharply defined, ordered and repeat patterns are more yang. Less defined, irregular or all-over mottled patterns are more yin. If patterns are pictorial (flowers, fruit, animals, country scenes) or have symbolic significance (stars, suns and moons), make sure the images have positive associations for you.

PATTERNED SOFT FURNISHINGS

The principles of choosing patterned fabric are the same as for choosing wallpaper. First check the direction of the curtains, soft furnishings or furniture from the centre of the room. Then, decide whether you want to maintain, enhance or calm the chi energy there. Consult the chart on page 73 for harmonious colours and the chart opposite to determine which patterns or shapes are harmonious.

Influential patterns
The basic pattern groups can be linked with Five-Element chi energies: (from top to bottom) irregular patterns with water, vertical stripes with tree, stars with fire, checks with soil and rounded patterns with metal.

harmonious patterns and shapes

DIRECTION	ENHANCE		STRENGTHEN		CALM	
NORTH		circles arches ovals		irregular clouds waves		tall and thin vertical stripes
NORTH-EAST		pointed stars zigzags		wide rectangles horizontal stripes checks		circles arches ovals
EAST		irregular clouds waves		tall and thin vertical stripes		pointed stars zigzags
SOUTH-EAST		irregular clouds waves		tall and thin vertical stripes		pointed stars zigzags
SOUTH		tall and thin vertical stripes		pointed stars zigzags		wide rectangles horizontal stripes. checks
SOUTH-WEST		pointed stars zigzags		wide rectangles horizontal stripes checks		circles arches ovals
WEST		wide rectangles horizontal stripes checks		circles arches ovals		irregular clouds waves
NORTH-WEST		wide rectangles horizontal stripes checks		circles arches ovals		irregular clouds waves

harmonious materials

To assess the effects of objects you wish to position, consider the materials they are made of. Plastic carries fire energy, but is undesirable in Feng Shui terms.

DIRECTION	ENHANCE	STRENGTHEN	CALM
NORTH	metal harder stone	glass	wood wicker, bamboo, rattan plant fibres
NORTH-EAST	(plastic)	ceramic and clay, softer stone, fabric	metal harder stone
EAST	glass	wood bamboo, rattan plant fibres	(plastic)
SOUTH-EAST	glass	wood bamboo, rattan plant fibres	(plastic)
SOUTH	wood, wicker, bamboo, rattan plant fibres	(plastic)	ceramic and clay softer stone fabric
SOUTH-WEST	(plastic)	ceramic and clay, softer stone, fabric	metal harder stone
WEST	ceramic and clay, softer stone, fabric	metal harder stone	glass
NORTH-WEST	ceramic and clay, softer stone, fabric	metal harder stone	glass

lighting

Light waves bring energy into a space and help activate the ambient chi energy there. Artificial light is usually harsher than candlelight. Ideally, windows and skylights should be large enough to let in plenty of natural light during the day, so that artificial light is confined to evenings and dark days. Pale colours on the walls and carefully placed mirrors can reflect sunlight into a room.

TYPES OF LIGHTING

INCANDESCENT LIGHT-BULBS   Used for general household lighting, these give a broad angle of uniform light. They increase the chi energy over a wide area in a relatively even manner.

SPOTLIGHTS   These allow you to focus light in a particular place, enabling you to activate chi energy in specific areas like dark corners, which are at risk of stagnation. Use them also to illuminate one area of a multi-purpose room for work while the rest of the room remains in natural or more subdued lighting.

UP-LIGHTERS   These encourage an upward flow of chi energy, which is particularly helpful if you have a low or sloping ceiling.

LOW-VOLTAGE LIGHTING   Ideal for increasing the flow of chi energy through stagnant areas, this produces a bright high-intensity light. It is easily recessed into ceilings and is also much used in free-standing lamps, which can be used for up- or down-lighting.

FLUORESCENT LIGHTING   This emits a different colour of light and also gives off more electrical radiation. In my view this can lead to headaches, loss of concentration and mental tiredness. The same applies to small energy-saving fluorescent bulbs.

COLOURED LIGHTING   This introduces a particular frequency of light. Check the direction of coloured lights from the centre of your home, and choose a harmonious colour from the chart on page 73.

Lampshades
Metal, glass or reflective shades create a less relaxing, more yang atmosphere; with fabric or paper shades it is softer and more yin.

decorative objects

The flow of chi energy in your home and garden is affected by any sculptures, works of art or decorative objects you place there. This includes paintings as well as three-dimensional items. The influence of an object depends largely on its shape and material. Images can also have an effect by their symbolic meaning, which influences your own flow of chi energy. A picture or sculpture of a couple in a loving embrace, for example, can encourage feelings of romance in you.

The influence of different shapes, colours and materials on chi energy is described on pages 72–8. By putting combinations of these properties together you can devise the ideal statue or sculpture for the effect you want.

Square boxes
These add metal energy. Use in the south-west to boost stability.

Clear glass
Place in the north to create a flowing atmosphere.

Shiny ceramics
Spherical shapes help concentrate energy in the west and north-west.

Clay birds
Low clay objects create a steady atmosphere. Use in the north-east.

Wooden animals
These add liveliness which is harmonious in the east and south-east.

Metal boxes and frames
Use these to add solid metal energy in the north-west and west.

Stone figures
Romantic images boost the playful energy of the west.

flowers and plants

As decorative objects plants are special because they are living things that generate their own particular flow of chi energy. Healthy green plants create a fresher, more alive atmosphere and can compensate for the relatively dead materials often found in the home – electrical appliances that emit radiation and plastic and other synthetic materials that emit static energy. Plants also provide fresh air in the form of oxygen through their metabolic processes.

Different plants have different effects, depending largely on their overall shape, the shape of their leaves and flowers, and their colour, which associate them with the Eight Directions, the Five Elements of chi energy and yin and yang. Plants with pointed leaves are more yang and help to move chi energy more quickly. Plants with round floppy leaves are more yin and calm chi energy. Bushy plants help slow fast-moving chi energy and are effective in long corridors or near doors. Tall plants generate more tree chi energy, prickly plants and those with star-shaped pointed leaves encourage fire energy, low spreading plants produce soil energy, round plants or those with small round leaves metal energy, and trailing plants water energy. The green of the leaves also adds tree energy, but the colour of flowering plants adds more of the energy associated with that colour.

Fresh flowers also bring lively chi energy to your home. The colour and to a lesser extent the shape of the flowers will influence the nature of chi energy in that part of the room. Flowers are most effective if they are healthy and well looked after. Wilting flowers have a negative effect on chi energy so change the water daily and trim stems diagonally to make them last longer. Remove dead flowerheads and wilting foliage.

Although they are fashionable and popular in the West, dried flowers are less acceptable in Feng Shui terms since, for some people, they symbolize death and decay. Artificial flowers are recommended by Feng Shui practitioners if they are made of suitable material such as silk or paper. Neither dried or artificial flowers are as effective as living plants.

Radiation remedy
Indoor plants, like this peace lily (Spathyphyllum wallisii), can be placed next to electrical appliances to remedy their detrimental chi energy.

indoor plants

A variety of plants in the home give a more balanced flow of chi energy. Consider the plants' relationship to ying and yang and the Five Elements when placing them.

YANG

DRACAENA (*Dracaena marginata*) The strong upward growth with sharp pointed leaves combines tree and fire chi energies. This plant is good for stimulating chi in a corner or under a sloping ceiling, but do not place it close to where you sit or sleep. Ideal in the east, south-east, south and south-west.

WATER

IVY (*Hedera helix*) The bushiness, upward growth and floppy leaves make ivy relatively well-balanced. But its clinging trailing habit means that it generates water chi energy. It is useful in any area that lacks sunlight (such as an internal bathroom) because, unlike many plants, it grows in shade. The ideal position for it is in the north.

YIN

SPIDER PLANT (*Chlorophytum comosum*) The long, narrow, pointed leaves cascading downwards create a calming more yin atmosphere. Ideal in the north.
SWISS CHEESE PLANT (*Monstera deliciosa*) Large floppy leaves create a more yin soothing chi energy. This plant is ideal in any area that needs calming, especially the south, south-west and north-east.

TREE

HYACINTH (*Hyacinthus orientalis*) Straight upward-growing plants add uplifting tree chi energy. From the pink, white, blue or cream flowers, choose one in harmony with its position. this tree is especially harmonious in the east and south-east.

Money

Hyacinth

Poinsettia

FIRE

AFRICAN VIOLET (*Saintpaulia*) Purple star-shaped flowers make this plant strong in fire chi energy. It is helpful for attracting attention and getting public recognition for your efforts. The ideal positions are east, south-east, south, south-west and north-east.

PALM (*Phoenix roebelenii*) These upward-growing plants with spreading pointed leaves add fire chi energy and create a more yang active atmosphere. They are ideal for corners. Avoid placing in the north-east where the energy is already sharp and place the plant positions are east, south-east, south and south-west.

POINSETTIA (*Euphorbia pulcherrima*) The star-shaped leaf clusters can be red, pink, yellow or cream and the shape is linked with fire energy. Choose a colour to suit the location.

SOIL

CYCLAMEN (*Cyclamen persicum*) This spreading plant adds soil chi energy. Choose a purple flowering one for more passion in your life, a red or pink one for romance and excitement, and a white one for stability. The ideal positions for this plant are south, south-west, north-east, west and north-west.

EYELASH BEGONIA (*Begonia bowerae*) This white-flowering, low spreading plant creates more yin soil chi energy, which is good for a settled, stable atmosphere. The ideal positions are in the south, south-west, north-east, west and north-west of your home.

METAL

MONEY PLANT (*Crassula ovata*) Round thick leaves represent metal energy, which adds stability. The name is apt as metal chi energy helps finances. Ideal in the west, north-west and north.

PEACE LILY (*Spathiphyllum wallisii*) This counteracts electrical radiation from computers (see page 81).

Cyclamen

(see page 81)

USING PLANTS

INTERNAL CORNERS Plants help avoid stagnation by getting chi energy moving. Use more yang plants associated with fire chi energy, especially those with long, sharp, pointed leaves.

PROTRUDING CORNERS Place bushy plants in front of corners to calm cutting chi (see page 8). Plants with round leaves and dense foliage are the most effective in this respect.

LONG CORRIDORS Stagger bushy plants either side of a long corridor to slow fast-moving chi.

BATHROOMS Plants here help keep chi energy moving. Tall plants increase tree energy and help drain excess water energy, especially if they are in the north of the room.

KITCHENS Plants add natural living energy to food preparation and storage areas. Tall plants add tree chi energy which is in harmony with the water and fire energies of the sink and cooker.

BEDROOMS Plants add healthy natural chi in bedrooms, some of which you absorb as you sleep. More yin, floppy plants help create a calm atmosphere.

SECURITY Prickly plants such as cacti give off a spiky energy which can deter burglars. Place them along window sills.

(see page 8)

flowers

If you feel the chi energy in part of a room or your home generally needs boosting, use the following: cream flowers in the north, white flowers in the north-east, tall greenery in the east, tall blue flowers or greenery in the south-east, star-shaped purple flowers in the south, low yellow flowers in the south-west and centre, round red flowers in the west, and round white flowers in the north-west.

Tulip
The bowl-shaped blooms carry metal energy. Red in the west adds romance, pink in the west brings pleasure, white brings motivation in the north-east, dignity in the north-west, and peace in the north.

Iris
These come in many colours especially yellows, blues and purples. In spite of these links with tree energy and with the centre and south, their delicate appearance gives them a more yin quality. Use them to introduce vitality and passion, but gently.

Sunflower
The jagged flower shape has fire chi energy, but yellow is closer to soil energy. They spread out chi and have a powerful stabilizing influence.

Different flowers for different chi energies
Depending on their colour and shape, flowers enhance the chi energy of particular directions.

Carnation

The round shape of the flowers and the reds and pinks enhance romance and pleasure, whereas white adds dignity and serenity.

Mimosa

Flowers composed of many small yellow spheres increase the chi energy of the centre. Place them in the centre of your home to keep your life more centred.

Anemone

The shape is linked with metal energy and this, with strong colours, helps keep chi energy in one place. Red anemones in a west-facing bathroom could help prevent chi from draining away.

Lily

Despite the tall stems, the flowers often point downwards giving them a more settling influence. Use them to quieten an over-active part of your home.

Daisy

The round white flowers are harmonious in northern locations. In the north they add tranquillity, in the north-west dignity, and in the north-east motivation.

Rose

Tight round rosebuds are linked with metal energy, but as they open this changes to a more fiery shape. Red roses will increase the chi energy of romance and style, especially if placed in the west.

furniture

People often buy furniture that seems ideal in the store, but somehow does not feel right once they get it home. Feng Shui can help you choose furniture that is harmonious with its intended position. It helps you understand why certain items seem out of place, how to find the right furniture to fill difficult spaces, and how to find the best position for an existing piece of furniture. Check the relevant charts for harmonious colours, shapes and materials (pages 73, 77, 78).

Obviously, in some cases, practical considerations may override the requirements of Feng Shui and you need to compromise. Where materials are concerned, you can choose wood for any part of the home since its effect is largely neutral. If you were looking for a bedroom chair for the north-west of your home, for example, you would probably reject the harmonious materials (metal, stone) on practical grounds and choose wood, but a round, upholstered shape covered in a circular-patterned fabric in grey and pink shades would also be an ideal choice.

New furniture contributes a fresh, virgin atmosphere to a home whereas old furniture has absorbed chi energy from the past and has a more substantial feel. The kind of chi energy absorbed depends on the past use of the piece. A butcher's table will have absorbed a different kind of chi energy to a table used for displaying china. Find out the history of old pieces and make sure that it is compatible with your intentions for it. Most furniture will take in the chi energy of its new environment within a short time. Exercise particular caution with furniture that has been used for the slaughter of animals, or comes from funeral parlours, hospitals or similar environments.

Avoid positioning furniture so that sharp edges point towards you. This can direct swirling chi energy, known as cutting chi, towards you which causes your own chi energy to swirl and can lead to feelings of disorientation and eventually ill-health. Also avoid over-furnishing or filling rooms with clutter, which make it harder for chi energy to circulate and may lead to stagnation

TYPES OF FURNITURE

BEDS Bedrooms with high ceilings can take high beds on legs, which enhances uplifting tree chi energy. Bedrooms with lower ceilings would be better served by a low beds or futons. These create a more settled, soil chi energy. (See also page 49.)

CHAIRS Rounded, soft, plump chairs are more yin and therefore more relaxing. Upright, straight-backed chairs are more yang and activating. Mix more yin and more yang chairs to create a balanced atmosphere. Use colours to create a contrast, for example a red yang cushion on a soft yin chair.

TABLES The shape of a dining table has a strong influence on the area used for eating (see page 19). Side tables and coffee tables should have rounded corners, especially if they are placed in seating areas, to avoid cutting chi. Yang materials, such as glass on the table top, will speed up the flow of chi energy and produce a more stimulating, wideawake atmosphere; yin materials such as light natural wood will have a more soothing effect.

DRAWERS Tall chests of drawers encourage a greater flow of upward tree chi energy whereas low wide chests of drawers bring out more settled soil chi energy. Round knobs, particularly if made of metal, enhance metal chi energy and give a chest a more solid feel.

DRESSING TABLES If this is in the bedroom it should have rounded corners to avoid cutting chi. Do not let the mirror face your bed during the night. Cover it with a cloth when you go to bed if necessary. An oval mirror matches the outline of your head and is better for feeling more relaxed while putting on make-up.

CUPBOARDS Built-in cupboards should be designed to avoid stagnation. Hard, smooth, shiny surfaces help to keep chi energy moving. Where possible they should square off a room. For instance, you might build the cupboards into an alcove to eliminate the corners of the alcove and avoid introducing more sharp corners into the room. This is particularly important in bedrooms. Place free-standing cupboards in alcoves, too, if possible, for the same reasons. Corner cupboards are particularly helpful as they cut off internal corners without adding any protruding corners.

Yang chairs
Ideal for a home office where you need to be alert and stimulated, yang chairs have hard shiny surfaces and are made of metal or dark polished hardwoods.

Yin chairs
Padded furniture with smooth, curved outlines and soft fabric coverings is more yin, ideal for living rooms and bedrooms where you need to relax and wind down.

windows

Windows allow chi energy to flow easily into and out of your home, and they let in light. The direction the light comes from changes the chi energy in your home so eastern sunlight, for example, is very different from western sunlight. To determine the chi energy entering through the windows, place the grid of the Eight Directions over your floor plan and check their locations.

Ideally, the windows should expose your home to light from all directions. Where this is not possible, you might like to consider installing skylights. These are a useful means of bringing in more light, especially in rooms with no windows.

Make sure all your windows are easy to open. Ideally, open them at least once a day throughout the year to allow fresh air and chi energy into your home, and make sure you clean them regularly. Replace cracked or broken panes promptly.

Finally, avoid sitting with your back to a window or sleeping near a window unless it is covered with thick curtains. Both these situations can be unsettling and make it difficult for you to relax or go to sleep.

window treatments

The type of window covering you have eases or inhibits the entry of chi energy into a room.

Curtains
When drawn in large rooms, full curtains create a cosy atmosphere, but in small rooms they entail a risk of stagnation. Curtains in bedrooms help you sleep.

Vertical blinds
These are associated with tree chi energy and are useful if you want to make the room seem taller.

TYPES OF WINDOW

Chi energy enters and leaves a home more easily through large windows, but too many windows encourages too great a movement, making the home difficult to relax in. Too few or small windows can cause chi energy to slow down and stagnate. Ideally, the number of windows should be balanced against their size, and the type of glass used can help to counteract any disadvantages of size. The window's shape is related to Five-Element chi energy and also has an effect.

Tall rectangular windows represent tree energy, producing an upward-moving atmosphere in the home. They are most harmonious in the east, south and south-east of the home.

Pointed or triangular windows represent fire energy but are rarely found in domestic buildings.

Wide rectangular or square windows create a more settled atmosphere. They are linked to soil energy and are best sited to the south, south-west, west, north-west or north-east.

Round windows are linked to metal energy. They create a more concentrated atmosphere and are most applicable to the south-west, west, north-west, north and north-east.

Venetian blinds
These prevent stagnation. They allow in plenty of light so are good for small windows. Wooden blinds have a neutral effect on chi; metal speeds it up and plastic blocks the flow.

Roller blinds
Similar in their effects to slatted blinds, these create a slightly softer atmosphere because of the fabric. Use coloured or patterned fabric appropriate to the direction.

Shutters
More light is shut out by these coverings than any others and, as they are relatively solid, their influence on the flow of chi energy is similar to that of walls.

mirrors

Mirrors are very important in Feng Shui. They speed up and redirect the flow of chi energy. The hard, flat, shiny surfaces help chi energy to move more quickly, and their reflective quality deflects some of the chi in other directions. The effect is similar to the way they redirect light waves. Mirrors can therefore be used to direct chi energy and light to a part of your home where chi energy is stagnant. They can also reflect energy away from an area that has an excess of chi energy and deflect channels of fast-moving chi energy, unfavourable chi or cutting chi.

Mirrors are the most effective objects in these respects, but anything with a reflective surface can influence the flow of chi energy in a similar way. Flat items, such as the glass in a framed picture, act like flat mirrors; shaped items, such as door knockers, like convex mirrors (see below). The more polished and reflective the surface, the stronger the effect on chi energy. They can be used like mirrors (see opposite), and are also useful in dark areas such as corners to keep chi energy moving.

To deflect cutting chi from sharp corners or busy road away from your home, use shiny reflective door fittings. These are more practical alternatives to mirrors.

MIRROR SHAPES

Flat and convex are the two types of mirrors used in Feng Shui. Flat mirrors redirect chi energy in one direction whereas convex mirrors spread it out in lots of directions. Convex mirrors are usually round, but flat ones can be rectangular, square, round, oval, octagonal and irregular. Octagonal mirrors have special significance in Feng Shui as the eight sides are in harmony with the Eight Directions, but the other shapes can also be significant, and the material and colour of the mirror frame can also have a subtle influence on the surrounding chi.

Circular and oval mirrors are associated with metal chi energy, but whereas circles are more yang and help to contain chi, oval mirrors are more yin and therefore tend to disperse chi. Tall, thin rectangular shapes encourage upward-moving tree chi energy. Low, wide rectangles are associated with soil energy and create a more stable, settled atmosphere in a room. Like circles, squares are compact shapes and have the effect of containing chi energy.

using mirrors

Mirrors are used in many Feng Shui remedies. Positioned carefully, they can help chi energy to move harmoniously through your home, and overcome the disadvantages of problem features such as long narrow corridors, small or L-shaped rooms and stairs opposite the front door.

Corridors
Stagger mirrors on either side of a long corridor to move chi energy from side to side, slowing the flow. The corridor will also appear wider. In a dark, winding corridor position a convex mirror on the bend so that you can see around it. If daylight is reflected in it so much the better; the mirror also helps chi flow round the bend.

L-shaped rooms
Use large mirrors to give the impression a room extends into an indentation. Hang them to reflect the space facing the mirror into the indentation. They will also encourage chi to flow across the room, making the mirror wall seem further away.

Small rooms
Large flat mirrors can make a narrow room appear wider by directing the chi energy across the room.

Entrance halls
Where stairs are positioned opposite the front door, place a convex mirror to reflect chi energy back into the house. Place a large flat mirror next to the front door so you see round the door as you open it.

other chi activators

Certain small items can be used to activate chi in a variety of contexts and in a particularly powerful way. These include crystals, lighted candles, things that make beautiful sounds and sea salt.

CRYSTALS

As sunlight passes through a crystal it refracts into the colours of the rainbow. Beams of coloured light radiate in all directions, each colour carrying the intensity of that particular type of chi energy.

The commonest crystals are round multi-faceted ones. Irregularly shaped or jagged crystals can also be used but take care to avoid creating too much spiky chi. Place them near plants whose own yin chi energy will help smooth that of the crystal.

CANDLES

Candles have fire chi energy, which encourages passion and helps attract attention. If you want to develop a more intimate relationship with someone, place a pair of candles close together. Tall ones are the most suitable as they represent tree energy which is supportive to fire.

The most favourable locations for candles are in the east, south-east, south, south-west, centre and north-east of your home or particular room. You can keep the candle burning continuously, or while you are in the room, or when that direction is most active (see pages 22–25).

Candles are helpful where a home or room is lacking sunlight. Place several candles in the south of the room or in the corner. In dark damp rooms candles make the atmosphere drier and brighter.

The shape, material and colour of the candle holder has a subtle influence on the surrounding chi energy. A tall, black, wrought iron holder, for example, is associated with tree, soil and metal chi energies. A tall, green, wooden holder has tree chi energy characteristics, and a flat white china holder soil chi energy.

White candles have the closest relationship to the flame of the candle and, in most situations, are preferable to coloured candles.

Using crystals
Hung in a window, crystals can bring chi energy from outside into dark or stagnant areas of your home.

SOUNDS

Sound vibrates the air, which stimulates chi energy. Chanting and singing can achieve this, but wind chimes, bells and gongs, ticking clocks and the sound of running water are also helpful.

WIND CHIMES The tone is intended to purify and cleanse chi energy, so choose chimes carefully for the sweetness and clarity of their sound. Chimes are usually made of metal, wood or pottery, which enhance the elements of metal, tree and soil respectively.

When you have decided where the chimes should be, check that direction from the centre of your home and choose an appropriate material (see page 78). To stimulate chi energy near a door in the north of your home, for example, hang metal chimes so that they sound when the door is opened. To calm chi energy of the south, pottery chimes are more suitable.

BELLS AND GONGS Traditionally, these have been used to clear chi energy in a part or all of the home. They can be rung by hand in areas that feel heavy or stagnant. Other ringing sounds have a similar effect. If the sound is generated by a metal bell rather than electronically, telephone and door bells can enhance the flow of chi energy.

Making sounds
Whether loud or soft, sounds can stimulate or cleanse chi energy, particularly in areas where it is prone to stagnation (dark corners, corridors, hallways or under sloping roofs).

SEA SALT

Salt is the most yang of the foods we eat. It is found in blood in the form of sodium and thus has a direct influence on your personal chi energy. It also has the ability to draw moisture out of the atmosphere, and in Feng Shui terms its effect is to pull chi energy into it, which tends to have a purifying and stabilizing influence. This contracting inward-moving chi is associated with Five-Element metal energy, so you can use sea salt in situations where it will be in harmony with that. Place one or two tablespoons of salt in a low white china bowl. Place the bowl on the floor, or on a shelf or table if you have children or pets. Alternatively, tuck it out of sight behind a piece of furniture

Sea salt is most effective in the north-east and south-west of the house where the metal energy of the salt will help stabilize the naturally less stable flow of soil chi.

water features

Water is one of the key solutions in Feng Shui as it has a special significance for the human body: it carries ingredients vital for human life
and is essential for growing food. Humans evolved from sea creatures
and most of our body weight is made up of water. By adding a water
feature either to your garden or inside your home you bring in fresh chi
energy that can be highly beneficial for your health and destiny.

The water feature can take the form of a garden pond, fountain,
swimming pool, bird bath, aquarium, or other indoor water feature.
Even a small bowl of fresh clean water can be effective. The water
should remain fresh and unpolluted. Place it either east or south-east
from the centre of your home; no other locations are recommended.

An aquarium is a favourite means of bringing moving water indoors.
Place the tank east or south-east from the centre of your home and, if
possible, to the east or south-east from the centre of the room. Use
pebbles and shells rather than plastic decoration. Appropriate living
plants in the water will add their own chi energy and help keep the tank
clean and the fish healthy.

Indoor fountains can vary from elaborate structures to a small rock
with an integral pump that moves water to the top of the rock and allows
it to trickle down again. As with aquariums, these should be located to
the east or south-east of the centre of your home or room.

If you do not have the space for a more elaborate water feature place
a bowl of water to the east or south-east of your
home. Refill it each day. Ideally, the bowl should
be refilled from a tap in the east or south-east
of the home before any other water is
taken from it.

FISH
Depending on their shape, colour and behaviour, the fish
you put into a aquarium can either be more yin or more yang.
Quick, aggressive fish darting backwards and forwards will create a
more yang dynamic flow of chi. Brightly coloured fish are also stimulating. Slow, peaceful fish, or fish with muted colours are more yin
and promote a gentler more relaxing atmosphere.

Acknowledgements

Carroll and Brown would like to thank the following:

Illustrations: D. Brown, Peter Cambell, Karen Cochrane
Model Making: Robert Bradshaw
Photography: David Murray, Jules Selmes
Design: Vimit Punater
Editorial: Madeleine Jennings
Production: Wendy Lawson

Author acknowledgements:

I would like to thank all those who have played their part in helping me to arrive at the place where I could write this book: all the Browns, especially my mother Patsy, Dragana, the love of my life, my children Christopher, Alexander, Nicholas and Michael; also Adam and Angela and their children; the Waxmans, especially Melanie and Denny for getting me started; an enormous thank you to Boy George for all his help; my friends and clients Kim Andreolli, Adrienne Brown, Jasna Cacik, Enno and Dusica von Landmann, Michael Maloney, the Mosbachers, and my oldest friend Jeremy Parkin; my teachers and colleagues Michio and Aveline Kushi, Shizuko Yamamoto; my colleagues Maria and John Brosnan; Stephen Skinner and Nimita Palmer at *Feng Shui for Modern Living*, Jon Sandifer and everyone at the Feng Shui Society; a special thank you to all my clients who have given me the opportunity to put Feng Shui into practice; and everyone at Carroll and Brown, especially Amy Carroll, Denise Brown and Madeleine Jennings.

Simon Brown

about the author

Simon Brown began his career as a design engineer and has had two inventions patented in his name. In 1981 he began studies in Oriental medicine and qualified as a shiatsu therapist and macrobiotic consultant. In addition to these healing arts, he studied Feng Shui. For seven years he was director of London's Community Health Foundation, a charity that ran a wide range of courses specialising in Japanese and Chinese healing arts. During this time Simon taught the first courses on Feng Shui to the UK general public. Simon has since made Feng Shui his full-time career. His client list ranges from large public companies (such as British Airways and The Body Shop) to celebrities (including Boy George). Presently, he writes regular features for the magazine *Feng Shui for Modern Living* and conducts training workshops in Lisbon, Munich, Paris, Rome and various cities throughout the UK and US.

All books by Simon Brown use the compass style of Feng Shui.

Also published by Ward Lock:

Practical Feng Shui
A complete do-it-yourself practical guide to Feng Shui. Explains how Feng Shui works with full colour photographs and drawings. Expanding on the material covered in *Essential Feng Shui*, this book provides additional information on how to carry out a Feng Shui survey and further design solutions for your home. It advises on how to make the most of the shape and location of your home, how best to tackle unusual areas such as utility and storage rooms, staircases, doors and fireplaces, and helps you to understand the effects of sunlight. It also includes information on Feng Shui astrology, based on the Nine Ki system.

Practical Feng Shui for Business
Ideal for anyone who wants to apply Feng Shui to their career. This book explains how to be more successful at work. Full of colourful drawings and photographs to help you to implement Feng Shui in real life situations, the book also includes successful strategies for offices, shops and restaurants.

Practical Feng Shui Astrology
Using the Nine Ki system, learn how to make and read your own birth chart, which can then be used to gain interesting insights into your relationships with lovers, friends and family. This book helps you to work out the best time to make important changes in your life and highlights the most favourable times of year for you. Also in full colour with quick reference charts that make it fun and easy to use.

Other publications include:

The Principles of Feng Shui
(Thorsons ISBN 0 7225 3347 0)
This is now also available as an audio cassette.

For information on Feng Shui consultations and courses with Simon Brown contact:
PO Box 10453, London NW3 4WD, England.
Tel/Fax 00-44-207-431 9897
e-mail 106025.3515@compuserve.com.

Visit his web site, including software for floor plans and Nine Ki information, on:
HTTP://ourworld.compuserve.com/homepages/simonbrown_fengshui

THE ROAD BENEATH ME

When Kate Swan's father demands that she marry a man she despises, she refuses and is cast out of her comfortable home in Whitby.

Meanwhile in Shetland, Malcolm McFadden, disagrees with his father's plan to clear the crofters from his land. He proposes to defy convention by marrying crofter's daughter Rowena Murray, but she hesitates and Malcolm leaves Shetland on his own.

When he and Kate meet, they are instantly attracted to each other, but while Kate fulfils her obligations to her new employer, Malcolm receives the news he has long dreaded. The Highland Clearances have begun, and old loyalties draw him back to Shetland.

For Jill
for showing me the way ahead.

THE ROAD
BENEATH ME

by

Jessica Blair

Magna Large Print Books
Long Preston, North Yorkshire,
BD23 4ND, England.

British Library Cataloguing in Publication Data.

Blair, Jessica
    The road beneath me.

    A catalogue record of this book is
    available from the British Library

    ISBN   978-0-7505-3631-8

First published in Great Britain in 2012 by Piatkus

Published in Large Print 2012 by arrangement with
Little, Brown Book Group

LP

Magna Large Print is an imprint of Library Magna Books Ltd.

Printed and bound in Great Britain by
T.J. (International) Ltd., Cornwall, PL28 8RW

PROLOGUE

Kneeling in a hollow, a young girl watched three children racing happily across a sandy bay. The breeze was light, barely rippling the sea that sparkled diamond-like under the Shetland sun and seemed to charge the three running figures with energy and joy.

She knew who they were but was certain they would not know her. She was envious of their privileged life and their companionship as siblings. Their laughter jarred on her ears. She saw the elder boy stop, rooted in curiosity. She knew he had seen her. Feeling she should escape, she scrambled to her feet. He waved again. His brother and sister came to him. All three, smiling, beckoned to her. Dare she join them?

After a moment's hesitation she raised her hand, returned their smiles and ran eagerly towards them, steps that would take them all into unforeseen worlds.

1

It was a day Kathleen Swan would never forget:
12 August 1832, the day that changed her life.

From the window-seat in her room, she looked
up from her copy of *The Last of the Mohicans* and
swept her gaze across the River Esk and Whitby's
red roofs climbing the East Cliff, to the ancient
church and ruined abbey at the top. From its
position high on the West Cliff, her room gave
her a panoramic view from the sea and all along
the river to the busy quays beyond the drawbridge. She sighed; not because of any real dis-
content but because, at nineteen, she felt that
maybe life was passing her by.

Most young women of Kate's age anticipated
marriage to an eligible beau, fearing the life of a
spinster who would be looked down on with their
future left dependent on the charity of relations or
others. Her elder brothers, Archie and Samuel,
were both married, and her sister Dorothea, a year
younger than Kate, had her eye on Ben Crichton.
It wasn't as if Kate herself had not received pro-
posals but, unlike some girls she knew, she had not
chosen the prospect of security over a love match.
Ever since she had been a little girl, she had
dreamed of the day she would meet the 'knight in
shining armour' who would sweep her off her feet
and into a world of pure happiness. She sighed
again. Had she been foolish? Had she allowed that

girlish dream to mislead her? Should she have married without waiting for love? She shook her head, annoyed with herself for doubting her own scruples. No, it was the right course for her. She could do nothing else.

She looked back at the printed words, hoping to direct her thoughts to this stirring tale of adventure.

She was aware of movement outside and a swift glance out of the window brought surprise – her father returning home in the middle of the morning? She had never known him do this; something very important must be bringing him back at this time. During the next ten minutes she heard various comings and goings which all seemed to centre around his study. Curious, but realising she would probably never be told what was going on, she turned her attention back to her book.

So absorbed had she become that she did not realise someone had approached her door until there was a knock on it. Kate looked up.

'Come in.'

The door opened and a maid took a step inside.

'Yes, Agnes?'

'The master wants to see you in his study, miss.'

Surprise brought a moment's hesitation then Kate said, 'Thank you, Agnes.'

The girl bobbed a little curtsey and left.

Kate sat still for a moment. Her heartbeat had speeded up a little. What did her father want? Was it connected with his unusually early return? She'd better not keep him waiting. She stood, flicking away a loose thread from her high-necked spencer before smoothing down the pale yellow dress that fell from its tight-fitting waist to her ankles. She gave herself a quick glance in the mirror, primed her copper-coloured hair with swift movements of her delicate fingers, and left the room.

Kate tripped lightly down the stairs, but slowed at the bottom. Her bright blue eyes lost some of their sparkle as she wondered what awaited her behind the heavy, dark-oak door. She could not account for it but the sense of foreboding that began to grip her then made her want to turn and run away. But she knew it would do her no good. She had to face her father. A far from easy man, he was hard if not cruel. She knew there were times when he had laid hand on her brothers in anger, but he had never once struck her or Dorothea, though they had felt the lash of his tongue. He always expected their instant obedience. It was understood he would direct their lives, and not them.

Kate took a deep breath and squared her shoulders. She crossed the hall, knocked on the door and entered the room with its heavy, forbidding atmosphere. Her father sat behind his desk, stiff and upright, his eyebrows drawn close, his dark eyes penetrating. The formality of his pose was matched by the room's furnishings: a dark-oak desk with matching sideboard and chairs. One wall was lined with books, another adorned with paintings of a dark forest. The gloom was alleviated only by light from a large window overlooking the garden.

But today, to Kate's surprise, another person was present. Her mother sat in a chair drawn up at an angle to one of the corners of the desk.

10

Another chair was positioned at the other corner; so that each of them could see the other two without having to turn their head. Kate realised this had all been carefully arranged and, coupled with her mother's presence, it suggested a serious matter was about to be broached.

Without a word, her father indicated she should sit in the vacant chair. Kate did as she had been bidden, and sat down, back straight, hands resting primly in her lap, waiting for him to speak.

Not being a man to ease his way gradually into a subject, Titus Swan came straight to the point. 'It's time you married, Kate. You have shown no inclination to accept any of the eligible young men who have come courting you, so I am making arrangements with Mr Garfield for you to marry his only child. Cyrus will be calling on you a week today,' he brusquely informed her.

This bare announcement, with no consideration for how she might feel regarding the matter, chilled Kate to the very core. She had never thought she would be offered to such a man. Cyrus Garfield? One word repeated itself in her mind. Never! Never! Never!

Kate glanced at her mother's pale, expressionless face and realised she was looking at someone who had herself been tied into a loveless marriage. Oh, Emma Swan had wanted for nothing; there was always sufficient money coming in from her husband's rope and sail manufactory, now well established in the thriving port of Whitby. She ran the house to her husband's liking, with the help of a housekeeper, but now Kate knew why, within this household, her mother had always turned for

11

companionship to her children.

In that moment Kate knew she did not want a life like her mother's. With that unshakable conviction came deliberate and immediate defiance.

She gave voice to the word that was crying out to be heard. 'Never!' Kate jumped up from her chair, shaking but determined not to back down. 'Never! I'll never marry Cyrus Garfield!' she yelled, and then lowered her voice to repeat, 'Never!'

Titus scowled, eyes dark with anger at this unexpected insubordination. 'Sit down, girl.' His voice was harsh but Kate defiantly remained standing. Titus's hands were resting on the desktop and Kate saw he had clenched them until his knuckles were white. She sensed her mother stiffen, but knew Emma would make no intervention. She would not dare. 'Sit down!' hissed Titus between tight-drawn lips.

Kate knew if she did her position would be weakened; her father would see this as a further chance to exert his authority. She remained standing.

His gaze was penetrating but Kate met and held it with equal tenacity. She did not waver and knew her father was shocked by the strength of her resistance. Keeping her tone even, she told him, 'I can see why you are promoting this marriage, I'm not stupid. An only son ... an ailing father. But I will *not* be used as a pawn in your plan to get your hands on the Garfields' business.'

'Don't dare to defy me! I *will* be obeyed. You will marry Cyrus Garfield!' Her father's voice was cold, filled with the certainty that his authority had never been challenged by any member of the family before and it was going to prevail now.

Still holding his gaze, Kate shook her head slowly. 'No!'

He did not reply immediately, allowing the seconds that passed to strengthen the finality of his words when he eventually spoke. 'Then you are no daughter of mine!' he declared.

'So be it,' Kate whispered.

Titus glowered with fury. 'Then go! Get out of my sight. But think carefully on the result if you do – no money; no help from me; cut off from your family; a life of poverty and hardship for which you are totally unsuited. You'll come running back eventually – when you accept that marrying Cyrus Garfield is the better prospect for your future.'

'I will not marry him.' Kate spoke determinedly, and forced herself to walk unhurriedly from the room. Her last glance was at her mother, a subdued and beaten woman without the spirit to speak up for her own child, though Kate thought she saw regret in her eyes and a tear slide from one of them.

She walked quickly upstairs and in to her room, sinking back against the door as it closed. It was only then that the enormity of what she had done hit her. She felt cold.

She had become an outcast.

Some would say she was stupid; others would think her stubborn and disobedient. But this was hardly a childish tantrum. She was nineteen, for goodness' sake, with the rest of her life ahead of her. Many girls in her position would have agreed to the arrangements made for them by their parents, hoping that love would eventually develop

13

in the marriage and thankful for the security they had gained by it. But Kate would stick to her convictions. She wanted none of that.

2

Leaning against the door, drained by the enormity of what she had just done, Kate felt sick and dizzy. She walked slowly to the bed and sat down. Reaction to its familiar softness jolted her back to reality. Never again would she sleep amidst the warm comfort of its feathers, or feel the soft blankets comforting her with the reassurance that she had a place to live where she wanted for nothing.

Not true! Hadn't parental love always been lacking here? Her defiance of her father's order to marry Cyrus Garfield had thrust into the forefront of her mind something she had known for a long time but had never allowed herself to dwell on. He had no true affection for her, but saw her and all his children as mere chattels, their wishes and feelings of no consequence to him whatsoever.

Nevertheless, she could still turn the clock back. She could, here and now, beg her father's forgiveness with all the humility she could conjure and hope that he would pardon her terrible insubordination. But that would mean marrying Cyrus. For one moment indecision clouded Kate's dazed mind, but then the horror of being married to a man she did not love closed in. It was as if Cyrus himself stood before her now – a weedy, insinuating sort of man of thirty or so, whose talk was often tainted with innuendos and whose hooded eyes always dwelt for too long on any half-attractive woman. Such a man would expect his wife's total subservience – an even worse scenario than the life her mother endured. At least Titus had some consideration for her since they occupied different rooms. Cyrus Garfield would show no such respect for Kathleen.

'Never!' She moved her lips silently, bolstering her own defiance. She had swiftly realised why her father was prepared to sacrifice her happiness. Cyrus was the only son of an ailing widower who had a small but successful ships' chandlery business. Her father knew it would be a useful addition to his own enterprise and planned to exert pressure on Cyrus through Kate. She was revolted by the lengths he was prepared to go to, to bolster his own wealth and status. Well, *she* would not be party to his scheming! She would not be used as a pawn to make her father richer. She would make what she wanted of her own life.

Kate crossed to the window and gazed out across Whitby. This was a view she loved, one which had sent a young girl's dreams soaring as she watched the ships sail down the river to the sea, and thought of the men aboard who did not know what they would face before once more sighting Whitby's welcoming landmarks of red roofs, ancient church and ruined abbey. Among them were young men more worthy of her affections than Cyrus Garfield. Kate impressed the view on her mind for she did not believe she would gaze on it from this room again. She let eyes drift over it then sweep down to the road below. She paused, wondering where her future lay, where that road might lead her ... what it had in store for her next.

Someone walked past with a resolute step; they knew where they were going. It jolted Kate back to the reality of her situation. She had to leave now. She could not remain in this house tonight. To do so might be interpreted by her father as a weakening of her resolve and a tacit acceptance of his order. She must leave at once. But where could she go?

Kate grabbed a valise and threw into it some clothes and necessities, taking only what she could manage to carry; she would have to make do as she went along. She needed time to think and consider her best course of action.

She was fastening her valise when there was a gentle tap on the door. As Kate turned to answer, it opened and Dorothea slipped inside, closing the door quietly behind her. She looked troubled as she faced her sister.

'Father's gone out. Mother told me what happened. Oh, Kate, what will you do?' Tears were welling in her eyes.

Kate took her sister in her arms. 'I don't know, but I can't stay here.'

'But you...'

Kate interrupted quickly, fearful of what Dorothea might say to try and change her mind. 'Say nothing. I couldn't possibly marry Cyrus Garfield ... I shudder at the thought. Father has only his own ends in mind. I'll not be used for gain.'

'Oh, Kate, I don't want to lose you. What will

16

happen to me now? Might Father want me to take your place? It's Ben Crichton who...'

'I thought as much,' Kate said with pleasure in her tone. 'Ben's made for you, and I doubt Father will frown on the match. He and Mr Crichton are close associates; he won't want to spoil that. If he has other ideas, it will be up to you to stand up to him.' She stood back a little, grasped Dorothea by the shoulders and instructed her, 'Don't let him force you into anything you don't want to do. You can make a good case for marrying Ben, if you try, and I'm sure Father will agree. But Cyrus... Never! Now, I must be away before Father returns.' She swung her redingote around her shoulders, tied on her bonnet, and picked up her gloves and valise.

'Will you see Mama before you go?' asked Dorothea.

'I don't think that would be wise. Give her my love.'

'Please let us know where you are.'

'I'll try to let *you* know, but not Mama. Father would only wheedle it out of her – she's so browbeaten after all these years. So, please, be discreet.'

'I will.'

They hugged again, and then Kate hurried from the room without a backward glance. Reaching the bottom of the stairs, she kept going briskly to the front door. Without hesitation she opened it and swept outside. The sound of it closing seemed to signal that a chapter of her life was over and a new one was about to begin.

Kate hurried down the garden path and out on to the road that she had observed from her room.

In the last few moments she had decided where it would lead her. Now she tried to bolster her confidence with quick steps, aware that her immediate prospects now lay in the hands of two people whom she dearly loved.

She took the road to the bridge, crossed to the East Side and headed along Church Street towards Green Lane, which formed the steep incline leading to the Abbey Plain. At the lower end of Green Lane stood a terrace of modest-sized houses known as Prospect Row. In one of these lived her brother Archie and his wife Rosemary. Though she loved Samuel and his wife Alicia dearly, Archie was Kate's favourite brother and she had a deep and long-standing friendship with her sister-in-law Rosemary. If anyone would help her, if only with advice, she was sure they would.

Kate rapped the brass doorknocker. A few moments later it was opened by the neatly dressed maid who smiled on seeing her and stepped back to allow her to enter.

'Good morning, miss.'

'Good morning, Polly. Is your mistress at home?'

'Yes, miss. I'll inform her...'

'That's all right, Polly,' said Rosemary, hurrying out of the drawing room.

'Ma'am.' The girl hurried away.

'The door was ajar, I heard your voice,' said Rosemary, coming to Kate with arms outstretched. Her warm smile changed to an expression of curiosity when she saw the valise Kate had with her. 'What...?'

'I'm sorry to intrude on your morning, but I need to speak to you.' At the urgency in Kate's

18

tone, Rosemary's expression changed to one of concern.

'Come in.' She took the valise, placed it on the floor beside a small table, and drew Kate by the arm into the drawing room. 'Let's have you out of your coat and get you a drink. You look as though you need it. Then you can tell me what's troubling you. That valise seems to indicate it's something drastic.' As she was speaking she had taken Kate's coat, placed it on a chair and sat her down on a comfortable sofa. She went to the oak sideboard where she poured two glasses of wine for them. Handing one to Kate, she sat down beside her and said, 'Now you can tell me.'

That was what Kate liked most about Rosemary: she always seemed to be in charge of any situation. She was besides attractive and charming. They had known each other since they were girls and had shared much together. Kate had been delighted when Rosemary agreed to marry Archie, believing they were perfectly matched and that Rosemary would be a great asset to him. So it had proved when she supported his desire to open his own ship-building business rather than work alongside his father. That had left the way clear for Samuel to stay with his father's business, which had satisfied everyone.

'I've left home!' Kate blurted out.

'As simple as that?' queried Rosemary calmly.

'Well, not exactly. Father ordered me to marry Cyrus Garfield!'

'What?'

Kate nodded a confirmation.

'And you refused and walked out?'

19

'I refused, yes, but Father told me in no uncertain terms to leave. He cut me off without a
penny. I believe he thinks that after I've had a
taste of the outside world, I'll be back begging to
marry Cyrus.'

Rosemary gave a little shudder. 'How could
anyone marry that horrid man? How could your
father order you to do so?'

'Because he has his eyes on the Garfields'
business and is used to getting his own way.'

Rosemary nodded thoughtfully. 'So what are
you going to do now?'

'I don't know.' The words caught in Kate's
throat as the prospect of her uncertain future
yawned before her.

'I see,' said Rosemary decisively. 'Does your
father know where you are now?'

'No.'

'Good, then you must stay with us for as long
as possible, though I fear that may not be very
long. I will have a word with Polly and Cook, tell
them to say nothing about you, but it is bound to
come out sometime. We'll deal with that when it
arises. Now let's get you settled in and we'll talk
with Archie when he gets home.' Rosemary rose
from the sofa.

As Kate followed suit she said, 'I am grateful
for what you are doing. I do realise that it could
be awkward for Archie so it will be best if I can
make other plans as soon as possible.'

'Have you any ideas?'

Kate shook her head. 'No. But I'll do anything
to keep my independence. I'll not relent and
submit to Father's wishes. Marriage to Cyrus

would be a fate worse than death.'

Rosemary took her hand, a reassuring gesture. 'Don't even think about it. Let's get you settled.'

Rosemary showed Kate the room she would occupy and left her to unpack. Even as she was doing so, Kate was trying to think of a way out of her immediate dilemma. She needed some occupation that would bring her an income. Her independent streak would not allow her to consider anything else.

When she came downstairs she found Rosemary, pen in hand, seated at her satinwood secretaire. Kate did not interrupt but stood looking out of the window until, a few moments later, Rosemary said in a satisfied tone, 'There.' She said no more to enlighten Kate but sealed the letter she had written, rose from her chair and went to the bell-pull. A few moments later Polly appeared. 'I want you to take this note to Mr Swan at his yard. You need not wait for an answer,' Rosemary instructed.

'Yes, ma'am.'

'And, Polly, I do not want you to mention to anyone, not even Mr Swan, that Miss Swan is staying here.'

'Yes, ma'am. Do I see to her room too?'

'Yes, until she leaves. I don't know how long that will be.'

The girl nodded and started to turn for the door.

'And, Polly, ask Cook to come and see me.'

'Yes, ma'am.'

As the door closed, Rosemary explained to Kate that she had asked Archie to come and take luncheon at home. 'I have not said anything about your being here, just that I have an urgent matter I wish to discuss with him and that it cannot wait until he comes home later.'

When Cook appeared she and Kate acknowledged each other, then Rosemary told her, 'Miss Swan will be staying with us for a while. I don't want that information going beyond this room.'

Rosemary and Kate were sitting in the drawing room when Archie arrived, his face grave; he had never been summoned home like this before. Seeing his sister, he immediately associated her presence with his wife's note.

'What's wrong?' he asked, alarm creeping into his voice.

Kate was about to explain but held back, allowing Rosemary to put the situation to him; she was pleased to do so because she knew Rosemary would explain things much more calmly than Kate herself would have done. Emotion would have coloured her version of events. Rosemary, as an outsider, put the facts more logically, presenting the problem they had brought about much more lucidly, with the result that when Archie spoke again, it was in a much more composed manner.

He started with the obvious. 'We have a problem.' Then he added, looking Kate straight in the eye, 'I hope you can see this from my point of view? It does me no good to offend Father.'

Her heart sank. Was there going to be no sympathy, no support, from the brother she loved? Surely Rosemary would bring her influence to bear.

Archie was going on, 'I know you will say that I

stood up to Father when I told him I wanted to establish a shipbuilding business, but he supported that because he saw it as an adjunct to his own enterprises, and besides had Samuel, who was far more interested in the sail- and rope-making business than I was. You have defied him for different reasons.' He stopped Kate when he saw she was going to protest at the instruction she thought he was about to issue: Go back and beg forgiveness. 'I support your stance,' Archie assured her. 'Marriage to Cyrus would be a disaster, condemning you to a hellish life. Father is blinded by the prospect of commercial advantage, which is no excuse when it comes to imposing his wishes on others, especially his own daughter. But that's his way. Now we have to consider you. Have you any idea what to do next?'

She shook her head. 'No. I had hoped you and Rosemary could help.'

'I have said Kate can stay here but that I would have to seek your thoughts,' Rosemary put in.

Archie nodded. He looked at Kate. 'Rosemary knows this but you probably don't. Father financed the start of my business and is continuing to do so until I have it on a sound basis. I am doing well but I am not yet at the stage where I can do without his support. I cannot risk losing that, which I surely would if we give you refuge here. He is sure to get to know.'

A chill had settled over Kate. She could feel her colour draining away, and with it all hope. 'You want me to leave?' Her voice, scarcely above a whisper, carried a sense of the betrayal she felt.

'No, Kate, we do not. Believe me, we will give

you all the support we dare. But please try and understand our position.' She saw him glance at Rosemary for her approval and knew, from the easing of his tone, that his wife had granted it; the reassurance of help she had given Kate was now sealed, within limits. 'We will try and find another solution as quickly as possible,' her brother continued. 'What about going to Aunt Clarissa in Newcastle?'

'Too risky to go to any relative. I would have to give a reason for going, and whoever it was would be bound to seek Father's approval,' Kate pointed out.

They both agreed that would not be a wise move.

'Besides, I need to gain an income. I've only a little money at my disposal ... in fact, what I have in my pocket ... and I cannot think of taking that sort of help from you.'

'We'll manage while you are here,' said her brother. 'What we need to do is find some permanent position for you.'

'Anything,' Kate declared, 'rather than yield to the plan Father has made for me. I'll gather seaweed for the alum works at Ravenscar. I'll scrat for jet for Whitby's workshops. I'll go as a domestic. I'll gut herrings ... I'll do anything.'

'Wait!' Rosemary broke in. 'Domestic – that's reminded me. Three days ago, when I visited Mama, the conversation turned to a friend of hers, Mrs Jordan, who lives at Peak House near Robin Hood's Bay.'

'High on the cliffs where the bay swings round towards Ravenscar,' explained Archie. 'It's a wonderful setting with views right across the bay.'

'I know it,' Kate said. 'Father allowed Dorothea and me to take a trap to Robin Hood's Bay one day.' She added with a little smile, 'We never told him we went a little further; we drove past Peak House.'

'So what's this got to do with our problem?' asked Archie, eyeing his wife.

'Well, I took little notice at the time but, hearing Kate mention a domestic position, I recalled Mama telling me Mrs Jordan's companion had recently left and that she was hoping to find another.'

Archie's eyes were bright when he turned to his sister and said with some enthusiasm, 'What do you think, Kate?'

This unexpected opportunity had occurred so quickly she had barely had time to take it in, but now the possibilities were making themselves apparent and excitement was gripping her. 'It could be the answer. It will give me my independence. Do you know Mrs Jordan, Rosemary?'

'I've never met her but I've heard Mother talk about her. A genteel lady in her early-sixties ... been widowed ten years. Her husband made his money in Scarborough and bought Peak House because they both loved this part of the coast. She is energetic, loves gardening and walking on the cliffs. A fine embroideress ... loves being read to while she is working on her latest piece.'

'You'd like that, Kate,' Archie enthused.

Already the situation was appealing to her. Why had she been so lucky? At that moment there flashed before her a memory of what she had

25

seen from her window: the road below. And she had wondered where it would take her. Was this the answer? To Peak House? And where would it lead beyond that?

That pulled her up short. What if the position with Mrs Jordan had already been filled?

3

Malcolm McFadden stepped outside Garstan House and let his eyes slowly scan his surroundings. This was one of his favourite views in Shetland, if not the favourite, and it was part of the estate he would one day inherit as its new laird.

He loved the house that had been his home for all twenty-one years of his life. It had been built by a seventeenth-century ancestor. With its winding passages, crooked staircases and many rooms, each with its own character, it had been a splendid house in which to play Hide and Seek with Angus, his younger brother by a year, and sister Lavinia, two years his junior. It was full of memories, most of them happy; the saddest being when his mother had died with her still-born child in 1814, eighteen years ago. Malcolm was only three at the time. Their father, Mungo, was devastated by the loss of his wife, and found solace in running his estate. Unable to manage such young children, he had sought help from his childless sister, Grizel, whose husband had been lost at sea. She had come to nurse the children's mother in the latter stages of her pregnancy, and had readily agreed to her brother's suggestion that she should live with them and look after the family. She had run their home since with kindness and love, a soothing influence on all of them.

In his young years, Malcolm was always eager to be outdoors where he loved to roam. He had watched the seasonal comings and goings of the birds, particularly the swift-weaving terns and the brilliantly coloured, comical puffins. He had roamed the cliffs and the beaches; watched the sea otters playing among the rocks unaware of his presence, and laughed at the seals' ungainly movements on land while admiring their agility once in the water. Everything an adventurous boy needed was here, but as he grew up he came to appreciate his life on Shetland more profoundly, though it was still tinged with the magic of those earlier days.

The time came when Angus and Lavinia insisted on accompanying him on his adventures: 'Otherwise we'll tell Papa.' He knew Angus, always more devious and sly, would carry out that threat, though he trusted Lavinia not to. She and Malcolm would explore together whereas Angus became more of a loner. Malcolm regarded him as a sneak. It was when they roamed the estate that Malcolm and Lavinia first came into contact with the crofters. At first the estate dwellers regarded the laird's children with suspicion, but once that barrier was breached and the crofters realised the children meant no harm, they were welcomed any time.

Malcolm's boyish charm, open friendly manner

and ready smile, together with Lavinia's charming innocence, won the trust of the tenants eking out a living on their father's estate. Although Mungo had forbidden direct contact with them, Aunt Grizel turned a blind eye to the association. The estate was a big place and neither their father nor his factor could be everywhere. The children trusted the crofters to hide them if authority was seen approaching.

The people grumbled about living on the edge of poverty, continually trying to wrest a living from their small landholdings, though income from that source was further compromised when they had to neglect their crops and animals in order to try and supplement their earnings by fishing. But they never complained or spoke out against the laird in the children's presence, offering them nothing but friendship instead. With his sharp mind and skilful hands, Malcolm quickly learned their boat-repair and fishing skills. That brought pleasure to those who had taught him, and he derived satisfaction from these sea-faring skills.

It was only as he became older that he realised the good things in life that he had taken for granted, and thought were experienced in the same way by everyone, resulted from the disparity in social position that led to poverty for some and riches for others.

Now, he stood in front of the house and fixed his gaze upon the land that narrowed between two voes and ran in a north-easterly direction to the high cliffs, beyond which were Yell, Fetlar and Unst, island jewels where the North Sea and the Atlantic met. He regarded this as his Shetland –

not in any possessive way, even though this part of it was his inheritance, but rather because of the love for it that sprang from deep within him.

He had welcomed his father's suggestion that he might take more responsibility for running the estate once he reached the age of majority, but had soon realised that they held differing views on how this should be done. Wisely Malcolm had kept most of his own ideas to himself, knowing that one day his time would come. But then he realised that might be too late for him to help the crofters who had generously befriended him as a child. He had recently heard conversations when other local lairds had visited Garstan House that had alarmed him greatly. Some admitted that they had already enforced eviction on their crofters, so that they could take back the land and use it more profitably by turning it over to sheep. Others were in favour of embracing this policy. Malcolm knew his father had listened to them. He also knew that so far as the landowners were concerned the policy made a great deal of sense, but it alarmed him that so little thought was given to the future of the tenants they planned to dispossess.

Mungo was so engrossed in managing his estate that everything else in his life revolved around it. His one aim in life was to leave it financially sound; he would make provision for Angus and Lavinia so that they would never want, while Malcolm as eldest son would inherit the land and the house. The income from the crofters' tiny holdings was always uncertain; an unproductive harvest or poor fishing always affected the returns. The more Mungo considered the situation, the more convinced he became that eviction and sheep-rearing could be the answer to fulfilling his ambition, even though he knew it would be disastrous for the crofters. But Mungo was not given to sentimentality. For him the future of the Garstan Estate was paramount.

Malcolm knew this and had been alarmed when yesterday his father had intimated that they should start drawing up a procedure to be followed for the eviction of the crofters. When that had been done, the plan would be handed to the factors and his men to implement. Malcolm realised the estate workers would show no sympathy to the crofters; they were there to see that their master's plans were carried out to the letter, no matter what. The crofters who had become Malcolm's friends and from whom he had learned much could face rough handling and a harsh future, maybe even forced emigration. And that could mean the loss of Rowena Murray...

The thought made Malcolm shudder.

Malcolm had been twelve the first time he had spoken to her. He, Lavinia and Angus had been exploring the beach close to the Murrays' croft. There had been an instant liking between the four of them and Rowena's heart had soared with the joy of gaining a friendship she had thought could never be. Thereafter they were often in each other's company. Rowena had taken the McFadden children home, a gesture that had gradually won them the friendship of the other crofters.

Gordon and Jessie, unable to have any more children, were protective of their daughter and cautious about this unexpected friendship. But, seeing the children's innocent happiness, they did not discourage it, only pointing out the consequences of their becoming too close.

Close they did become but, as sometimes happens in maturing childhood friendships, and aware of the social distinctions between them, Rowena and Malcolm shyly held back the stirrings of a deeper emotion.

Now Malcolm feared the thought of her emigrating. Losing her from his life would leave a void he hardly dared to contemplate. There was fear in his heart. The spectre of eviction loomed large. Friendships would be tested to the extreme. Upheaval was coming to disturb the tranquillity of this beloved land. He let his gaze run along the coast then sweep down the drive from his home to the road below; wherever it led, nearby or far away, he sensed his future lay with it.

4

Rosemary's mother, Georgiana Hawkesley, was a slight woman who, after bearing five children, still retained her youthful figure, which was the envy of others who had not been so successful. She had fussed over her brood ever since the birth of the first and still continued to do so into their adulthood, but it was all done with love and never overbearing. So it was no surprise to Kate, when she and Rosemary called on her soon after luncheon, that Mrs Hawkesley was immediately on her feet, greeting them effusively with hugs and kisses.

'Gaynor,' she called to the maid, who was closing the drawing-room door after showing the two friends in, 'take the coats.' She glanced at Rosemary. 'You'll be staying? Of course you will. It's lovely to see you, Kathleen.' When the maid had taken their coats and left the room, Georgiana said, 'Do sit down. Are you comfortable on that chair, Kathleen?'

'Yes, thank you, Mrs Hawkesley.'

Georgiana held herself straight when she sat down, and smoothed her pink silk dress to her liking while she continued to speak. 'Rosemary, your note saying you would be calling together with your sister-in-law had a touch of mystery to it.' She left a slight, tantalising pause then let her words rush out even faster. 'Quick, quick! Tell me what it is you want.'

'Mama, all in good time,' replied Rosemary calmly.

Georgiana gave a flick of her finger at her daughter, as if dismissing her caution.

'Mama, I must request that whatever passes between us in this room should remain a secret, at least for the time being.' Rosemary fixed her mother with a hard stare.

'Of course! Of course! You know well enough I can keep a secret when there is one to keep.' Georgiana's eyes widened. She was eagerly anticipating what might be coming next.

'Well, see that you do.' After the briefest of pauses Rosemary added, 'Kathleen has left home.'

Georgiana gasped. Expressions of disbelief and

shock followed in quick succession as her eyes darted from one to the other of them. 'Why? What has happened?'

'Kate's father was trying to force her to marry Cyrus Garfield.'

'Oh, my goodness!' Georgiana flung up her arms in honor. 'Not that horrible little man?' She shuddered.

'Yes, but Kate refused and walked out – well, her father told her in no uncertain terms to leave.'

'Oh, you poor girl.' Though it was difficult for Georgiana to support Kathleen against her parents, the instinctive sympathy she felt for her overpowered any loyalty she might have had to Titus Swan in this matter. 'What will you do?'

'That's why we are here, Mother,' replied Rosemary. 'Kate came to us for refuge and help. I sent a note to Archie to come home for luncheon. He's well aware of the situation, supports Kate's stance, but because of the financial support he receives from his father, does not want it known that she is living with us.'

'It would be best if I could move on as quickly as possible, so that I bring no trouble down on Rosemary and Archie.'

'That is commendable but...'

'Father believes that, cast out with no prospects, I'll soon be begging his forgiveness and agreeing to marry where he wishes. But I won't. I'll die first.'

'Oh, my dear, we won't let it come to that! We must think of something...'

'I had a thought,' put in Rosemary. 'I remembered your mentioning that Mrs Jordan was seeking a companion. Could you get us an introduction? If the position has not been filled, it might be the answer to Kate's problem.'

Georgiana's eyes brightened at the thought of being involved in an intrigue to outwit Titus's unreasonable demand. 'Splendid.' Her slight hesitation turned to open doubt when she asked Kate, 'Would being a companion suit you?'

'Yes, Mrs Hawkesley. I'll do anything.'

'Very well.' Georgiana got to her feet, went to the mahogany secretaire, sat down and started to write, chattering all the time. 'I'm asking if it will be convenient for me to call tomorrow morning with someone I think might fill the position of companion to her, if it has not already been taken. I'll mention no names. I think that would be best.' She added a little personal note hoping Mrs Jordan was in good health, then signed, sealed and addressed the letter. She went to the bell-pull and gave it four tugs. A few moments later the maid appeared. 'Gaynor, tell Harry to leave his kitchen chores and take this note to The White Horse. He must request the landlord to dispatch a post-boy to deliver it immediately and I will settle the cost later. The post-boy is to await an answer and deliver it to me on his return.'

As the door closed behind the maid, Kathleen felt some of the tension ease from her. But, in spite of Mrs Hawkesley's and Rosemary's efforts to lighten the atmosphere, unease slowly returned as the clock ticked the afternoon away.

They took tea and sent word to Archie to dine with Mr and Mrs Hawkesley that evening. When Mr Hawkesley returned home, he was quickly acquainted with the bare facts and sworn to secrecy.

34

They were all gathered together in the drawing room when a loud knocking at the front door brought a hush to the room. Kate, anxious for news, almost leaped to her feet, only just managing to control her reaction, but there was no disguising the anxious glance she gave Rosemary. A few moments later there was a knock on the door and Gaynor came in.

'A note for you, ma'am. No reply, the post-boy said.'

'Thank you, Gaynor.'

Georgiana broke the letter's seal as the door closed. She glanced at the contents. Everyone else, with eyes fixed on her, was held in suspense. She looked up. 'Mrs Jordan will see us at eleven o'clock in the morning.'

When Kate lay down that night her thoughts were full of her dramatic, life-changing day. There were some regrets, there were bound to be as much of her life to date had been happy, but lately... She shut those thoughts out and fell asleep, wondering what tomorrow would bring.

She woke to a sunny morning, hoping that its brightness was a portent of her future. Though thoughts of the past recurred as she dressed, Kate resolved that whatever happened at Peak House she must grasp the future and mould it her way; she was resolved there would be no turning back.

A horse and trap large enough to convey four passengers arrived at the precise time Mr Hawkesley had designated when he had left the request at The White Horse on his way to his banking business in Grape Lane. Once the driver had seen the ladies comfortably seated, he left Whitby on the trackway to Robin Hood's Bay, turning off it on to a drive that passed between two stone pillars with the words 'Peak House' painted on them. Georgiana chatted all the way, believing she was easing the nervous tension in Kate and Rosemary. They said nothing but Rosemary, sensing her friend's anxiety heightening as they neared the house, gripped Kate's hand and hoped she had reassured her with a whispered, 'Everything will turn out well.'

The driver was quickly off his seat to help Mrs Hawkesley out of the trap first. By the time he had assisted the young women to the ground, Georgiana had given the bell-pull a good tug. The door was opened by a young maid, smartly dressed in a black close-fitting skirt and white high-necked blouse plus an embroidered apron and small white cap set well back on her head. Kate was impressed by her smartness and thought it augured well for a life led in this household. She was reassured too by the ready welcoming smile with which the maid greeted them. Though she was nervous of how Mrs Jordan might appear and the way the interview might go, Kate felt her first impressions easing her trepidation.

'Mrs Hawkesley, daughter and friend to see Mrs Jordan,' Georgiana announced.

'You are expected, ma'am.' The maid held the door open while they stepped inside.

Kate took in her surroundings quickly. The medium-sized hall had four doors leading off it as well as a dog-leg staircase.

'Please follow me.' The maid led the way to a

door that was partly hidden by the staircase. She knocked on it and announced, 'Mrs Hawkesley and companions, ma'am.'

Kate almost gasped at the size of the room they entered, but more especially at the number of windows it contained. They not only flooded the room with light but afforded a wonderful view over the edge of the cliff, out to sea and over the bay that swept beyond the small village in a majestic curve towards the soaring cliffs at Ravenscar.

'Welcome, Georgiana.' Mrs Jordan rose from her chair with a smile that embraced them all. 'It is good to see you again. We really should meet more often.'

'We should,' Georgiana agreed as they embraced. 'And thank you for seeing us at such short notice, Evelyn. Not correct etiquette but...'

'Fiddlesticks to etiquette between friends,' said their hostess with a dismissive wave of her hand. 'Besides, I did not want to delay when you said you had probably found me a companion.' She turned to the two young ladies and, looking at Rosemary, said, 'You have your mother's features – you must be Rosemary. So I take it the position of companion does not concern you?'

'You are correct, Mrs Jordan. We have never met before so may I say how pleased I am to meet you. It is an honour to do so.'

Mrs Jordan smiled. 'We have met before, my dear, but you were only tiny and would not remember it.' She turned to Kate then. 'You must be the one looking for a position?'

'Yes, ma'am,' she replied.

'This is my friend and sister-in-law, Kathleen

37

Swan,' put in Rosemary quickly. 'I hope you will be able to help her.'

'We shall see, my dear,' Mrs Jordan replied gently. 'I suggest we all take a cup of chocolate together, and then you and your mother could take a stroll in the garden or along the cliffs while I talk to Kathleen.' As she was speaking she went to the bell-pull.

Kate realised it had been a prearranged signal because within a very short time the maids appeared with the chocolate. They served it and handed round sweetmeats before departing.

Kate realised that Mrs Jordan was using these informal moments to form her first opinions of her without appearing to do so. Kate smiled to herself; she was doing exactly the same with this lady who might be the answer to her present dilemma.

Kate liked what she saw; a slim, impeccably dressed, self-assured woman who exuded an air of competence. Kate supposed these attributes had been held in check to a certain degree while her husband was alive, but, facing life as a widow, Evelyn Jordan had resurrected them in order to make her life bearable, and then progress as far as possible to finding it enjoyable. In fact, she was seeking a companion who could contribute to that. She interested Kate, and by the time they had finished their chocolate Kate wanted to live here. So much now depended on how Mrs Jordan saw her.

Kate made an effort to keep her nervousness concealed. She entered the conversation only when it was appropriate, and showed a proper interest in Mrs Jordan's observations and opinions. She was aware that her hostess was subtly learning about her interests and abilities, and that her deep brown eyes missed nothing without appearing to be probing. Kate felt herself falling under the spell of her gentle, soft voice. She was a gracious lady whose features still showed signs of the grief she had suffered at the loss of her husband, but that could not disguise the fact that she had once been beautiful.

'Well now, if you have all had enough, I would suggest that Miss Swan and I remove ourselves to my small drawing room.' Mrs Jordan looked at Georgiana. 'You and Rosemary make yourselves comfortable or, if you prefer, take a walk in the garden. Those glass doors are unlocked.' She indicated the doors at the end of the room. Then she rose from her chair and Kate did likewise, appreciating her tact when, in the corridor outside, Mrs Jordan walked beside her, negating any feeling of their being prospective employer and employee.

When they entered the adjacent room Kate found it to be both cosy and elegant. The furniture was of the best, reflecting Mrs Jordan's innate good taste and the careful thought that had gone into furnishing this room. Kate could imagine the pleasant evenings that Mr and Mrs Jordan must have spent here, especially when a winter fire blazed in the hearth and filled the room with its warmth. The more she saw and sensed the friendly atmosphere here, the more she hoped Mrs Jordan would be impressed enough to appoint her to the position of companion.

Mrs Jordan indicated a chair to Kate and then sat down so that they were facing one other.

She looked steadily at the young woman. 'I

believe you are the daughter of Titus Swan.'

'I am, Mrs Jordan.'

'A man with a very successful rope and sail business, as well as a number of smaller interests in Whitby.'

'That is correct, Mrs Jordan.' Kate had feared this might be her initial approach, but she managed to keep her own voice firm.

'I have never met him or any members of your family, but I have heard something of his success from Mrs Hawkesley when I showed interest in her daughter at various stages of her life, and you were mentioned then as Rosemary's friend. So I am not altogether ignorant of your background. Which makes me wonder why you are seeking a position as my companion?'

Her eyes had never left Kate who, aware of their gentle scrutiny, gave an honest response.

'Ma'am,' she replied firmly. 'I will not try to deceive you in any way. The truth is that I had a dispute with my father and was told to leave home.'

If Mrs Jordan was shocked by this bold announcement, she did not outwardly show it. 'I see,' she commented thoughtfully.

'I will explain further,' put in Kate quickly. She believed that she had raised doubts by her admission and felt she must seize the initiative. She went on to tell Mrs Jordan about how she had come to be sitting here hoping for employment.

Mrs Jordan listened intently, her gaze never leaving Kate's face as she unfolded her story. Kate did so simply and directly, allowing her natural expressions to reveal the full trauma of what had happened.

40

When she had finished a silence fell between them. Anxiety began to stir in Kate. The next few moments could decide her whole future.

Mrs Jordan broke the silence by clearing her throat. Then she said, 'I appreciate your frankness, Kathleen. That is in your favour.'

'Thank you, Mrs Jordan.'

'But I hesitate to come between father and daughter in what is after all a family matter.'

Kate's heart sank.

'Yet I do sympathise with you. You see, I know something of Cyrus Garfield and his father. My husband, God rest his soul, had dealings with them through his legal practice in Scarborough. I remember him coming home one day and telling me he wished he had never set eyes on them. I never heard him speak so strongly about anyone, before or after that. My husband was normally an understanding and tolerant man, but his dealings with the Garfield family brought out a side in him I never knew existed. He was fixed in his abhorrence for them.' She gave a little shrug of her shoulders. 'I never saw it again and never expected to recall it.'

'Oh, Mrs Jordan, I'm so sorry if I have revived unpleasant memories for you,' protested Kate.

She held up her hand. 'Don't be, my dear.' She gave a little smile. 'Just think about the unexpected way in which those dealings with the Garfields are having repercussions today. Life can be surprising. I have liked what I have seen of you. Though I don't want to interfere in family affairs, I could not possibly condemn you to life with the Garfield family, which is what might happen if I turn you down.'

'Mrs Jordan, I don't want to gain this position purely by appealing to your sympathy,' replied Kate sharply.

'I realise that from what I have seen of you today. Even if the Garfields had never been mentioned, I would have offered you the position, never fear. I think you will fit in here admirably, and that you and I will get on famously.'

'Oh, Mrs Jordan, thank you! Thank you from the bottom of my heart.' Kate felt relief sweeping over her, and with it came joy that the road she had seen from her window had brought her here to Peak House, and to this kind, considerate lady.

5

Rowena trailed her toes with irritation through the soft, sun-warmed sand as she reluctantly left the beach. Every morning for the last eight weeks she had walked the same stretch of sand – their usual meeting place – but Malcolm had not so far appeared. Disappointment deepened with every passing day and brought with it ill temper and surly moods. She stared morosely at the ground, as if her reason for living had been torn from her.

From the window of the croft, a troubled Jessie Murray watched her daughter wander slowly back towards the dwelling. She did not like what was happening to Rowena. Disturbed by her changing moods, she had observed her daughter's usual placid approach to life disrupted lately by peevishness and grumbling. Jessie decided it was time to talk to her straightforwardly. She took her grey shawl from the wooden peg beside the door and went out to meet the girl.

They were close together before Rowena realised her mother was there. 'Ma!'

'Walk with me, Rowena.' Jessie's voice was gentle but it carried a note of command.

Rowena recognised that tone; she knew something serious was about to be imparted. Her heart started beating.

Deliberately, Jessie took the path back to the beach, which Rowena had just abandoned. As they moved on to the sand, she said, 'So he didn't come again?'

Rowena automatically shook her head and said, 'No, Ma.' She tried to hide her feelings but failed to subdue the catch in her voice or the truth revealed in her eyes.

'Do you remember how when you first became friendly with the laird's children, I told you not to allow that friendship to become too close?'

'Yes, Ma.'

'I should have warned you again months ago but I held back, not wanting to blight the feelings I thought you had under control. But I have seen some worrying changes in you recently. I should have spoken out sooner.'

'Ma, what are you talking about?' said Rowena in annoyance. 'I'm still me.'

Jessie gave a small smile. 'There you have it! You would never have spoken to me in that tone previously.'

'But I...'

'You forget or overlook the possibility that I too have experienced young love. I know the signs; know what you go through when he does not come to meet you. I know how it hurts, Rowena, but I'd rather it hurt now, so that you recognise the futility of this relationship. End it, and save yourself from a future that could otherwise be dogged by tragedy.'

'That's not going to happen, Ma. We're just friends, as we always have been,' Rowena protested.

'Don't lie to yourself. That won't solve your dilemma.'

'What on earth are you talking about?' The girl stopped walking, antagonism flaring in the look she gave her mother.

'You're not helping yourself. You think you are subduing the feelings within your heart by denying them to me. You fail to see the outward signs that betray your love for Malcolm.'

Rowena bit her lip thoughtfully.

Jessie knew she had struck home – to the very core of the feelings that were troubling her daughter. She knew it was no use demanding an end to the relationship; it was of too long a standing for that. Best to try to make Rowena see reason for herself, and trust her to take the right action.

'Think carefully, Rowena. Innocent love is one thing, but you have both become adults and the childhood love you felt has slipped into something more serious. You probably weren't even aware of the change until this prolonged absence brought home the depth of the love you are feeling now. If you let it go on, you will be badly hurt. As your mother who loves you deeply, I have to make you aware that such feelings can lead only to heartache. The laird would never agree to his son marrying a crofter's daughter. There's no telling what lengths he would go to in order to prevent it. We could be cast out. Malcolm could be exiled "until he comes to his senses", as his father would no doubt put it. Think very carefully, Rowena. Very, very carefully.'

As her mother's words struck home, the enormity of what might lie ahead overwhelmed Rowena. She just wanted to be free to express her love for Malcolm McFadden. Why was that forbidden to her? Tears welled in her eyes and could not be stemmed. With a mind ravaged by the heartbreak she faced, she ran and ran across the sand.

Jessie, with sadness in her heart and her own tears flowing in sympathy, stood and watched until Rowena was far across the bay. She shook her head sadly and turned back for the croft that was her home. But for how much longer?

The matter was not raised again when Rowena arrived home. Jessie knew from her daughter's attitude that her words had taken effect; she only hoped they had been powerful enough. Nor was it mentioned to Rowena's father when he returned with a good catch of fish that would help them pay the dues on the croft that belonged to Malcolm's father.

In the days that followed, Rowena walked in the place she and Malcolm had christened 'our bay', still without a sign of him. Her thoughts dwelt on him, but then her mother's words rang in her mind. She saw reason in them but also a mother's concern; she could not really know the strength of her daughter's love for Malcolm, a love Rowena hoped could surmount all obstacles. Only love mattered. It would survive every trial and be stronger for it. Then the euphoria of these thoughts came crashing down as the daunting reality of her position assailed her mind. It was then that her mother's warning clamoured to be considered seriously. Though she tried to rid herself of this persistent train of thought, Rowena often failed. With Malcolm's continued absence she wondered if his feelings remained fixed in friendship and had not matured as hers had. Or had his father learned of their meetings and issued an ultimatum that Malcolm dare not refuse?

Two weeks after her talk with her mother Rowena came again to 'our bay', slipped off her light shoes and walked along the beach, letting the waves run over her feet. With her head bowed and her eyes fixed on the swirling water, her mind filled with disappointment that he was not here to share these moments with her. Something terrible must have happened to keep him from her for so long. Maybe he was gone from her for ever...

Malcolm topped the rise, stopped and sharpened his gaze to scan the small secluded bay. The path that had brought him here was little-trodden and almost lost among the stunted heath that swept gently down to the strand. His eyes drifted towards the rising ground that hid the next bay where the Murrays lived.

Recently, with his father wanting him to take more interest in the way the estate was run, Malcolm had been unable to get away as he would have liked; it had been two months since he had last seen Rowena. He had longed to walk with her again or even run as they had done in childhood. But now as he searched for her amidst the landscape that was special to him, his feelings assumed a depth he had never experienced before. The prolonged absence had strengthened his desire to see her. He recognised now that their old familiar friendship had turned into a love that could not be denied. He wanted to be with her, to touch her, hold and kiss her. But Rowena was nowhere to be seen. He let out a deep sigh and tightened his lips in annoyance that his expectation of seeing her was not fulfilled.

He scolded himself. Why should she be in one of their old haunts at precisely this moment? He had let his expectations run too high. They had over-ruled cold logic. He could easily find her at the croft, but that wasn't what he wanted. After two months' separation, he wanted to be alone with her.

Disappointed, he started down the long slope leading to the beach, his mind dwelling on the happy times they had shared there: bare feet in the warm sand, ignoring the waves that broke around their calves, escaping from Lavinia when she was talking with Rowena's mother, running together or strolling hand in hand ... then there was always laughter in their eyes and on their lips, for in childhood and youth there are no troubles, no doubts.

The path swung round a slope that hid sand and

sea for a few minutes. When they came into view again, Malcolm saw her. She was coming round the promontory that separated the bay where she lived from 'our bay'. He stopped, transfixed, his eyes only for her. He took in her every movement, recalling every feature that he must have preserved in his mind without being truly conscious of doing so. In that moment he knew that he was in love with this girl. Rowena was walking slowly, allowing the sea to lap across her bare feet. Her auburn hair was loose to her shoulders, and he knew that when she looked up from the lapping water it would frame an oval face of perfect symmetry. Her bow-shaped lips were set beneath a small nose with a slight upturn that he had always found attractive. He stood watching her, not wanting to move and spoil the new emotions running through him, yet at the same time wanting to fulfil his sharp desire to take her in his arms.

Rowena looked up, stopped and stood still, ignoring the surf that broke across her feet, wetting the hem of her dress. Malcolm! She curbed the urge to run to him, wanting to savour the sight of him, distant though it was. Memories almost overwhelmed her but were replaced by an intense hunger to feel his arms around her. With that came a powerful need to be with him always. But within moments her mind beat back this thought and she whispered, 'If only.' Exasperated by her own words, that dashed so much long-cherished hope, she savoured these moments of reunion.

Neither of them moved. It was as if they both knew that each wanted to lock this moment in their mind for ever; as if they foresaw it would become a precious memory.

How long they stood there they never knew, but then the need to bridge the distance between them became irresistible and as one they started to run.

The rough slope almost brought Malcolm to his knees. He stumbled, fought for balance and felt exhilarating laughter burst from his lips. Then he was free of the obstacle and on the open beach. He ran.

Rowena's eyes brightened with every urgent step that sent the water splashing higher; two months of wondering had been banished by the sight of him. She realised how much she had missed him; how long the days had been. She sensed a new stirring within her that brought joy, but even as she ran towards him her mother's words silently warned of the need for caution. Dare she allow young love to change into something that burned deep within her and carried the promise of so much more? Then she was in his arms. The time to make decisions that would affect her future was later. Malcolm held her so tight that it seemed as if he was bent on keeping her there for ever. Feeling the need to lock these precious moments in her heart, she held on to him with all her strength until she felt his embrace ease a little. At last she was able to look up at him. Their eyes met. There was no need for words, but they said them nevertheless.

'I love you, Rowena.'

'And I you, Malcolm.'

Their lips met, gently at first but then moving

with a passion that disclosed what each had kept hidden – an adult love, now made all the more intense by its bursting into full expression.

'I've missed you so much, Rowena,' he said quietly.

'I walked this beach every day, hoping you would come.' She looked at him with eyes beseeching an explanation.

Malcolm took her hand and they started to stroll close to the water's edge, as they had done many times before. But now the words had been spoken, they both realised their lives had changed for ever.

'You knew Father was involving me more in the running of the estate. That is what has preoccupied me. I just could not get away. I daren't risk him finding out.'

His last sentence struck a chill in Rowena's heart. Her mother's words, 'The laird would never allow his son to marry a crofter's daughter,' echoed in her mind and brought with them a question: Did Malcolm know this?

The ecstasy of their declarations of love for each other had almost overwhelmed Rowena, but the implication behind Malcolm's words had soured those first moments and reinforced her mother's warning. She knew that if she did not exercise caution now, both their lives would suffer and what they had enjoyed together would be tarnished for ever. They would be lost to each other. She stopped and turned him towards her.

He saw that her first mood of elation had faded; a guarded expression had replaced the joy that had been so evident a few moments ago.

'What's wrong, Rowena?' he asked tenderly.

She bit her lip as if trying to hold back what she felt she must say. 'This can't be,' she replied, her tone revealing how much she regretted her own words.

Malcolm frowned, puzzled. 'What do you mean?'

'Our love is wrong.'

'How can it be when we feel as we do?'

'You are the son of the laird and I am a poor crofter's daughter.'

'It makes no difference.'

'That is easily said, but it takes no account of the dangers we face if we declare our love for each other. I think you know it too, otherwise you would not have spoken of being afraid of your father finding out...'

'I can deal with that,' Malcolm cut in curtly.

His tone sent a chill through her but Rowena kept that to herself. 'Again, easily said.'

'I can.'

'Believe that if you will, but your father would never condone what we feel for each other.' He was about to answer when Rowena stopped him by pressing her fingers to his lips. 'Our friend-ship, established when we were children, became more than that as we grew up, but we both kept a tight rein on our feelings. I found great joy in our young love. Oh, Malcolm, I'll not deny that many nights I went to sleep with dreams of what might be! Then with adulthood came the cold light of reason and I realised I could never be-come the lady of Garstan House. It would never be sanctioned by your father. You love this land, this estate, so much. I could never, never ask you to give it up, as you would be forced to do if you married me.'

'But I'd willingly sacrifice my inheritance for you! I would!' The pleading she saw in his eyes tore at Rowena's heartstrings. She wanted to fling herself into his arms then and say that they would be together for ever, no matter what, but cold reality dictated her reaction.

'No, Malcolm. I would feel for ever guilty that you had given it up for me. Besides, what else would you do? What...?'

'I'd move in with you until...'

She laughed. 'You could never settle to life in a croft! You may have learned some things from my father but you'd never cope with living on the poverty line, always wondering if we are going to be able to pay the laird's dues. And he'd still exact them even if you were living with us. In fact I would bet that once you had declared your intention, he would evict us ... even hound us out of Shetland.' She saw from his eyes that he knew she was right. 'Oh, Malcolm, I love you more than anything, but we cannot allow it to blight our lives and that of others.' She could hold back the tears no longer.

He took her into his arms and held her tenderly. 'And I love you, Rowena. I suppose I always have, ever since childhood, but it was only through our separation these last two months that I realised how much you mean to me.'

'Then I ask you to keep it that way,' she pleaded, 'a love preserved in a deep and special friendship. That way we can mean a great deal to each other and continue to meet in a relationship that we both hold dear, but one in which we are not bound by any ties and are able to go our own way, as life dictates.'

Malcolm kissed her gently on the lips. Placing his hands on her shoulders, he looked into her eyes. 'I must respect your wishes. I see you would be hurt if I did not do so, and that might destroy the emotions that we share. I don't want that to happen. You are a wonderful person. My love will ever be yours. You will be always in my heart, no matter what life deals us.' He paused and then made one last plea. 'Change your mind, Rowena, please?'

With tears streaming down her cheeks, she shook her head slowly. With her eyes fixed on his, she said a quiet but firm, 'No.'

Malcolm's eyes betrayed his disappointment. 'Then I ask you to wait for me. Times are changing – this land will change too. I can see it looking very different five years from now, and with that may come a change in attitudes. Let's wait until then.'

Rowena's heart was near breaking point. Five years seemed such a long time, anything could happen; her childhood dreams were being shattered. She nodded. 'Very well,' she said quietly, then added cautiously, 'but without any serious commitment on either side.'

He kissed her. Malcolm's touch tempted her to stay longer but she pulled away. He let her go. As Rowena strode across the sand she called over her shoulder, 'What will be, will be.'

6

Five years! It seemed like eternity when Malcolm woke the next morning. He cursed himself. Why had he even said it? It had only come to his lips because, during those moments yesterday, he had visualised the changes that would affect everyone during the years to come. He hoped he could influence those new developments even though his views might be stifled by his father and other powerful lairds. And he hoped prejudice against a crofter marrying into Shetland's 'aristocracy' would ease, or at least that he would be able to persuade Rowena that it could work for them. That their love would triumph over all. In the meantime, he would have to tread carefully.

He escaped his increased burden of duties around the estate whenever he could in order to meet Rowena in their bay, but those meetings were not as they had once been. The old carefree atmosphere between them was marred by caution not to offend or upset the other by referring to 'that' meeting which both felt had become a watershed in their lives. But both still held the other in a love and respect which they hoped, one day, would surmount the obstacles life had put in their path.

Six months later, a July storm lashed the windows of Garstan House. Malcolm's thoughts went to the Murrays' croft. Protected though he was by

54

the house's solid walls and roof, he knew the severity of the rain would be finding ways to penetrate the crumbling walls and rotting thatch of the old croft. Only a few weeks ago he had reported on the conditions of the crofts on the estate and had given his opinion that the one occupied by the Murrays should be the first to be repaired.

'Gordon Murray could do more to keep it in better condition, but he's a lazy blighter,' was all that Mungo replied.

Malcolm had countered that criticism with, 'He has the land to till ... fish to catch, to try to meet your dues...'

'Aye, and they take priority. Even so he should make time to do something at the croft.'

'Maybe, but we have our responsibilities too.'

'All right, all right,' said his father with marked irritation. 'I'll see to it.'

But nothing had been done.

The recollections were driven from Malcolm's mind when Aunt Grizel looked across the breakfast table at her brother and said, 'If you'll excuse me, I've some things I must see to.'

'Of course.' Mungo gave a wave of his hand. He looked at his daughter. 'If you'll leave too, Lavinia, I've something to say to your brothers.'

'Yes, Papa.' She rose from her chair and, as she was leaving the room, flashed a glance at Malcolm and Angus that said, 'This must be serious!'

Malcolm twitched his eyebrow in response but Angus remained impassive.

As the door closed Mungo's glance swept over his sons. 'I've been bringing you both more and more into the running of the estate,' he began, 'because its future will lie in your hands – particularly Malcolm's. He will inherit by right when I die. Angus, whether you move on then or even before is up to you. There will be financial provision for you made in my will, some of which you may draw on before then, if you elect to leave. Regarding the estate itself... I've been giving considerable thought to new ways to obtain the best financial return. I'm coming more and more to the conclusion that sheep would pay better than crofters.'

Malcolm's mind froze. His friends!

'I wondered when you would come round to thinking that way,' said Angus calmly.

The remark surprised his father. 'I didn't know you were so interested?'

Angus smiled and tapped his forehead. 'I see, I hear, and it's all stored in here.'

Mungo pursed his lips. 'So you agree we should turn the land over to sheep then?'

'It's your estate, you dictate the policy.'

'Father, you cannot be serious?' Malcolm's heart was racing with fear.

'We cannot ignore the figures. The last two years have brought in little revenue from the crofters. If we take our land back, we could use it more profitably by turning it over to sheep.'

'But surely it's about more than just money?'

'What else?'

'The crofters' livelihood. Take back the land and what do they have?'

'Nothing,' put in Angus.

Malcolm didn't like the note of satisfaction in his voice.

'They'll have to move on,' added his brother.

'But where? And what will they have to live on?'

'That will be up to them. I can't run their lives for them,' said Angus dismissively.

'You're doing just that by taking their living away from them,' Malcolm pointed out, with some hostility.

'It's out of our hands,' said Mungo complacently.

Malcolm looked disgusted.

'They are human beings – like us,' he protested.

'And what have they made of themselves?' argued Angus. 'Nothing.'

'They never had the opportunities we did.'

'Why should we sympathise with them because of an accident of birth?'

'Surely they deserve our compassion.'

Angus gave a derisive laugh.

'Does your championing of their cause perhaps run deeper than that?' Mungo asked coldly, eyes fixed on Malcolm in a penetrating gaze.

He did not answer.

'Come on,' snapped Mungo. 'I'm no fool. I know you used to visit the crofters, play with their children. Inevitably you got to know them – developed friendships that could colour your attitude now.' His frown held a sternness that Malcolm didn't like. 'Let me tell you, you cannot afford to be soft if you are to run this estate properly. People will take advantage of you. You've got to be strong, even if you have to make decisions you don't like. You cannot grow attached to people. If you cannot use the estate to its full potential, you'll go under. And right now, I see our future in sheep.'

'But what about the crofters?' Malcolm persisted.

'I'll offer them the cost of two sheep to move on.'

'A pittance!' he stormed.

'Better than nothing,' put in Angus, seizing this opportunity to support their father; grasping this possibility to turn the future to his own advantage. 'Why should we give them more?'

'Because they'll be losing their income and a place to live.'

'Why should we care?'

Malcolm cast his brother a withering look. 'You have no heart.' He swung his gaze towards his father. 'What if they won't move?'

'If they oppose me, then the factor and all his men will move in and evict them.'

'What? Turn them out bodily?'

'If it comes to that. I'd only be taking back what is mine.'

'At what cost?' stormed Malcolm.

Mungo's face darkened. He pointed a finger at his eldest son. 'That's enough! Now listen to me. This is not going to take place immediately. This year the yields from the land look good, the fishing too, so the dues from the crofters for the last twelve months plus their debts from the last two years should be met.'

'But imposing the full back rents will cripple them,' Malcolm protested.

'They are rightfully mine! Give way on this and they'll try to take advantage of my generosity in the future. Besides, we could be faced with the opposite situation next year; we must make preparations against any setbacks, and so I am. In a year's time this land will be turned over to sheep: crofters gone, crofts destroyed and cleared.' By now Mungo was on his feet, bringing an end to the discussion.

'But ...' Malcolm began to argue.

'There's nothing more to be said.' His father glared at him and started for the door.

'Yes, there is, Father!' The strength of his words, carrying an ominous note, was enough to stop Mungo in his tracks. 'If that is your final word, then don't expect me to be here this evening or to sit down at that table with you again.'

Mungo bristled at his son's threat. His lips tightened for a moment before he said coldly, his eyes darkening as they bored into his son's. 'Don't you dare threaten me! Leave if you must, but it will be a step that will rob you of your inheritance. Think hard on this ... you will be left with nothing. Nothing!'

As the door closed behind his father Malcolm heard a chuckle. He turned to find his younger brother smirking at him. 'And your precious Rowena won't care to lay with an impoverished laird, will she?'

Malcolm's fury rose at the implication behind this. He strode towards his brother who scrambled to his feet, but before Angus could defend himself Malcolm's fist smashed into his face, sending him crashing back into his chair and toppling on to the floor with a split lip and bloodied nose.

Malcolm swung round and strode out of the room.

Half an hour later he was securing the pack into which he had stuffed some clothes. He looked around and immediately felt a pang of sadness. This had been his room since he was born; much of his life had revolved around it, and now...? He drove down the thoughts that might keep him here and replaced them with practicalities. He left his room and went along the corridor. His knock on Lavinia's door was answered by her soft voice, bidding him to come in.

'Malcolm,' she said, looking up from her sewing. She watched him cross the room and, as he sat down beside her on the window seat, said, 'You look serious. Has it something to do with what Papa had to say?'

He nodded. 'Regrettably, it has. I'm leaving.'

Lavinia's eyes widened in disbelief. 'Oh, no!' She felt her world collapsing.

'I'm afraid so,' he confirmed, and went on to tell her what had happened.

Lavinia listened intently, her features becoming more grave as his story unfolded. When he had finished she said, 'I cannot pretend to understand all the economic details of running an estate, but I can understand your concern for the crofters. And knowing Father, I don't expect he will change his mind.' She swallowed hard, tears coming to her eyes. 'Malcolm!' she cried. 'I don't want you to go. Do you have to? Angus and I very rarely see eye to eye. I'll miss you so much. Couldn't you help the crofters more if you stay?'

Malcolm shook his head. 'I fear not. You know how Father is when he gets his mind set on something. He won't tolerate any opposition.' He left a slight pause during which he leaned forward and took his sister's hands in his. 'The change to sheep may not happen next year or the year after, but when it does may I ask you to do what you can for the crofters?'

'Of course,' Lavinia agreed readily, but added more cautiously, 'I don't know how I'll be able to do that, but I'll try.'

'Thank you.' He stood up and kissed her on top of her head.

She came with him to the door and placed her hand on his as he took hold of the knob. 'Where will you go?'

'I'm not sure. I must see Rowena first. Maybe I can stay with the Murrays for a day or so until I make up my mind.'

She nodded, kissed him on the cheek and said, 'God go with you.'

Twenty minutes later, with his pack slung across his back, Malcolm was striding down the path to 'our bay', glad that the rain had stopped. He had almost reached the beach when he saw Rowena appear at the opposite side of the bay. His heart beat a little faster with joy but his mind was uneasy. What would her reaction be when he broke his news? Maybe his hope of seeing these latest developments solve their problem had been premature.

'Malcolm, it's good to see you.' Her smile faded. 'You look serious ... something is wrong?'

He nodded. 'Yes, it is.'

As they strolled along the beach he told her what had happened. Rowena listened attentively without interrupting him.

'So that is it,' he said in conclusion.

'And you've left already?'

'For good and all. Marry me, Rowena. It will solve everything.'

She stopped and looked up at him. 'That sounds easy, Malcolm, but it will only present you with more problems, not solve them. Your father would oppose it with every means at his disposal. He'd not tolerate you marrying a crofter. And my parents wouldn't approve of our marriage either.'

'Why not? It would mean a better living for them.'

She gave a weak smile that echoed the doubt in her eyes. 'Would it?'

'I would see that it did.'

'How? You've walked out of your home.'

Malcolm shrugged his shoulders. 'I can't answer that now. It would depend on circumstances at the time.'

'Exactly! We said five years, Malcolm. Your father might relent and want you back by then; you might relent and seek his forgiveness.'

'Never!'

'That's easily said. How will you live? Where are you going now?'

'I was hoping I could stay with you.'

She threw up her hands in despair. 'Oh, Malcolm, you haven't thought this through, have you? You've acted on the spur of the moment, in anger probably at what your father is proposing to do.' Her lips tightened. 'Mother warned me not to get too involved with the laird's son; that it would only lead to trouble. Now it has. I fell in love and was not strong enough to resist it. My mother and father will have no sympathy if I take you home and ask shelter for you. They'll see it as bringing trouble from the laird down on their heads; they would not dare risk it. You'd not be able to stay.'

'But if we...'

'Stop. Malcolm, stop!' Rowena cut in sharply. 'I simply could not ask them to change their whole way of life for me, and I could not leave them to face the worst that the change to rearing sheep might bring. I would have to stay and help them.'

Malcolm could see where this was leading. He felt bitter. He turned abruptly and walked away.

She stood watching him, tears streaming down her cheeks, his name unspoken on her lips.

7

Malcolm's stride was firm and determined. He used its momentum to drive away the disappointment that threatened to overwhelm him. He had seen Rowena and her parents as the answer to his future, but her rejection, and he could only see it as that, had thrown his ideas and prospects into disarray. As disturbed as he was, in his heart of hearts he saw reason in Rowena's resistance to his plan, but that did not make him feel any better about the situation. As far as his father and the estate were concerned, he would not turn back; his own principles, linked to concern for the crofters and what they would face on expulsion, would not permit him to do that. As for helping them himself, he knew he was all but powerless. His father would make sure his attempts were useless; his authority over the estate workers would prevent any interference by Malcolm.

But what should he do now? What of his own future? What could he turn his hand to? Boat-building? The sea? Maybe the answer lay in Lerwick.

Four days later, after sleeping rough, he stood on a hill looking down over the town. His spirits were not lifted by the sight. The clouds, threatening rain, hung low, making the grey buildings huddling around the harbour look even more dour. What had this place to offer him? Little by the look of it, but he was here now and must make the best of it. He strode down the hill and found a lodging house. The lined, pale face of the middle-aged woman who offered him a room with the basic necessities reflected the harsh life that had followed the loss of her husband while hunting whales in the Arctic. He learned from her that work was scarce in Lerwick and that anything available was given to local men; those from elsewhere were always last in the queue. In spite of this discouraging information, he knew he would have to find something; his funds would not last long.

As he looked around his room, with its iron bedstead, washstand and wardrobe that had all seen better days, he recalled the comfort of the room he had left behind and wondered if he had acted too hastily.

During the following days he walked the streets, enquiring at boat-builders; he sought out fishermen, pleaded to be hired on the docks ... but all to no avail. He knew he was eyed with suspicion. He had come from 'the country'; his accent, his way of speaking, were not of this town; he was not one of 'them'.

Then one late-August day he was wandering around the quays, wondering if he should return to Garstan House and seek... He pulled his thoughts up short. No, he could not do that. He had to be true to himself. He had been so wrapped up in his thoughts that he had been unaware of a vessel coming into Bressay Sound until an outbreak of activity on the quay aroused him. Several men hurried down the stone steps on the side of the quay and, without wasting any time, were into two boats and rowing strongly in the direction of the ship.

With his attention drawn to the vessel, Malcolm saw that she was a whaler; one mast was broken, her bow had suffered damage and a hole, fortunately above the waterline, in her starboard side had been roughly repaired. From the calls and shouts that came across the water he realised that some of her crew had suffered injury and needed instant attention. This information soon percolated through Lerwick and horse-drawn wagons began to assemble on the quay where two doctors awaited to assess the state of the injured. When the two boats returned they brought several men, the ship's captain showing great concern for the welfare of his crew members as he talked to the doctors.

Once he was satisfied that his men would be in good hands, the captain turned to the harbourmaster. 'I will need men to make up my complement, sailing the *Lady Isobel* to Whitby.'

'I'm certain that can be arranged and you can sail on tomorrow morning's tide if you don't wish to delay,' replied the harbourmaster with confidence.

'Excellent. My crew will be pleased to hear that, after our terrible experience. The sooner we are all home the better.'

The harbourmaster nodded. 'I'll have the men you require ready to come aboard by first light.'

'Sir, I couldn't help but overhear what you just said. I'll volunteer to be one of the crew to take the *Lady Isobel* to Whitby,' said Malcolm, seeing his chance to seek a new life elsewhere.

Both men eyed him. Because of an accent that spoke of a better upbringing than the usual types, he encountered around these parts, the harbourmaster asked Malcolm doubtfully, 'Have you served on such vessels before?'

'Aye, sir. Not whalers, but vessels sailing to the mainland.'

'He'll do for one,' put in the captain.

'Thank you, sir,' returned Malcolm. 'There's just one thing ... I won't be doing the return trip on the vessel that I expect will be accompanying us, to bring the Lerwick men back home.'

'Makes no difference to the complement required to bring the escort vessel back,' confirmed the harbourmaster.

'Thanks,' said Malcolm. 'Then I'll be here at first light.' He touched his forehead in salute and hurried away. His step was light and eager, in marked contrast to the leaden pace he had adopted as his lack of prospects had begun to weigh heavily on him.

The sky was touched with pale early-morning light when he reached the harbour the following morning to join a group of men eager to put some money in their pockets. Two boats were waiting to take them to the *Lady Isobel*. Once on board they came under the orders of the captain and first mate, who were eager to be underway.

As the ship slipped out of Diessay Sound, Malcolm looked back, wondering if he would ever see Shetland again.

Evelyn Jordan laid her knife and fork neatly on her empty plate and glanced across the table at her companion who was reaching for a second slice of bread. 'Kathleen, you have been with me for a year now. I enjoy your company and am grateful for what you do for me. Above all, I value your friendship.'

Kate gave her employer an appreciative smile. 'It is I who should be thanking you. A year ago I was at my wits' end. It was a godsend when I heard about you. Though I did not know what I was coming to...'

Evelyn laughed with amusement. 'You thought I might be a dragon!'

Kate blushed as she said, 'I was apprehensive, but you have been so good to me.'

'You had every right to be suspicious, just as I had every right to wonder if I was making a wise decision in employing you. Well, it turned out right for both of us.'

'It certainly did for me,' agreed Kate.

'And I have no complaints. You have been like a daughter to me, and still are. You replaced the one I was never able to have.' A catch came into Evelyn's voice but, not wanting to cast gloom on the moment, she quickly drove away the memory. 'At times it worries me, though, that you are a young person tied to an older woman, living the kind of life which restricts you from meeting people of your own age.'

'Mrs Jordan, I am content enough.'

'Maybe, and I appreciate your saying so, but I think I am being too selfish tying you to me here.'

'We have our occasional shopping visits to Whitby.'

'True, but I always sense your uneasiness there – brought on, I suspect, by fear of meeting your father.'

'I must admit that is true. I am sorry if it spoiled your visits.'

'No, no. Please don't think that.'

'And I am most grateful that you have allowed me visits here from Rosemary. They have kept me in touch with family news. So, as I say, I am content.'

'But I do think you should have more freedom … get out and meet people of your own age.'

'You are saying you wish me to leave?' Mrs Jordan could not mistake the note of distress in Kate's voice then.

'No,' she replied quickly. 'Far from it. But if ever the time comes when you wish to leave, to spread your wings, I hope you will not hold back from telling me? You have become dear to me, and it is your happiness I seek. What I am suggesting is that you should have every Wednesday free, to do as you please. Also that we mix with people rather more than we do at present. It would be good for you, and no doubt for me too. I had become a little too much of a recluse but, without you knowing it, you have reopened my eyes to the world beyond this haven of security.'

'I don't know how I have done that, when I needed to escape from the world that was being forced on me.'

'Ah, but you brought with you your youthful views and new thoughts. Once you were comfortable with me, you expressed them and they threw new light on to what was becoming a very narrow world for me.' Evelyn left a little pause before she added, 'Now, I am going to arrange for us to spend a week in Scarborough, and if that works well for both of us, then we might think of travelling some more.'

'That sounds exciting. I shall look forward to it. Thank you very much.'

Evelyn waved her hand as if to dismiss any notion of thanks. 'I will do something about it right away.' She rose from her chair as she continued to speak. 'You finish your breakfast while I write a note.' She left the dining room and crossed the hall to a small room with a pleasant view of the garden. A small Regency mahogany desk was positioned so that the light from the window fell across it from the left. Evelyn sat down, laid a sheet of paper in front of her, picked up a quill and began to write. With her message completed, she sat back and reread her letter. Satisfied, she sealed and addressed it then rang the bell. A few moments later a maid appeared.

'Give this to George and tell him to take it into Whitby at once, to catch the mail coach to Scarborough.'

Lily hurried away, knowing the houseman would be pleased to escape from cleaning drains for a while.

Mrs Jordan followed her from the room and went to the drawing room where she found Kate collecting the book she had been reading the previous evening.

'There, it's done,' she said, with a degree of satisfaction in her voice. 'I've sent a letter off booking us two rooms at Donner's Hotel. We should hear back in a day or two.'

'You know it, Mrs Jordan?'

'Oh, yes. My husband and I often dined there when we were living in Scarborough and stayed there when we visited after coming to live here. It's in Long Room Street and is very convenient for shops, the theatre, the two assembly rooms – one of them in Donner's itself. It's close to St Nicholas Cliff where there is a fine garden used for promenading by the local well-to-do and visitors of the same standing. And, of course, there are the South Bay sands which are used for the same purpose.'

'This all sounds very exciting,' said Kate, eyes shining with the thought of spending some leisure time in Scarborough. She was wondering if she dared hope for a ball in one of the assembly rooms. 'I'm so grateful to you.'

'If you want to repay me...'

'Oh, I do, I do!' broke in Kate.

Evelyn laughed, recalling her own youthful enthusiasm whenever a treat was in the offing. 'You can repay me by enjoying your visit to Scarborough.'

A fortnight later they walked back into Peak House, to be greeted with pleasure by the housekeeper Mrs Stabler who expressed her hope that they had had an enjoyable time. Lily and Enid were fussing around, taking their outdoor clothes, and with George's help took the luggage to their respective rooms.

'I'll have a cup of tea ready for you in the drawing room in ten minutes, ma'am,' Mrs Stabler informed them.

They had just arrived there when the maids came in with tea and a welcome home cake.

'Ah, it is good to be back,' said Evelyn as she poured the tea. 'As much as I enjoyed Scarborough, it can't beat what we have here.'

'It certainly can't,' agreed Kate, and then, feeling her employer might interpret that as indicating she had not enjoyed her stay in Scarborough, added quickly, 'Don't take that wrong, Mrs Jordan. It was all delightful and I derived a great deal of pleasure from it.'

'I thought you did. It pleased me to see you mixing readily with people, especially the younger ones at the balls.'

'We were fortunate to have pleasant people staying in the hotel. And I enjoyed promenading with you, especially on the sands.'

'Well, now we have ventured forth, we shall do it again. I have been toying with another idea but I am not going to say anything else yet. In the

71

meantime, you must not think you should be staying in with me all the time. You should get out more. Go for walks along the cliffs, use the trap and go into Whitby or...'

'I'm perfectly happy being with you.'

'I appreciate that, Kate. But Scarborough has shown me that you should not be tied to my apron strings. Get out more on your own.' She left a little pause to add emphasis to what followed. 'And that's an order!'

8

Thankful that they had not met any adverse weather, the crew of the *Lady Isobel* nursed her towards the Yorkshire coast and her final destination in Whitby. Malcolm had enjoyed the voyage, short though it was, and had got on well with the Whitby men, admiring their pride in the ship which had bravely endured Arctic conditions. Duties done for the time being, he stood by the rail gazing at the ever-nearing coast, wondering what awaited him there far from his island home.

'I hear tell you aren't returning to Shetland,' a quiet voice broke into his thoughts.

Malcolm looked at the Whitby man who had come to stand beside him. He gave a nod. 'That's right, Tom.'

Malcolm had got on well with Tom Davis from the moment they had met. They had both felt an immediate rapport and Malcolm enjoyed the company of a man of his own age who had been sailing with the whalers since he was ten, steadily gaining promotion until on this voyage he had sailed as one of the harpooners. His strong open face spoke of confidence in his own ability and drew trust from others. He had the sharp eyes of a sailor, ever probing the distance but focusing intently on whoever he was talking to.

For his part Tom had recognised in Malcolm someone who stood apart from his fellow Shetlanders, but not in any superior or snobbish way; he mingled too easily with them for that. Nevertheless Tom detected that Malcolm was from a better-class family. That made him wonder why he was crewing a disabled ship back to her home port. This latest information had made him even more curious.

'What do you intend doing in Whitby?' he asked.

Malcolm shrugged his shoulders. 'I'll see what comes up.'

'Got anywhere to stay?'

'No.'

'Then take care. There are unsavoury places in Whitby, as in any port. There are those who'd rob you as soon as look at you. I'm not one to butt in, but if it's of interest I reckon my widowed mother would not be against letting you have a room. She lives three doors down from where my wife Ada and I live in Henrietta Street.'

'Tom, that sounds too good an offer to miss. I'm grateful to you.'

'Good.'

Malcolm sensed his mood lift after this stroke of luck. Was this a good portent for the future?

73

They stood in their own silence, which the swish of the sea along the sides of the ship, the creak of the sails and rap of ropes seemed to emphasise without intrusion.

'There!' Tom straightened up.

Malcolm followed the direction of his pointing arm and saw what he could only make out as the silhouette of a building on the cliffs.

'Whitby Abbey! A homing landmark for Whitby sailors.'

'So where's the town and harbour?' asked Malcolm, who could see only high cliffs.

'Look closely and you'll see the stone piers ... the west one has the lighthouse near the end of it.'

'Got it,' said Malcolm. 'But where...?'

'They mark the entrance to the River Esk, which flows between high cliffs and forms part of the harbour upstream.'

Before any further exchanges about the town and its position could be made, the two men were called to their task of helping to see the *Lady Isobel* safely into port.

'What's going on?' Malcolm asked, surprised to see the crowds of people gathering on the piers and cliffs as the ship closed in towards the port.

'A whale ship always receives this sort of welcome whenever she returns from the Arctic. Men have been away for anything up to six months. Their dangerous trade deserves a welcome and Whitby folk are keen to show their appreciation of what the whale men do for the town. Everything around the town will come to a stop until the ship is safely berthed.'

74

Malcolm was overwhelmed and moved by the reception that extended all the way from the piers to their berth upriver, beyond the drawbridge crossing of the Esk. It seemed to him that all of Whitby must have turned out to greet the ship. He sensed concern amongst the joy; the vessel's broken timbers told their own tale; he knew Whitby folk must be searching for their loved ones, fearing the worst if they could not see them. The final news would come only when the ship neared her berth. The relief amongst relations on the quay was unmistakable when information was called down from the deck that no one had been killed and those left behind in Shetland to receive medical attention were not in any danger.

'There's Ada!' cried Tom rapturously. 'And Ma! Come on, Malcolm, meet them.'

'Off you go. I'll follow,' he returned, not wanting to intrude on those first precious moments of a sailor home from the sea. When he walked down the gangway a few minutes later he nonetheless felt a pang of lonely jealousy. He had no one to greet him in this way. As he came towards his friend, he saw the pretty girl who was holding Tom's hand turn towards him. Her dark hair was loose and peeped out from under the shawl thrown loosely over her head. It framed an expressive face that attracted by its air of seductive innocence. Her sharp blue eyes were shining with the joy of having Tom close to her again. Her whole expression seemed to say, 'I'll be friends, but no more than that. I'm Tom's woman.' Malcolm liked her for that; he knew that in Tom and Ada Davis he had found true friends.

That impression was reinforced when Tom's mother, Maud, greeted him. She gave him a warm welcome, and instantly made him feel accepted. The friendliness in her deep brown eyes contrasted strongly with the lines of suffering on her face, caused by the loss of her husband to the Arctic and the constant fear that her only son might suffer the same fate. Malcolm also saw there a strong resolve that she would never voice those fears to him. She might do so to Ada whom she knew would have the same fears, and in the sharing both of them would draw on the strength known only to whale men's wives.

'Tom tells me you are wanting lodgings,' said his mother, once the introductions were over.

'Yes,' replied Malcolm. He knew she had been making an assessment of him in these first few minutes and felt he had passed muster when she said, 'When you have finished your duties come and have a cup of tea with me.' She gave a knowing little smile. 'We'll leave the other two to themselves.' She turned to face them. 'Six o'clock then. You know the score, Ada.'

'Aye, Ma. Tom's favourites – tattie and onion pie, then bread pudding as only you can make it.'

'Flatterer,' replied Maud, with a pleased smile.

Once family greetings had been exchanged on the quay, the crew set about completing their arrival tasks as quickly as possible.

Malcolm received his pay from the captain and, before joining Tom, said goodbye to the Shetlanders, who, in a couple of days, would be returning home on the ship that had followed the

76

Lady Isobel south.

Tom led the way along Church Street on the east side of the river towards the Church Stairs, the one hundred and ninety-nine stone steps that led up to the old parish church and ruined abbey on the clifftop. He took the street that ran along the cliffside from the bottom of the stairs.

'Henrietta Street,' he announced. 'Named after the wife of Nathaniel Cholmley who used to live in a big house near the abbey.' Tom saw Malcolm glancing dubiously at the cliff towering over them to their right. 'Pa bought two houses along here – a fashionable street for ships' masters and the like – but I'm looking to move, and Ma also. Those cliffs are none too safe.'

'I would think it a wise decision.'

Before any more could be said, Tom stopped, knocked on a green door to his left, opened it and walked in. Malcolm followed and found himself in a passage leading towards the back of the house, with a flight of stairs leading up on the left.

'Just us, Ma.' Tom's call brought Mrs Davis hurrying from a room at the back.

'Welcome,' she said, smiling at Malcolm.

'This is very kind of you, Mrs Davis,' he said, laying his bag on the floor.

'We'll see you at six, Tom.'

He nodded and left the house. Mrs Davis ushered Malcolm into the front parlour. 'Sit down,' she said, 'I'll be back in a moment with the tea.'

As he surveyed the room, Malcolm blessed his luck at falling in with Tom Davis. The house was not big but it was cosy and tastefully decorated, furnished with an eye to comfort. The delicately patterned wallpaper of small pink roses against a white background gave the room a feeling of light. He was standing looking at a framed drawing resting on top of the mantelpiece when Mrs Davis hurried in, carrying a tray of tea.

'Your husband, Mrs Davis?' he asked.

'Yes,' she replied.

'A fine-looking man,' he commented.

'He was.' Maud's voice filled with pride. 'That was sketched by a local artist just before Jack sailed on his last voyage three years ago.' Though her voice remained firm, Malcolm could detect the sadness of loss in it. 'A good man who controlled his crew firmly but kindly.'

'He looks a man of the sea through and through.'

'He was. His heart was there and I never tried to stop him sailing. If I had asked him to he would have done so, but he would never have been truly happy. Tom is the same. Thankfully, Ada understands that.' She paused then added quickly, 'So, Mr McFadden, you are thinking of staying in Whitby?'

'Yes, for the time being.'

'Until you find another ship?'

'No, Mrs Davis, I'm no sailor. I only volunteered to help bring the *Lady Isobel* back to port as a means of travelling on. I've no intention of returning to Shetland. Trouble at home,' he added in explanation.

Maud did not pry. It wasn't in her nature. Whatever had brought about his decision was Malcolm's affair and his alone. She liked him; he had an honest face, and seemed like someone who was naturally considerate. His build and the set of his jaw told her he was capable of looking after himself. She read gentleness in his alert deep blue eyes, and felt she could listen all night to the soft Scottish lilt in his voice.

'So what do you intend to do in Whitby?' she asked.

'Find work, I hope.'

'Have you any skills?'

'I'm good with my hands. Love working with wood, no matter what.'

'Then you are in the right place. There's plenty of ship-building in Whitby, and more so at the moment. I've heard tell that one of our newest shipyards, run by Archie Swan, is on the point of closing an order. He'll be likely taking on more men.'

'That sounds hopeful,' replied Malcolm enthusiastically as once again he blessed his luck in meeting Tom Davis.

'Then, when Ada and Tom arrive, we'll tell him to take you down to the yard in the morning.' As Malcolm was making his thanks, Maud said, 'Drink up, then I'll show you the room I have spare and you can decide whether to stay or not.'

'Mrs Davis, I know now I'll take your offer.'

'Without seeing it, and without hearing the rent and conditions?'

'I know without looking that the room will be just as attractive as this one, and I know you will charge no more than you think right.'

She smiled, grateful for his trust. She knew it would have pleased Jack.

Ada and Tom were delighted when they were told what had transpired, grateful to know that there would be someone in the house with Tom's mother, whom they both knew would revel in having someone to look after once more.

Kathleen Swan kept the horse to a steady pace as she left Peak House for Whitby after bidding Mrs Jordan goodbye. She had made no prior arrangement to visit her sister-in-law but hoped she would find her at home.

Rosemary had visited her at Peak House on two occasions during the past year but knew nothing of Kate's time in Scarborough or of the new arrangements for Wednesdays. Kate looked forward to surprising her with the news.

The sun was warm, making the drive pleasant; the countryside was lush with new growth, and glimpses of a tranquil sea added to Kate's feeling of well-being. Though she regretted her dispute with her father, she knew that if she had not defied him she would now be condemned to a life of servitude to the unsuitable man he had chosen for her. She settled herself more comfortably on the seat and drove those thoughts away, replacing them with the eager anticipation of surprising her sister-in-law.

She found suitable stabling for the horse and trap opposite one of the quays close to Prospect Row. On leaving the stable, she paused and took in the activity on the quays along the river side of Church Street. Here was the beating heart of Whitby; trade that took her ships to countries far and wide. Kate had been close to it throughout

80

her childhood and formative years. Now, as she watched the activity that swirled around the quays and the ships, she felt a touch of nostalgia. But did she really miss it? Was it not now replaced for her by the peace and tranquillity surrounding Peak House?

Her reverie was sharply interrupted by the sight of her father shaking hands with a man whose peaked cap signified he was the captain of the vessel berthed nearby. Titus turned and strode down the gangway with an air that could only indicate satisfaction with whatever had passed between him and the ship's master. He reached the quay, paused and looked in both directions.

Kate froze. She saw him stiffen as their eyes locked. The moment seemed to her to last an eternity. Then Titus turned and walked briskly away, making no acknowledgement of her in any shape or form. She stared after him, unable to move. Scenes from her childhood passed through her mind. She felt choked. But then they were replaced by memories of the tumultuous upheaval of their last meeting, and the tears that had started to come were suppressed. Kate turned away sharply and, though physically shaken, strode towards the house in nearby Prospect Row.

Her pull on the bell was quickly answered.

'Is Mrs Swan at home, Polly?' she asked.

The maid, a bright-eyed, tidy girl, smiled upon recognising Kate and answered briskly. 'Yes, miss.' She stood to one side, allowing Kate to step into the small, tastefully decorated hall. 'It's nice to see you again, miss.'

'Thank you, Polly.'

The maid closed the door and crossed the hall to the drawing-room door. She went in and Kate heard her say, 'Ma'am, Miss Swan is here.'

A moment later Rosemary hurried into the hall, smiling broadly. 'Kate, how delightful to have you call!' She took her sister-in-law in her arms and kissed her on both cheeks before hugging her warmly, an action that Kate reciprocated without any hesitation; she suddenly felt safe, and the pleasure of being with her sister-in-law wiped away any thought of the dark, unpleasant look she had received from her father.

'This is an unexpected surprise,' said Rosemary. There was a query in her tone but she knew better than to voice it in front of the maid, who stood by ready to take Kate's coat and hat.

Once she had shed them, Rosemary linked arms with Kate and led her to the drawing room.

'You look a bit piqued. Is something the matter?' she asked as she closed the door.

'I had just dismounted from the trap I drove here when I saw Father leaving a ship. He saw me too and it would be obvious to him I was coming here. Oh, Rosemary, I hope my visit will not cause trouble for you and Archie with Father.' The anxiety in her voice and expression did not go unnoticed.

'Did he speak to you?'

'No. His look said it all.'

'Well, I think you need have no fear of any repercussions from your visit.'

'But...'

Rosemary raised a hand to stop her. 'I know we were concerned because of Father's investment in

82

Archie's business, but things have changed. Your father came here one evening only last week and announced in angry tones that he knew we had taken you in when you left home, and that I had visited you at Peak House. He threatened to withdraw his help from Archie's business, but Archie was able to counter that threat by informing him he was on the point of closing a deal to build a new ship and, with the advance he was being paid, would repay the outstanding sum owed to his father. So he no longer has any say in our lives.'

Kate felt relieved but said, 'I hope there is no permanent rift between Archie and Father?'

Rosemary shook her head. 'No, even though Father-in-law clearly does not like relinquishing power of any sort. But with Archie now well established, their relationship is on a more even footing, and he can no longer dictate to us how we conduct our private lives. So, you see, we can be open about our friendship now. We can meet openly, and you can come here without any need to keep the news from him. I was going to come to Peak House and tell you next week, but here you are now...' She let her voice trail away expectantly.

Kate smiled and told her, 'I have so much to tell you! But first, let me say how delighted I am with the news of Archie's success.' She went on to tell Rosemary of the latest arrangement between her and Mrs Jordan, of their visit to Scarborough and Mrs Jordan's offer of further outings. 'But best of all, she has suggested Wednesdays should be my free day – a day to myself. Today is the first. I just had to take the opportunity to tell you.'

'Oh, I'm so pleased you did! You must stay all

day. I'll tell Cook you'll be here until after our five o'clock meal, and then you'll see Archie too. I'll send him word so that he can hire a horse to escort you back to Peak House this evening.' Rosemary paused then and a flash of concern crossed her face. 'Have you to be back by a certain time?'

'No. I told Mrs Jordan I was going to call on you, and she said I was not to be tied by any thoughts of time, though I know she would prefer me to be back before dark. I do not want to cause her any anxiety; she is so good to me.'

'You must tell me more, but first let me ring for Cook. Then I'll write a note to tell Archie he must be home by five and not a minute later. I won't say why. He'll get a nice surprise.'

So it proved; the three of them were much relieved that they could now see each other openly. Though they knew Titus would not approve, they sensed he would not want to lose another member of his family either and would be forced to ignore Archie's continued friendship with his sister.

9

'Mrs Davis, you're spoiling me,' said Malcolm, eyeing the dishes set on the table the following morning. Freshly baked bread filled the kitchen with its tempting aroma. To accompany it were cheese and cold minced meat. The golden brown of the apple pie crust spoke of Mrs Davis's light touch. She was standing by the fire, stirring something in a pan hanging from the reckon.

'This all looks very tempting ... and that bread smells wonderful. You must have been up early,' commented Malcolm.

'Aye, I am most mornings; best part of the day.'

'Well, I'm grateful to you.'

'You can show that by tucking in, enjoying it and making yourself at home. Would you like some porridge first?'

'Can't say no to that,' he replied with a smile of appreciation.

They talked pleasantly while he ate.

Maud was curious about him but asked no questions. She had heard other Shetland men on occasions when a ship from those northern islands arrived in Whitby. Malcolm spoke with the same lilt, but there was a difference in his tone and delivery that told her he was from a better background.

His plate was clear, the last piece of bread gone and only the mug with his second filling of tea remained on the table when they heard the front door open.

'Only me,' came the call, followed by the appearance of Tom a few moments later. 'Did he give you any trouble, Ma?' He grinned at Malcolm.

The twinkle in Maud's eyes teased him back as she replied, 'Aye, he did that. Noisy all night.'

'Slept like a babe,' replied Malcolm.

'Good, then you'll be ready to face Archie Swan.'

Malcolm nodded, drained his mug, got to his feet and, a few moments later, as the two men started along Henrietta Street, commented, 'The way you delivered your last remark made it sound as if I'm about to face a hard man?'

Tom laughed. 'I didn't mean it to come out like that. You should get on all right with Archie. He's a considerate taskmaster, but he won't stand any slacking. He knows what he wants and how a job should be done. He'll look for good honest work.'

'How old is he?' asked Malcolm.

'Twenty-two.'

'With his own business? I'd expected him to be older.'

Tom smiled. 'Who wouldn't? But he's a capable young man. Inherited his business talent from his father, Titus Swan. He's principally a rope and sail manufacturer but has his fingers in many other enterprises and is always on the lookout for more. He put his son into the family business when he was sixteen, but Archie had this talent for shaping wood, an ability he says he inherited from his great-grandfather.'

'And did he?'

'More than likely. He wanted to get out of working alongside his father and insisted he wanted to be a boat-builder. It went against Titus's plans but he was shrewd enough to see his son's talent as an investment for the future so financed the start of his business. Archie wanted his independence, though, wanted to escape his father's interference, so he insisted on a contract being drawn up which provided him with the chance to repay his father and take control of the yard. Now the time has come when that could happen, if the rumours circulating around Whitby are correct. According to Ma, Archie is about to acquire order for a

86

merchant ship. You and I will soon know if he's signing on more men.'

They walked at a brisk pace down Church Street and turned into Bridge Street.

'Archie Shaw's yard is on the other side of the river and upstream from the bridge. Most of Whitby's shipbuilding yards are there,' Tom explained.

As they proceeded across the bridge, weaving through the flow of people crossing it in both directions, Malcolm was surprised by all the activity until Tom told him that Whitby was one of the busiest ports on the east coast.

The sounds of hammers and saws mingled with the shouts of men as they passed the yards where boats and ships were being built by rival firms. A notice announced 'A. Swan, Ship- and Boat-builder'. They turned through the open gates and started across a patch of wasteland with the river on their left. Along its banks were four slipways, empty at present, but further along four more were occupied by cobles in various stages of construction.

'Not dissimilar in size to what we were making in Shetland,' commented Malcolm.

They reached a small block of buildings where Tom knocked on a door. He opened it on hearing the call 'Come!' They stepped into a square room containing a desk on their left and a long table against the opposite wall. Malcolm's quick eyes made out that the sheets of paper spread out on the table were plans. From behind the desk a young man looked up at them.

Recognition crossed his face. 'Tom Davis! Good

to see you, and to know the crew survived the battering the *Lady Isobel* took. I've seen the owner Sam Beadmore. The ship's condition means more work for my men.'

Tom made no comment at this but said, 'I've brought Malcolm McFadden to meet you.'

Archie nodded, his eyes intent on the stranger, assessing the man before him.

'Sir, Tom tells me you might be looking to take on more men.'

Archie did not answer immediately. Malcolm reckoned he was weighing up what his reply should be. Then he glanced at Tom. 'Where did you hear this? You've only just got back from the Arctic.'

'Rumours in the air,' replied Tom.

Archie grinned. 'There always are in Whitby.' His gaze swept back to Malcolm. 'And you are a Shetlander.'

'You have a sharp ear, sir,' said Tom. 'Malcolm is a Shetlander; he helped sail the *Lady Isobel* back from there. It was a one-way voyage for him as he aims to make a new life for himself elsewhere ... possibly here, if he can find work.'

'So you came here after hearing the rumours?'

'Aye, sir. No sense in missing a chance.'

Archie stood up and went to look out of the window. After a few moments' pondering, he said over his shoulder, 'Rumours are just rumours.' He paused, during which time Malcolm and Tom exchanged grimaces of disappointment. Then suddenly Archie spun round. 'And if they aren't, what interest is it to you, Mr McFadden? If anyone comes to work for me, I expect them to have the

88

necessary skills. I would question if you are likely to have them. Your voice and bearing tell me you are something different from the usual run, and that leads me to wonder why you need shipbuilding work and if you have the qualities required.'

'Mr Swan, I will be frank with you. I am leaving Shetland because of a dispute with my father ... nothing that could lead to any upset in Whitby, I assure you. The *Lady Isobel* was there and I took the opportunity to leave Shetland on her. Her captain knew I would not be returning. The dispute was merely a family matter.'

Archie looked thoughtful. 'I have heard rumours about of my intention to build a new ship. How they sprang up, I don't know.' He paused and looked hard at the two young men then continued, 'There is some truth in what you have heard. It will be for a group of investors living in and around Whitby. If that happens, I will be looking to employ more men. Nothing is certain yet but a final decision is close. Now, nothing of this must be said beyond these four walls until I make the announcement.'

Both men nodded and gave their undertaking to keep the information secret.

'Good. Now, Mr McFadden, you interest me but are you sure you have the woodworking skills I require?'

'I have them, sir.'

Archie sat down behind his desk again. 'How?'

'I became friendly from an early age with some local crofters. They built their own boats to work an inshore fishery and supplement their income. I watched and learned; they encouraged me. I

89

found I had a natural skill at the work, so practised and developed it. I discovered that I love wood and working with it. Hopefully I can now turn my favourite occupation into my livelihood.'

Archie nodded thoughtfully. He liked what he heard, which echoed his own love of wood. He could tell by the timbre of Malcolm's voice when he spoke of it that here was a man after his own heart.

'All right, here's what I'll do. I'll sign you on now for two weeks. I'll introduce you to Mark Jackson – he's in charge of one of the gangs working on those cobles you saw when you arrived. He could do with another man. He's also my foreman. We'll see how you get on and, after two weeks, what Mark has to say.'

'That suits me,' replied Malcolm. 'You won't regret it, sir.'

'Make sure I don't. Any adverse report about your work from Mark, and that is it.'

'Yes, sir.'

'And one other thing.' Archie glanced at Tom, including him in what he was about to say. 'Remember, I don't want anything said about what you have heard in this room. Ostensibly I am employing Malcolm to work on the coble, and that's all.'

When the two men left Swan's yard they were in high spirits.

'Thanks for your help, Tom,' Malcolm told him.

'It was nothing.'

'You've given me a new life.'

'You'll miss Shetland?'

'Aye, I will. Some aspects I'm glad I'm escaping, but others I will miss.' With that thought Malcolm felt a pang. Rowena... He shut the thought of her away. Let it take hold and there was no way of knowing what he might do; but of one thing he was certain – he would not return to Shetland and beg her to come with him. Rowena had made her decision. There was no road back.

'You wanted to see me, Mr Swan?' Mark Jackson put the question as he entered Archie's office.

'Yes, close the door and sit down.' He indicated the chair on the opposite side of his desk. Once Mark was seated Archie went on, 'We've had McFadden with us for two weeks. What do you think of him?'

Mark did not hesitate. 'He's a good worker with natural skills; knows what he's about. Tell him the job and he gets on with it with only a few questions, and they are getting less and less as he falls in with our methods. It's obvious he's worked on boats before even though they haven't been cobles.'

Archie nodded. 'You've verified my own conclusions about the work he turns out. Now tell me, how does he get on with the rest of the men?'

'Very well, sir. They were a bit suspicious of him at first but there's been no trouble from them. He won them over with his friendliness, and never pushed Shetland and his past life there down their throats.'

'Has he ever spoken of it?'

'No, and I don't pry. I take the view that he'll

91

tell us what he wants us to know in his own time. And if he doesn't, that's his privilege.'

'Quite right,' Archie agreed.

'But I will say this,' Mark went on. 'He's not the normal run of Shetlander we see here whenever they come south. There's something about him that is different.'

Archie nodded, pursed his lips thoughtfully for a moment, and then said, 'Good, then I'll sign him on permanently.'

Mark started to rise from his chair but Archie stopped him. 'I have something to tell you.' Mark sat down, his expression serious. 'As my foreman,' went on Archie, 'who has worked tirelessly with me from the start of this firm, I think you should be the first to know that late yesterday I signed a contract to build a new ship.'

Mark's sombre eyes brightened, betraying his excitement. 'That's marvellous news, sir! This will raise everyone's spirits.'

'Say nothing yet, but call the men to a meeting outside here twenty minutes before knocking-off time, when I'll make an announcement.'

Rumours about the possibility of new work for the yard had dwindled during the last two weeks. Knowing work on the cobles was almost complete, the men were seeing hard times ahead for them. Speculation ran rife among them as they gathered before Archie's office and the buzz of conversation only subsided when their employer stepped out.

He held up his hands, signalling for quiet. The air became charged with a dour sense of expectancy. 'Men, I appreciate the way you have worked for me, especially on these cobles – the last of our current orders.' A murmur of disappointment ran around the men. Archie paused. Then, strengthening his delivery, he added, 'You have two weeks in which to get them finished and delivered and make ready for building a new ship of three hundred tonnes...'

There was a brief moment of disbelief, as if this news could not possibly be true, but then its impact hit home and cheers rang out amidst cries of undisguised delight. Men hugged each other, slapped each other on the back and punched each other in playful exuberance. Excitement ran through them like wind through the corn, and culminated in three cheers for Archie Swan.

With a broad smile on his face, he held his hands high to try to win silence. Eventually the joyful noise subsided. 'This is a big order. It could pave the way for a secure future for all of us. Let us make sure we build this ship in the proud tradition of Whitby vessels that sail around the world. I will have to take on more men, mostly skilled ones, and I want you to work with them to the advantage of this firm – where all our futures lie.'

Only when Mark had raised another cheer for Mr Swan did the men begin to disperse, anticipating the joy this news would bring their families. Archie turned to Mark. 'Tell, McFadden to come to my office.'

A few minutes later Malcolm arrived. 'You wanted to see me, sir?'

Archie fixed him with a steady gaze. 'Your trial period is up. My foreman has given you a good report. If you wish to remain in Whitby, I can, as you heard, offer you work. The decision is up to you. You know what you want to make of your future.'

'I'll be more than delighted to take up your offer, sir,' replied Malcolm with a broad smile.

'You like our town then?'

'I do, and I am happy living with Mrs Davis. She's like a mother to me.'

'Have you no desire to return to Shetland?'

'No, sir.'

Archie was surprised by the speed of his reply. 'Not even in the future?'

'Who knows what the future holds for each one of us, sir?'

There was no reply to that. Archie just nodded.

'Thank you again for taking me on.'

'Your work is good, I've seen that for myself. In fact, it's better than good.'

When Malcolm left the office, Archie sat staring at the closed door. He was no nearer knowing any more about this man's background. Why was he curious about this stranger who had come to work for him? Archie had a natural curiosity about people which was often quickly satisfied, but he was not finding it easy to dismiss thoughts of Malcolm McFadden.

The Shetlander had settled easily among the Whitby men and they had readily accepted the quiet dignity and reserved friendship of the man. McFadden had said he had left Shetland because of a family dispute; it must have been serious to tear him away from his roots. The desire to find out more piqued Archie who now regretted he had not had a word with the Shetlanders who had brought the *Lady Isobel* back to Whitby. Maybe one day he would satisfy his curiosity, but for now he had to organise the building of a ship.

10

When Kate arrived at Rosemary's the following day, she sensed excitement in the air but when she made an observation about this her sister-in-law's smiling reply was only, 'I do have some good news – in fact, two pieces of it – but you will have to wait a little while to learn what they are. Come, have some refreshment while we wait.'

'Oh, come on, Rosemary, don't keep me on tenterhooks,' said Kate, shedding her outdoor coat.

'No, you'll have to wait,' she replied, enjoying her subterfuge as she led the way into the drawing room.

Kate gave a mocking pout and said, 'Maybe I'll stop coming.'

'I don't think you'll do that,' laughed Rosemary.

Her rejoinder was so full of conviction that Kate had to laugh and admit, 'You're right. It has been very comforting to be in touch regularly again, and it brings me such pleasure.'

'It has brought me pleasure, too, to know we can meet more frequently from now on.' Rosemary had rung the bell, a signal for refreshments to be served. Five minutes later the maid came in with a tray which she set on a low table in front of her mistress.

'Three cups? Are you expecting someone else?' queried Kate, hoping that the anticipated guest would not intrude too long on her time with Rosemary.

'Yes. It is someone I think you should meet.'

'One of your two surprises? Who is it?'

'You'll see.' At that moment a bell sounded deep in the house and a few moments later they heard quick footsteps making for the front door. 'Ah, timed to perfection.' Rosemary smiled, getting to her feet ready to greet the new arrival. The door opened; the maid stood to one side to allow someone to enter.

'Dorothea!' Kate gasped on seeing her sister.

Dorothea, eyes widening with astonishment, stood still in amazement. 'Kate!'

She jumped to her feet, and the two sisters hugged each other tightly, realising how much they had missed each other during the last two years.

Amidst the laughter, Dorothea managed to say to Rosemary, 'So *this* is who you wanted me to meet?'

'She told me the same,' put in Kate, then looked at Rosemary. 'This is so good of you.'

Rosemary's gesture dismissed the thanks. When she had accepted a cup of tea, Kate said, 'Now, the second surprise?' She followed the question immediately with one to her sister. 'Has she another surprise for you too?'

'Not that I know of,' replied Dorothea.

'Well?' Kate asked Rosemary.

'I know it will be a surprise to you,' replied her sister-in-law. 'I'm not sure if it will be to Dorothea ... she may know about it already.'

The sisters looked askance at her. 'You'll have to wait. And in the meantime, I think you two will have much to talk about,' said Rosemary, to avoid any further badgering from them.

So it proved as Kate asked about their mother and tentatively about their father and how things were at home, while Dorothea wanted to know all about her life with Mrs Jordan. When she heard of the possibility of their meeting more often in the future, Dorothea was delighted.

'I'll not let anything or anyone, not even Father, stop us meeting,' she informed them. 'You've set me an example, Kate.'

'Don't incur his wrath to your own disadvantage,' warned Kate.

'I won't. I recall you telling me how to handle him since he approves of Ben. It has served me well.'

'Good. Then keep it that way,' Kate approved, pleased that she saw a new brightness come to her sister's eyes at the mention of Ben; she knew Dorothea's love for him still burned brightly.

Chatter in the drawing room of the house in Prospect Row was lively; the time passed quickly and they were all surprised when Archie walked in.

He greeted his sisters with enthusiasm, pleased that they were in contact again. Then he turned to his wife. 'So this is why you wanted me to come home for luncheon?'

Rosemary smiled and slipped her arm through

his. 'Yes, I wanted you to tell Kate your news yourself. And I suspect from what has been said here that Dorothea may not yet know it either.'

'I don't think she will. Father's in Scarborough on business for four days, so he won't have heard.'

'Now you are making all this sound very mysterious,' put in Kate, glancing at Dorothea for agreement.

'You are,' she said, and added to her sister's observation, 'And so exciting! What's it all about, Archie?'

He looked at Kate first. 'I told you about the deal that was in the offing. Well, it has materialised. Contracts have been signed for me to build another ship.'

'Splendid!' enthused Kate. 'You deserve to be successful.'

'What's this?' asked Dorothea.

Archie explained the situation and she added her own enthusiastic congratulations.

'What about the second ship?' asked Kate.

'That didn't materialise but I have in mind that, while I have everything set up to build one ship, I might build a second on my own account. I'll seek out investors, but retain the major share for myself and trade her under my name.'

'This sounds an exciting venture,' said Dorothea.

'And one I'm sure you will turn into a major success,' agreed Kate.

'It has possibilities, but I will need to find some backers first.'

'Father?' put in Dorothea tentatively.

'No,' replied Archie, quickly and firmly. 'He

must not get a finger in this pie or he'll try to take it over. This must be my enterprise, an offshoot of my ship-building. Oh, I'll still buy my rope and sails from him; there isn't a better firm for those in Whitby.'

'Can I tell Ben?' Dorothea asked.

'Of course. Maybe he or his father would like some shares.'

As Kate drove back to Peak House she had much to think about. It had been an informative visit, and so good to be reunited with her sister again.

'Hello, my dear. Did you have a good day?' Mrs Jordan asked from the comfort of her armchair when Kate walked into the drawing room at Peak House.

'I did, Mrs Jordan.'

'You went to see your sister-in-law again?'

'Yes,' replied Kate, sitting down opposite her. 'I had a big surprise there too: Rosemary had arranged for my sister Dorothea to join us. I have not seen her since I came here.'

'Splendid! I'm so pleased. No doubt there will be other meetings in the future?'

'Most certainly. My brother joined us for lunch; again planned by Rosemary because he had news they wanted us to hear from them before it became generally known in Whitby.'

'It sounds as though it is something exciting,' said Mrs Jordan with eager attention.

'It is. Apart from the order to build a three-hundred-tonne ship, my brother plans to build another for himself if he can get some investors to take shares in her.'

'So he would be building two ships at the same time? That would be of great benefit to Whitby. When will he start?'

'I don't know any more than that. Archie has to work out all the details yet and will have to look to hire more men. There'll be a lot to arrange before they start work.'

'Of course.'

'It was only yesterday, when the men were finishing work, that Archie told them. It was a great fillip for them because the work they were doing on some cobles was almost finished.'

'Then this was a most fortunate time to obtain these orders.'

'Well, the second is by no means certain yet. He will have to find other interested parties.'

'I'm sure he will, so let us have a glass of Madeira and toast the new enterprise.'

The following morning at breakfast, Mrs Jordan laid down her knife and fork, dabbed her lips with her napkin and said, 'Kate, I want you to go back into Whitby and see your brother Archie. Tell him I might be interested in making an investment with him.'

'In his new ship?' asked Kate with mounting excitement.

'Yes.' Mrs Jordan smiled. 'What else? Ask him to visit me here as soon as he wishes. If this idea of his is going to come to fruition, I must make my interest known to him before his subscription list is completed.'

'Are you sure about this?' asked Kate cautiously.

'Of course I am,' Mrs Jordan reassured her.

'Since you came into my life, you have given me new horizons. I could have stagnated, grown old without any change of outlook, but you, young and vibrant, have brought my life a new perspective. I've money put away; it will be better for me to put it to work as a means of increasing my income. Kate, if this comes off, think of the excitement of knowing what the ship I have invested in is doing. Where she is sailing, what goods she will be carrying. Oh, Kate, it was a kind fate that brought you into my life.'

Kate's eyes dampened at the joy she saw in Mrs Jordan's expression. She had not realised how much she had changed her employer's outlook, overwhelmed as she had been with joy and relief to enter her household.

'Mrs Jordan, I owe you a great deal. I too regard fate as kind for stepping into my life, at such a moment of upheaval, and bringing me to you.'

'Then we both have fate or some more divine influence to thank.' Evelyn paused briefly, then stiffened her back and said firmly, 'If we go on like this, we'll spend the day weeping. So off with you ... go and bring your brother.'

'Very well, I'll lose no time.' Kate dropped her napkin on her plate and rose from her chair. On her way to the door, she paused beside Mrs Jordan and kissed her on the cheek. 'Thank you,' she said, and hurried from the room.

The closed door prevented Kate from hearing Mrs Jordan's whispered, 'And thank you.'

When Kate pulled to a halt in front of her brother's yard, one of his workers who was passing at the time recognised her. He touched the peak of his cap and said, 'May I help you down, Miss Swan?'

'Thank you,' Kate returned with a smile, and took his hand as she stepped from the trap.

'I'll tie the horse to that post, miss. Do you want it unhitching from the trap?'

'No, thank you. I'll be leaving soon.'

The man led the horse away, and Kate went into the office. 'Oh, I'm sorry,' she said hastily when she found someone was already with her brother. She started to turn back.

'No, Kate, it's all right. Come in, come in. This is Malcolm McFadden. Malcolm, this is my sister Kathleen.'

He touched his forehead. 'I'm pleased to meet you, Miss Swan.'

She inclined her head in acknowledgement, at the same time noticing the admiring light in his deep blue eyes. 'That accent tells me you are from the north,' she commented.

'Shetland to be precise, miss.'

'McFadden helped bring the *Lady Isobel* back and has stayed on in Whitby. That's my good fortune. I've found a man who is highly skilled with wood.'

'Your brother praises me too highly, Miss Swan.' Malcolm turned to Archie. 'Give me time to consider your offer then I'd like to talk some more, sir, if I may?'

'Of course. There is no immediate hurry.'

Malcolm bowed to Kate. 'Miss Swan.'

She returned his courtesy with a smile and watched him leave. As the door closed, she said to her brother as he offered her a chair, 'He's different.'

'You noticed it in even those few minutes?'

Kate gave a small laugh. 'Women's intuition... No, his voice gives him away. A more genteel sort than the men you usually employ.'

'That's what I think.'

'Haven't you found out anything else?'

'I'll wait for him to tell me himself. All I know is that he left Shetland after a family dispute.'

'Ah, intriguing,' she said, with curiosity shining in her eyes. 'We need to discover more.'

'Leave things be, Kate. I don't want him leaving.'

'He's as good as that?'

'I have plans for him if I am to build the second ship. But what brings you here?'

'It's just that – the second ship.'

'In what way?'

'Yes. It was mentioned when I was telling Mrs Jordan of my day with you all yesterday. This morning at breakfast she told me she would be interested in being one of the investors in the new vessel, and told me to come and ask you to visit her, to discuss the possibility. She doesn't want to miss her chance. So here I am. Can you come and see her now?'

'Of course!' Archie's eyes danced with excitement at such an unexpected development. He jumped to his feet. 'I'll send someone to hire me a horse at The Angel and then we'll be off to see Mrs Jordan!'

Hearing the crunch of wheels and the clop of hooves approaching Peak House, George the handyman came hurrying to the front of the house. He steadied the horse in the trap, spoke a quiet soothing word to it, and then helped Kate to the ground.

'Thank you, George,' she said. 'Can you take Mr Swan's horse too?'

'Yes, miss,' he replied pleasantly. 'Leave her, sir, she'll be all right,' he called to Archie who was swinging from his saddle.

'Thank you,' he replied, then straightened his coat and jacket.

'This way.' Kate started for the front door and he followed.

Before they reached it, it opened to reveal Mrs Jordan attended by a maid.

'Mr Swan, we have not met, though of course I have heard of you. Welcome to my home.'

Archie swept his hat from his head, bowed and raised the hand Evelyn had offered him to his lips.

'It is a privilege to meet you, Mrs Jordan. I have heard of you too. May I say I have heard nothing but praise for you from my sister? Thank you for your kindness to her.'

'Kate is a wonderful help to me, Mr Swan. Now come along in.' Mrs Jordan glanced at the maid. 'Enid, take Mr Swan's things.'

Once they were enjoying a glass of Madeira in the drawing room, Mrs Jordan said, 'Now tell me about this ship you intend to build.'

'The plan is only in its very early stages, but I must say that when Kate told me of your interest and that you wanted to see me, it took a step forward in my mind. If you make a positive decision, it will help me to convince others to invest.'

'I suppose you will be working in sixteenths?'

'Yes. I will retain nine-sixteenths and the rest will be distributed according to the amount a person wishes to invest.'

'And we will only know that when you have the ship's full costing worked out?'

'Yes.'

'Then when you have those figures, come back to me before you approach anyone else.' Evelyn gave a little smile. 'That is an order, Mr Swan.'

He replied with an amused smile, 'Yes, ma'am.'

'Now that we have reached that understanding, tell me more about this proposed ship. Why you are building her, and what you see as her role in the maritime trade of Whitby?'

'I decided that with a firm order for one large ship, it would make sense to build another at the same time rather than layoff the men when the first was completed and then probably have to reassemble them at a later date.'

'A sensible idea if you really see potential in another ship.'

Archie went into detail of what he had in mind: about the ship itself, his building schedule, what he would expect of his men and what he visualised the trading potential to be.

He was struck by the interest and knowledge Mrs Jordan showed. He knew he was dealing with an astute woman and guessed that much of her late husband's acumen had rubbed off on her. Their talk continued over a pleasant luncheon and only finished in the early afternoon.

As Archie was leaving, he thanked Mrs Jordan for her interest and hospitality.

'Let me have the figures and projections of timings as soon as possible. Once I get my teeth into something, I want it to happen quickly. I absorbed as much from my husband, God rest his soul. I must say, the possibilities of this project have given me a new interest in life. I very much look forward to seeing its fruition.'

11

Two weeks later Archie arrived at Peak House for a morning appointment with Mrs Jordan.

After greetings were exchanged with her and his sister, he remarked, 'If today's weather is a portent of success then we will have a thriving business.'

'You'll have had a pleasant ride here?'

'Indeed I have, and much to think about on the way,' he replied as he tapped the folder he had laid on the table.

'I'm very excited about this venture,' Mrs Jordan remarked, but halted Archie as he was about to open the folder. 'Wait, Mr Swan, a cup of tea first.'

As if on cue the maids came in carrying trays, placed them on a side table and proceeded to pour the tea. The conversation was restricted to pleasantries and it was only when the refreshments had been cleared away and Kate had left them that Archie detailed his venture to Mrs Jordan.

She listened carefully, asking pertinent questions. Archie realised once more he was dealing with no fool.

Her final comment and question were, 'I like the explicit and detailed nature of your presentation. I thank you for that. I admit, I know nothing about the actual construction process, but if we reach an agreement, I would hope you would better educate me in that and keep me informed regularly of progress. You have not mentioned any other investors?'

'I have investors for my first ship but for the second one, because you indicated you wished for first refusal of shares offered, I have not as yet approached anyone directly. But two merchants living in Pickering have previously indicated interest in any trading venture, and will no doubt decide whether or not to join us when they hear what I have to offer by way of shares.'

'This all sounds very promising,' commented Mrs Jordan. She looked thoughtful. Judging that she was considering her position, and not wanting to influence her unduly, Archie did not speak for a few moments.

'You propose to keep nine-sixteenths for yourself?' she queried.

He nodded.

'Quite right,' she agreed.

He remained silent.

'If I were to say I would be interested in taking four-sixteenths, would that fit in with the likely stake of your other two interested parties?'

'I do know that, as they are close friends, they would like to have equal shares. I would therefore be willing to reduce mine to eight-sixteenths; yours would remain at four, which would mean I could offer them each two-sixteenths, which I believe would satisfy them.'

'That is thoughtful of you, Mr Swan.'

'Not at all. It will keep the situation on an even keel while I remain the majority shareholder.'

'Good.'

They stood up and Evelyn held out her hand. 'I believe you men shake hands on a deal and then have the necessary documents drawn up.'

He smiled at her grasp of business etiquette. 'Quite right, Mrs Jordan.' He took her hand and felt her firm clasp setting the final seal on their business commitment to each other. 'I will have the necessary documents drawn up.'

'Very good,' said Evelyn sitting down again and indicating for him to do the same. 'One or two things more,' she said. 'When you have the documents drawn up, present them to my attorney in Whitby, James Walker in Baxtergate.'

'Certainly,' agreed Archie.

'Maybe, if the two gentlemen in Pickering agree to your proposal, we could all meet and sign the agreements there. It seems appropriate for the investors to meet each other; we would then be able to put faces to names, and know with whom we share this enterprise.'

'That's a splendid idea, Mrs Jordan. It should be easy enough. I share the same attorney as you.'

'Then that is settled. Now I suggest we break the news to your sister, who will be close to this venture through both of us.' As she was speaking Evelyn went to the bell-pull. A few minutes later a maid appeared. 'Enid, tell Miss Swan she is wanted.'

When Kate came into the drawing room, Mrs Jordan immediately told her, 'Your brother and I have reached an agreement about the new ship.'

'Oh, I'm so pleased. I'm sure you won't regret this investment, Mrs Jordan.'

'I'm sure I shan't. Now, Kate, be so good as to charge some glasses. We must drink to the success of our enterprise.'

They made the toast amid much pleasant speculation, then Archie said, 'Mrs Jordan, I would like you to name this ship since you have the biggest stake in her after mine.'

'But surely you should...'

Archie raised his hand to stop her. 'No, I want you to do it.'

Evelyn beamed at him in gratification.

'Well, that is very kind of you. I have plenty of time to decide. No doubt I'll chop and change my mind many times, and then, I dare say, will come back to the first one I thought of. I will put my mind to the task, Mr Swan, never fear. And your sister shall help me. Together we will decide on the perfect name.'

During his ride back to Whitby, Archie laid further plans. Reaching the port, he went straight to the offices of James Walker and told him of the agreement he had made with his client.

'Please draw up the legal documents for signature. I will go tomorrow to Pickering where I am certain Mr Walter Gibson and Mr Richard Moss will also be interested in investing in this new ship. I believe they both share the same attorney.'

'Good, that will make things easier,' said James

109

Walker. 'Do you know who it is?'

'Thomas Pierson of Bridge Street in Pickering.'

'Better still. I have had dealings with Thomas before. Everything should be straightforward.'

Two days later Archie walked into James Walker's office to inform him that he had had profitable exchanges with Mr Gibson and Mr Moss, followed by a meeting with their attorney and a pleasant overnight stay at the Black Swan in the Market Place.

He left everything in Walker's hands, and a fortnight later Archie and the three investors signed the necessary documents in front of the two attorneys.

When Archie said goodbye to them, he left a satisfied group whom he knew had high hopes of seeing a splendid ship sailing out of Whitby to bring them a good return on their investment. He acknowledged the burden of responsibility that he had brought on himself but knew he would revel in constructing this ship. The first thing he must do was to recruit a skilled workforce. When he returned to his yard, he paused to view the progress being made on the first new order. Recruits to the task had been readily forthcoming and, under the watchful eye of Mark Jackson, had worked well, keeping abreast of the time-scale laid down, though these were still early days.

Archie called his foreman to the office and indicated for him to sit down.

'You'll be pleased to know that the agreement for the second ship has been signed by all parties.'

'Good.'

Archie knew that behind this almost non-committal reply lay genuine heartfelt pleasure at what this would mean for the shipyard and its workforce.

'I do not want to upset the team you have working on...' Archie paused. 'I think we had better give it a temporary name – Number One. And the new ship will be Number Two, then there'll be no confusion.'

Mark nodded his agreement.

'As I say, I don't want to upset Number One team. I'd prefer to recruit a separate team for Number Two rather than chop and change between the two. I know it can be done that way and you would handle it well, but it could lead to speeding up on some jobs, which might result in shoddy work. I know you will say you would see that it didn't, but you can't be everywhere. As you know, some of this work is hidden from the eye. We can't afford to hold work up for your inspection while you are seeing to things on the other project. So it has to be a completely different workforce for Number Two, and that includes hiring a new foreman.'

Mark had listened to his employer with thoughtful attention. He pursed his lips and frowned.

'I see you don't agree?' said Archie.

'It's not that. It does make sense. A steady worker doesn't make mistakes. He'll do good work if he's not pushed unnecessarily. There would be danger in switching the men about from one ship to another. You are right to think of employing a separate team. My only doubt is about filling the foreman's position. I'm not saying I'm irreplaceable, but I'm not sure if there is anyone in Whitby who fulfils the role of good man-handler along with the necessary construction knowledge, and is available.'

'I am going to propose someone and I would like to know what you think.'

Curiosity appeared on Mark's normally imperturbable face.

'Malcolm McFadden,' Archie declared.

Mark raised his eyebrows in surprise. 'But he has no experience.'

'I've kept a close eye on him. He showed much skill in working on the coble. He has fitted in well, and gets on with the others even though there is something about him that sets him apart. I believe he has had dealings with men from a position of authority – as a leader. I believe he could use that experience while working as foreman on the new ship.'

'It's a bit different from building a two-hundred-tonne ship.'

'Aye, that's true,' admitted Archie, 'but I've seen his interest in the construction of Number One even though it is still in its early stages. He asks questions constantly without appearing to do so. It will be a while before we start on the new ship; he can learn from you, if you'll help him?'

Mark still looked doubtful. He gave a little grimace then said, 'Are you sure about this?'

'I think it is worth a try.'

'Well, all right. You're the boss.'

'Let's have him in then. Give him a shout.'

Mark left the office. Archie heard him shout, 'McFadden!' and a few minutes later both men walked in.

Archie eyed Malcolm for a moment, weighing him up, and then said, 'I want a foreman to work on the new ship in a position similar to Mark's; that is, overall foreman for the project. The shipwrights, caulkers, oakum boys, joiners, carpenters, sawyers and so on all have their own foremen, but you will oversee them, check that the work each foreman gets out of his team is up to the standard I require. Like Mark, you will keep the interests of Swan's first and foremost in your mind. That's the job I'm offering you, McFadden.'

Malcolm was stunned. He glanced at Mark as if looking for agreement from him.

'You heard what Mr Swan said.'

Malcolm turned his eyes to Archie. 'Are you serious, sir?'

'I wouldn't have you in here now if I weren't.'

'But I know very little about ship construction.'

'You've learned quite a lot while working on the present ship. I've seen it in everything you do. You can build on that and carry on learning. I know you pick up things quickly; you learn by observing. You can go on doing so in the time left before we start on the new ship. Mark will teach you. I think you said you have been around sailing ships?'

'I have on occasion crewed on one sailing from Shetland to the mainland of Scotland.'

'So you know ocean-going ships, their parts and so on?'

'Yes, sir, but not the actual construction.'

'As I've said, Mark will help you widen your knowledge.'

'But won't Whitby folk expect one of their own

to take the position?'

'Maybe, but I don't think they'll protest. You are liked and have a way with you. I think you can handle them. The job is yours, if you want it.'

'I appreciate your faith in me, sir. I'll take it.'

'Good.' Archie was relieved and it showed in the glance he gave Mark, who gave him an almost imperceptible nod. Archie was buoyed up by that as he knew it was Mark's usual sign of approval – no exuberance, no histrionics, just a small nod.

'For the time being, while we are recruiting men and getting everything ready you will stay on the same wage. Once construction work starts, I will put you on a wage slightly lower than Mark's. Then, if you continue to progress satisfactorily in this new role, you and he will be viewed as being on the same level.'

'That is more than generous, sir.'

'Good. Then it is settled.'

'Sir, might I ask when the timber will be arriving for the new ship?'

'Yes, but first, with no name decided, your ship is to be known as Number Two; Mark's is Number One. Elm for the keel and oak for the main construction will be coming in two weeks' time. I've long had in mind the hope that one day I would construct ships of this size, and accordingly ordered timber to be cut and held in readiness on estates around Helmsley.'

'Helmsley?'

'South across the moors. Quite a haulage job to get the timber here, but they've done it before for other shipyards.'

114

'Yes, sir.' When nothing else was forthcoming from Archie, Malcolm added, 'I'll see our storage sheds are suitably roofed and have good circulation, to counteract any fungal decay in the stored timber.'

As Malcolm left the office, Archie turned to Mark. 'I believe our faith in him will be justified.'

By observing the way Mark handled his responsibilities, Malcolm learned quickly and involved himself in the early developments of the task ahead. Labourers were engaged to clear overgrowth on land that had once held a slipway for a large craft; others repaired the storage sheds. Stocks of copper sheeting, necessary tools and other equipment were brought in.

Malcolm greatly looked forward to the day when he would be overseeing the actual building of Number Two. He was eager to see the drawings for the new ship; eager to oversee the first laying of wood – the English elm for the keel laid on the keel-blocks.

But his first sight of the plans, pored over with Archie and Mark, was followed by a surprise.

'McFadden, I told you Mrs Jordan of Peak House has invested in this ship. She's expressed a desire to be kept informed of progress. I want you to visit her, tell her what has happened so far, show her these plans and answer any questions.'

'Yes, sir.'

Malcolm and Mark left the office. Archie sat down behind his desk, pleased with the way things were developing and hoping that his latest appointment would bring him results. He also reckoned that if anyone could sum up Malcolm McFadden and learn more about the man and his background, Mrs Evelyn Jordan could.

12

Three days later Malcolm called on Archie at the end of the working day. 'Sir, when you told me to see Mrs Jordan, I sent a letter to her early the next day via one of the stable boys at The White Horse, asking if I could call on her today. I was unable to tell you yesterday because the boy's horse had gone lame, delaying his return. When I received her reply, you had gone home.'

'So you are telling me you need to be absent today?'

'Yes, sir.'

'Perfectly all right, but you'd better inform Mark.'

'Yes, sir.' Malcolm started for the door but was halted when Archie spoke again. 'Well done. I'm pleased you got it organised so fast. Take care to keep on the right side of Mrs Jordan; she's got a big stake in this ship. She's a pleasant lady – but she'll expect you to be on your toes while you explain where her money is being spent.'

Malcolm nodded to him and left.

Archie sat staring thoughtfully at the closed door for a few minutes, impressed by Malcolm's show of initiative. He would dearly have loved to see the letter his foreman had sent Mrs Jordan.

Kate viewed herself in her dressing-table mirror. She gave her hair a final brush, gathering it from the back of her neck and fastening it in a pile on top of her head, then pushed a wayward strand firmly into place. After carefully considering what she should wear, she had finally settled on a pale green skirt, tight-fitting at the waist, falling with a slight flare to her ankles. It was topped by a dark green, high-necked, silk spencer, pointed at the waistline. Satisfied with the results, she sat looking at herself in the mirror and pondered the coming visit of Mr McFadden.

When Mrs Jordan had told her he would be calling with the drawings of the new ship her brother was going to build, Kate had immediately recalled her first impression of him during their brief meeting in Archie's office. Even in that short time, and it was short – a bare introduction – she had been aware of his eyes. They had been blue, kindly-looking, yet interested and with an awareness of her. She had felt flattered by his attention, and at the same time drawn to him. Afterwards her desire to meet him again was strong, so that when Mrs Jordan told her about his coming visit Kate had felt an excitement she had never experienced before.

Malcolm collected the plans of the new vessel and, after informing Mark of his mission, left the bustle of the shipyard and hurried to the nearby stable where he hired a horse.

He enjoyed the ride to Peak House and, on approaching, slowed to admire it and its setting. Even though it was not in any way like Garstan

House in Shetland, it stirred a momentary nostalgia in him. Annoyed by his own sentimentality, he tightened his lips and shook off his reflective mood. He was here to do a job, one he must do well to impress an influential investor.

The sound of a horse's hoof brought George away from the patch of ground he was weeding. He saw a young man sitting well in the saddle and carefully guiding his horse. George waited for him at the foot of the steps in front of the house.

'Good day, sir,' he called as Malcolm brought the horse to a halt.

'Good morning,' returned Malcolm pleasantly as he swung out of the saddle. 'I'm here to see Mrs Jordan.'

'You will be the person she told me about – Mr McFadden?'

Malcolm nodded and said with a friendly smile, 'That's me.'

A maid led him into a large drawing room.

Mrs Jordan and Kate turned from the window where they had been standing admiring the changing light as white clouds played over the sea in the dazzling sunshine.

'Ah, Mr McFadden, welcome to my home.' Mrs Jordan stepped forward to shake his hand.

'My pleasure, ma'am.' Malcolm took her hand gently but not diffidently. He seemed unusually confident for a foreman. He turned to Kate and gave a small bow. 'Miss Swan.'

She acknowledged him with an inclination of her head. She noted the surprised, questioning expression on Mrs Jordan's face, so quickly made an explanation. 'Mr McFadden and I met briefly

118

that day you sent me to see my brother.'

'Ah, I see.'

'This is a lovely room, Mrs Jordan,' commented Malcolm, 'with a marvellous view.'

'It is,' she agreed, pleased that a young man should notice. 'When we moved here we had the room altered to enhance its outlook.'

'A very sensible idea, ma'am.'

'You've brought me the drawings?'

'Yes, ma'am. These are the preliminary ones only but are good enough to introduce you to the outlines of a merchant vessel. You will see amendments and enhancements made in the subsequent drawings I will bring, until eventually we won't require any more. From then on, I hope I will be able to escort you and Miss Swan to view the various finishing stages. Mr Swan informed me that you wish to be kept in touch with every phase of the building of the ship which, at the moment, we are calling Number Two. I understand that at some time you will name her?'

'Yes, I shall. Now, let us take some refreshment and then we will discuss the drawings.' Mrs Jordan went to the bellpull.

She had been very favourably struck by the demeanour of this young man. He carried himself well and was undeniably handsome, with deep blue eyes that sparkled in a lazy enticing way. And his voice – well, she felt she could listen to that without ever tiring of it; it told her he came from Shetland, a fact that indicated there was more to Malcolm McFadden than appeared on the surface. Even at her age she liked this man; her female curiosity was raised. She must find out more about him, not only to satisfy that but because she sensed and saw that Kate, who was of a much more eligible age, had been affected too.

Kate felt joyous now that Malcolm was actually here, not only in the same room but sitting opposite her and Mrs Jordan, talking over a cup of tea. It took all her will-power not to betray the rush of pleasure when their eyes met, but she felt that he knew what she was thinking.

'Mr McFadden, I know that accent, the lilt in your voice ... it is a Shetland intonation. You are a long way from home,' commented Mrs Jordan.

'I am indeed, ma'am.'

'You are not long arrived, I believe, but it would seem you are well settled in Whitby?'

'I am.'

'Do you not miss Shetland?'

'There is much there that I do miss, yes.'

'That sounds as if there are some things you don't mind leaving,' put in Kate.

'Is that not true of most places we leave?'

'I suppose so,' Kate agreed, recalling the things she hadn't regretted leaving when she'd made her decision to leave home. With that thought she felt a new kind of bond with this man – of shared experience even though they and their circumstances might be vastly different.

'You have not experienced it for yourself?' queried Malcolm, wondering why Kate, a girl from a comfortably off family, should be living with Mrs Jordan.

'Indeed I have, but the experience was tempered by the kindness of Mrs Jordan.'

'Then you were lucky. You didn't have to break

with an area you no doubt love.'

'And you did, Mr McFadden?' put in Mrs Jordan.

'Yes, but it was of my own choosing, if dictated by circumstances. I needed to get far away.' He interpreted the look in her eyes and added quickly, 'I should reassure you there was no pressing reason for me to leave Shetland; it was purely a family matter, a disagreement with my father.'

'Your mother...?'

'She died when I was three.'

'I'm sorry,' offered Mrs Jordan.

'And you so young,' commented Kate.

'I had a brother, Angus, and a sister, Lavinia. Their company was a comfort.'

'That must have been hard on your father, though.'

'No doubt, but we were fortunate in having my aunt's care and attention, together with the help of a governess.'

This brought a pause in the conversation. Mrs Jordan thought it best not to probe more at this juncture. There was sufficient evidence in what he had already told them to indicate that he came from a well-to-do family. The ice had been broken; she knew Malcolm McFadden felt at ease with her and Kate. There would be time enough to learn more, so for now she changed the subject.

'Should we turn our attention to the ship?' she suggested.

Malcolm felt some measure of relief. He had talked enough about himself, more than he had done to anyone else since leaving Shetland, but he had found Mrs Jordan and Kate Swan easy to talk

121

to. As he had talked, he had experienced a feeling of release; maybe it was not good to keep things pent up; maybe he should... But that would depend on the future he made for himself here.

'Spread the papers on the table, Mr McFadden,' Mrs Jordan suggested when she caught his enquiring glance.

He nodded and moved to the table, unrolling a sheaf of papers.

Kate came to his side. 'Let me,' she offered, and placed one of the Georgian silver candlesticks on the edge of a sheet to hold it down.

He smiled his thanks to her, continued to roll the sheet out and placed the matching candlestick at the other end, to hold the paper flat.

As he did so it was not the drawing that was revealed that caught Kate's attention, so much as Malcolm's fingers and hands. They did not resemble a workman's hands. They were slender, his fingers long, but they had strength. They moved easily across the paper as he smoothed it out, treating it gently, as if he prized it above anything else at that moment. Kate was mesmerised by the sight and found herself wondering what it would be like to feel their touch. She pulled herself up with a start. What on earth was she contemplating? But even as she brought her straying thoughts under control, she knew that later in the silence of her room would remember them, and wonder even more about Malcolm McFadden.

'These look interesting,' commented Mrs Jordan when she came to the table. 'But, Mr McFadden, you'll have to explain them to me.'

During the next hour and a half, he explained

the drawings and what they indicated about the stages of construction, but was careful to point out, 'These are preliminary ideas only. Basically they are the skeleton around which the ship will be built, to produce...' he paused, allowing the moment to become charged with tension as he swept the paper at which they were looking to one side to reveal a full-page sketch of how the finished ship might finally look '...this!'

Mrs Jordan and Kate gasped.

A two-masted ship in full sail leaned into the sea, cutting through it with a grace that indicated she was in her rightful element.

'Mr McFadden, if the completed vessel looks as beautiful as this, I will be proud to be her part-owner,' said Mrs Jordan, delight shining in her eyes.

'Who drew this?' asked Kate tentatively. In the moments of silence that followed her question she guessed the answer. 'You did?'

He nodded. 'Yes.' Then added quickly, 'You must not take this as a faithful representation of how the ship will finally look, but it will be very near it.'

'This is how my brother sees her?'

Malcolm gave a little laugh. 'No. I did this in my own time, just for my own satisfaction. Then, when your brother asked me to keep Mrs Jordan informed about the ship, I thought I would bring it...'

'I'm so pleased that you did. It has helped me understand a lot of what you have been telling us,' said Mrs Jordan.

He glanced at Kate as if looking for her comment also.

She smiled. 'I think you are very talented, Mr McFadden. Did you have lessons?'

'Not really. I liked drawing and used to amuse myself by sketching the coast near home. There were otters there. I used to spend hours watching them, then I started drawing them. One day my aunt and governess saw my sketches and they encouraged me to keep on.'

'They were very wise,' commented Mrs Jordan.

'Do your brother and sister draw?' asked Kate.

Malcolm pursed his lips thoughtfully for a moment, and then gave a little grimace. 'Angus, no, couldn't draw a straight line and has no eye for beauty.' It was almost undetectable but Kate was conscious of a slight animosity in his tone. Could a clash with his brother have driven him from Shetland? 'Lavinia has an artistic eye but her talent lies more in embroidery.' At the mention of her name Malcolm's tone had softened and Kate recognised his love and respect for his sister.

Mrs Jordan had been looking at the drawing intently. She said quietly, 'She's beautiful. You have made her so graceful. Mr Swan said I could name her. My first impulse was to wait. I'm glad I did because now I have seen this lovely sketch portraying such beauty and grace, I think that she can bear only one name, one I am sure Mr Swan himself would have chosen had he not been kind enough to ask me to do so. I shall name this ship the *Rosemary*.'

Kate gasped with joy. 'Oh, Mrs Jordan, Archie will be delighted.'

'Kate, your sister-in-law has natural grace.

Though Mr McFadden may not be aware of it, such grace is epitomised in this ship.'

'I shall tell Mr Swan of your decision,' he said.

'No, please don't,' countered Mrs Jordan. 'I would like to tell him myself.'

'Of course, ma'am. I will not say a word.'

'Kate, you and I will visit your brother to-morrow. Mr McFadden, tell him we will be at his office at eleven o'clock unless we receive a note telling us otherwise.'

'Yes, ma'am.'

'Now, I think a light luncheon will be ready. You'll stay and partake of it with us, Mr Mc-Fadden?'

'That is extremely kind of you.'

'You don't have to be back at the shipyard?'

'No, ma'am. When I told Mr Swan I was coming here with the plans, he placed no time limit.'

'Splendid.' Mrs Jordan turned to Kate. 'Please inform Mrs Stabler we are ready to dine.'

She noticed how quickly Malcolm sprang to the door to open it.

With Kate gone, Mrs Jordan said to him, 'A fine young woman.'

'Indeed.'

Malcolm's agreement was so quick that, taken with his attentive manner to Kate, Mrs Jordan knew she had no need to test the waters further.

The meal passed pleasantly with a flow of effortless conversation, Mrs Jordan noting with approval the ease with which Malcolm sustained his part in it.

With the meal finished, she announced, 'I'm feeling a little tired, I must have concentrated too hard on the plans. If you'll excuse me, Mr McFadden, I will take a little rest.'

'Of course.' Malcolm was on his feet, ready to walk her to the door. 'I'm sorry if I've been the cause of...'

'No, no, it has nothing to do with you.' Mrs Jordan gave a dismissive wave of her hand. She turned to Kate who also showed concern for her employer. 'Mr McFadden indicated he was not constrained by time. So, Kate, show him our wonderful garden and take a walk along the cliffs together. The scenery is spectacular.' She had been walking to the door as she was speaking. Malcolm was beside her to open it. She thanked him and added, 'I will see you later.'

When the door closed Kate looked at him with a teasing light in her eye and said lightly, 'Well, that compels you to stay, Mr McFadden.'

Malcolm's response to her flirtatious suggestion was only marred by the brief vision of Rowena running across the sand and the thought 'five years'.

'It certainly does, Miss Swan, but it will be a pleasure and your company will make it more so.' He left a slight pause then added in a soft voice that did not contemplate a refusal to his question, 'Shall we do as Mrs Jordan suggested?'

Rowena, tight-lipped and holding back tears, kicked at the sand in the little bay that held so many memories for her.

Her mind cried out: Why, oh, why, were there social barriers between people? Why did convention frown on certain relationships? Why didn't love conquer all? Were her mother's well-meant warnings about her friendship with Malcolm wrong? Should she have ignored them?

It was I who raised the barrier, she realised. But why didn't Malcolm tear it down? He didn't, but that was really my fault. I didn't encourage him. How I wish I could turn back the clock, but I can't and Malcolm has gone. Where? I wish I knew. Will I ever see him again?

13

'George keeps the garden looking beautiful,' commented Kate as she and Malcolm strolled in the garden.

'Indeed he does, and I am seeing it on a beautiful day. I expect you have seen it on many such days. How long have you been with Mrs Jordan?'

'Two years. I was most fortunate in being appointed to the position. I happened to be in the right place at the right time. I needed to find a job and Rosemary's mother gave me an introduction to Mrs Jordan whose companion had just left her.'

'You were fortunate but...'

'Should we walk on the cliffs?' said Kate, needing a few moments to decide how much she should tell this stranger whom she had just met. But did he feel like one, and did time really matter when it came to such things? They stepped from the garden and walked towards the cliff edge. 'You are wondering why I needed to find a job.'

Kate, reading his curiosity, did not think it intrusive. She was still finding Malcolm unusually easy to talk with. 'It was because of a dispute with my father. He wanted to compel me into a marriage I did not want, so I walked out. I stayed with my brother and his wife until it was settled that I should come here.'

Malcolm let the silence that followed this revelation lengthen. Realising Kate was expecting it to be filled by an explanation for his own arrival in Whitby, he said, 'I too antagonised my father.'

'Over a marriage?'

'No. I left over his future plans for the estate, ones with which I did not agree.'

'And you, as his son and heir, would inherit the consequences?'

'Yes.'

'So, will you return to Shetland when you come into your inheritance?'

'No. There'll be nothing there for me. Father threatened to cut me off. I expect that has been done and my brother, who does not contest his plans, will now inherit.'

'The policy must have been drastic for you to take a stance with such serious repercussions for yourself.'

'It was.' Malcolm found himself explaining, in the simplest but most telling terms, the Shetland lairds' attitudes towards their crofters.

'Turning people out of their homes to reclaim the land is a terrible thing to do. I can see you felt strongly about it. Has your father actually implemented the plan yet?'

'I don't know. I am very anxious for the welfare

128

of crofters on my father's land; one family in particular whom I have known since childhood. I seek a Shetlander, hoping for news, every time a ship from the north puts into Whitby, but so far I am out of luck.'

'One day you will find someone.'

'I hope so. Not that it will do me or them much good.' Malcolm gave a little start. 'I shouldn't be burdening you with this, but it has been comforting for me to talk about it.'

'If I have helped you then I am pleased.'

'Miss Swan, talking to you...'

'Wait!' she interrupted. 'Kate or Kathleen, please.'

He smiled and gave an inclination of his head in acknowledgement of her permission. 'Very well. And remember, I am Malcolm.'

'I won't forget.'

'Now, Kate, I was about to say that talking with you about the crofters has been a relief to me. I had it all bottled up inside me. It doesn't ease the frustration of being unable to help them, but at least my anxiety has been expressed. I am most grateful to you for listening.'

She stopped, placed one hand on his arm and looked into those entrancing blue eyes with all the sincerity she could muster. 'Any time you want to talk, I will be only too pleased to listen, if it will help.'

He kept his gaze on her. 'I thank you for that.'

In the moment's silence that followed a spark flared between them. He leaned forward and kissed her lightly on the cheek. Not a word passed, but their eyes and his kiss told of the magic that had stirred in these few moments spent alone together.

Kate realised they had better not linger. 'I think it might be best if we returned to the house. Mrs Jordan's rests are generally of short duration.'

He nodded. As they started to walk Malcolm said with a note of caution in his query, 'I hope I have not offended you in any way?'

She read the implication and reassured him quickly, 'Of course not. You could never do that.'

'I hope I never shall.'

Later, as she snuggled into the softness of her feather bed, pulling the crisp white sheets around her, Kate recalled the sight of Malcolm's fingers and the desire they had raised in her. Then she had quelled her thoughts; now she let them run riot.

Finally she took them under control again by wondering what else and who else had been previously part of his life. Maybe she would learn more about his Shetland life during his coming visits to Peak House when he would bring information on the progress of the ship. Kate drifted into a contented sleep, revelling in thoughts of those days drawing them closer together as they came to understand each other more and more.

Rowena tossed and turned on a mattress of heather in her wooden box-bed, curtain drawn across for a little privacy in the cramped confines of the one-room croft. She recognised they were lucky to have more space than most; she knew of families of three generations sharing the same space as she did with her father and mother. She

130

pulled the rough blanket up to her chin, seeking warmth against the chill of the Shetland wind howling around the croft. She tried to shut out the sound of her father's hacking cough that came through the wooden doors of her parents' box-bed across the room from where she lay. It had worsened over the last six months, sapping his strength until he could no longer handle his boat, and tilling the ground was exhausting to him.

Rowena dozed until a piercing scream brought her wide awake. She sat up in bed, trying to gather her wits.

'Rowena! Rowena!' The distress in her mother's voice was something she'd never forget. She swung out of bed, grabbed her shawl and pulled back her bed curtains to find her mother standing over her own bed, holding a limp figure in her arms. Tears streamed down her face and an unearthly wailing sound came from the depths of her grief.

'Ma!' yelled Rowena wildly, clutching at her mother.

'He's gone!' Jessie screamed.

'No, Ma, no!' Rowena's howl stormed the heavens as if she could somehow fend off the inevitable.

The next few days went by in a daze. With help from neighbours, a visit from the minister and one from the laird's factor, her father was laid to his rest. The final sod covered his grave close to the tiny church on a windswept cliff.

Alone by themselves, in the croft she had known all her life, Rowena voiced a question. 'What do we do now, Ma?'

Jessie's shoulders sagged. 'Try and live.'

'What did the minister mean when he said that a new beginning faced us?'

Jessie gave a grunt of contempt. 'New beginning? What's he know of poverty? Of facing life without a man?'

'We could have been secure if you had let me marry Malcolm,' said Rowena quietly, but the barb struck home.

Jessie's lips tightened. 'Don't blame me for...'

'We'd have been comfortable. Da would probably still be alive...' snapped Rowena.

'Don't say that,' rapped Jessie. 'You are cruel.' The fire in her eyes admonished her daughter.

'He might!' Rowena screamed. 'You should have let me...' Her voice cracked and she burst into tears.

The rage that had erupted in Jessie subsided. She held out her arms. 'Come here, love.'

Mother and daughter wept in each other's arms. Ten minutes later they were calm and united again by their bond of love.

A knock on the door while Rowena was hanging the kettle on the fire brought Jessie to open it.

'Hello, Jamie, come in,' she said.

The young crofter stepped over the threshold. He smiled at Rowena as he said, 'Hello.'

She nodded. 'I'm making a cup. Would you like one?'

'Thank you.' He turned to Jessie. 'Mrs Murray, I've called to say that if there is anything I can do to help, please ask.'

'That's kind of you, Jamie, but your time will be fully occupied helping your own family.'

'I'm willing to do what I can. Don't be afraid to let me know.'

'Thank you.'

During the next half-hour Rowena was aware of the attention Jamie paid her. So it was no surprise to her that, when he had gone, her mother said, 'Jamie's taken a liking to you. You could do worse.'

'He's nice enough,' replied Rowena, 'but I don't love him.'

'You can't always have the one you love. Jamie would make you a good husband. He's kind, as you've seen, considerate, hard-working, he's...'

'Ma, stop going on about him!' snapped Rowena. 'I don't love him.'

'You've still got your head in the clouds – Malcolm won't come back. He's been gone two years; you've never heard from him. You probably won't see him again.'

'Ma! Please!' With tears streaming down her face, Rowena rushed from the croft to the tiny cove that still held memories of happier childhood days. Her thoughts tumbled back and forth until finally they drew her back to her present predicament.

She fought the despair that threatened her; she must not give way to it. She and her mother needed to survive in a world where the laird took what he thought was appropriate from their tenuous income, dependent on conditions beyond their control. More often than not, it left them with little to live on, becoming especially harsh if the harvest yielded little or the fishing was poor. Now they had no man to wrest what he could from the land and the sea, and the threat of eviction hung over them. If Mr McFadden chose to follow what other lairds were doing, reclaiming all the land to turn it over to sheep, what would happen to them then? Rowena shuddered.

'Ah, there you are.' A soft voice startled her. She looked up.

'Lavinia!' Rowena leaped to her feet and the two young women flung their arms around each other.

'I thought I might find you here when your mother told me you had gone out.'

'I've missed you, Lavinia. I know you told me you were going away but I didn't know if you were back.'

'I was in Lerwick longer than I expected. I'm so sorry about your father, and sorry not to have been here to help you and Jessie.'

'Don't worry, Lavinia. I understand. Did you hear anything of Malcolm when you were away?' Rowena, eager for some news, no matter how slim, had to ask.

But disappointment struck deep when Lavinia answered, 'Nothing. It's as if he has vanished off the face of the earth. I wish I knew where he was. I miss him.'

'I miss him too.'

'I know you do,' said Lavinia.

'Thank goodness I have you.'

'I'll always be here.'

'But will we? What will we do if your father evicts us?'

'I'll oppose him. I'll do all I can to stop it.'

'You know that will be difficult, probably impossible?'

Lavinia grimaced. 'I do, but I will try by whatever means possible.'

After Malcolm's first visit Mrs Jordan had sensed a romance developing, and was more certain of it than ever when at the end of a later visit he approached her with a request. 'Mrs Jordan may I invite Ka– Miss Swan to accompany me to a theatrical production? I see one is advertised to take place in the large room in the Freemasons' Tavern next Thursday evening.'

'What might that be, Mr McFadden?'

'I understand it will be a play that will relate something of the history of Whitby through the eyes of one family. There will be refreshments and music to follow. Admission is by ticket only so I am sure, from what I hear about the Tavern, it will not be a rowdy affair but something of a sober, though enjoyable, occasion.'

Mrs Jordan smiled. 'You are trying to impress me. I know of the Tavern's reputation for such events; the proprietors are to be commended for stepping into the breach when the old theatre in Scate Lane was destroyed by fire. Of course you may invite Kate.'

'Thank you, Mrs Jordan.' His delight was obvious. 'If she accepts, I will hire a trap and pick her up here. I'll see she is back promptly after the evening's entertainment is finished.'

'I'm sure Kate will accept, Mr McFadden. I see she is in the garden. Off you go and ask her.'

Kate's smile was warm when Malcolm joined her and it became tinged with delight when he told her of the request he had made of Mrs Jordan. 'I will look forward to that with the

135

greatest enthusiasm and I thank you for the invitation,' she told him.

'Rosemary, I had such an enjoyable evening yesterday,' said Kate while visiting her sister-in-law the day after seeing the play.

'You went with Mrs Jordan?' queried Rosemary. 'No, no,' replied Kate, her voice and eyes filled with excitement. 'Mr McFadden.'

Rosemary's eyes widened in surprise. 'Mr McFadden who works for Archie?'

'Malcolm McFadden, the son of a Shetland laird.'

Rosemary looked astounded. 'But why is he working for Archie? And why are you on first-name terms with him? What have you been keeping from us?'

The questions poured out and Kate told her sister-in-law all she knew about Malcolm McFadden. 'There's more to him than I know,' she concluded, 'but I can tell it will all be good.'

'And I detect you are falling in love,' said Rosemary. 'If that is so then I hope everything turns out in your favour.' She hugged Kate. 'Be happy.'

'I will if he thinks as much of me as I do of him.'

'I don't want to put a damper on your feelings but have you considered the future? Is he likely to return to Shetland? Surely he must, if as you say he's the eldest?'

'Like me he had a dispute with his father and...' Kate told Rosemary as much as she knew.

'Archie has got to know about this straight away. Better from me than if he finds out some other way,' suggested Rosemary when Kate was about to leave for Peak House. 'He has your welfare at heart. After your casting out by your father, he feels he should assume the role. He wants the future to be better for you.'

'I know and I am grateful. Neither he nor you need have any worries, though. Malcolm is an honourable man.' Kate gave a little smile. 'And he's a very different proposition from Cyrus Garfield.'

'That's certainly true,' Rosemary agreed with a knowing grin. 'You are well out of *his* clutches. I know Archie will not try to influence your choice of husband. We believe love is central to any successful marriage.'

'You are wondering if I am truly in love with Malcolm?' Kate paused then added, 'Yes, I believe I am.'

'And if his obligations mean he must one day return to his rightful home, what will you do then?'

'Go with him.'

'To a different land, a different culture, so far away? It needs careful thought, Kate.'

'I know, Rosemary. And it may never happen. He might not ask me.'

'You have something to tell me,' said Archie to his wife when he reached home later that day.

'I've had a visit from Kate. Did you know you have the heir to a Shetland estate working for you?'

Archie looked askance at her. 'You can only mean McFadden?'

'Yes.' Rosemary went on to tell him what she knew.

'I've always thought there was something different about him, but I never expected him to be the eldest son of a laird.'

'And your sister's in love with him.'

'What?' Archie was startled. 'Never!'

'She is. If it turns out as Kate hopes you had better get used to it.'

'And if it does we had better start inviting McFadden into our circle of friends.'

So it was that other invitations to plays, lectures, musical evenings and soirées followed at suitable intervals during the next six months.

From her window, as she had done during every visit from Malcolm, Mrs Jordan watched Kate and him walk along the path from her garden to the cliff edge. She was not spying. Sentimental and romantic as she was, she hoped their relationship would develop into lasting love, but it also raised concern in her – their love had not been tested. Given the circumstances under which Kate had come to her, Evelyn felt some responsibility for her wellbeing, but, not being her parent, did not wish to approach Kate head on about it. But she could test the strength of their love for each other without them knowing it...

As the couple passed from her sight, Evelyn Jordan went to her secretaire and wrote a letter to a life-long friend living in Grasmere. She sealed the letter and went in search of George. Finding him, as expected, in the potting shed, she instructed him to take the letter with all haste to catch the next mail-coach leaving Whitby.

Ten days after sending her letter, Evelyn received

a reply that pleased her.

When Peak House came in sight Malcolm drew the trap to a halt. He and Kate had spent the afternoon and early evening with Archie and Rosemary. The light was fading over the Yorkshire coast, but far to the north brightness still clung to the sky. Kate caught a wistful look in Malcolm's eyes that intensified in the silence surrounding them.

After a few moments she said quietly, as if even a whisper would shatter the moment, 'You miss Shetland?'

There was pause, then he admitted, 'On nights like this, yes.'

'It tugs at your heart?'

'Yes.'

'You miss someone?'

He swung round on the seat towards her, letting the reins slip from his fingers so that he could grasp her shoulders. His expression as his blue eyes met hers was so intense that it jolted her heart. 'Marry me, Kate. Marry me!'

The words she had longed to hear overwhelmed her. The blue pools of his eyes were sweeping her into depths from which she did not wish to escape, and his grip on her shoulders was so fierce that it should have hurt, but all she could feel was a love she wanted to cling to for ever. But...

'You did not answer my question,' she said.

How much should he tell her? Would it ruin things between them? Even as the questions rose in his mind, he knew he had to tell her. His penetrating gaze intensified the honesty of his reply. 'I cannot say no.'

'You loved her?'

'Yes. We had known each other since childhood. She was a crofter's daughter.'

'And you a laird's son.'

Malcolm nodded. 'We loved each other, I know that, but Rowena said anything other than friendship between us would not work. I thought it could, in spite of knowing how strong my father's opposition would be. Circumstances have changed and I don't feel compelled to be bound by our promises, besides our paths have now gone in different directions.' He left a slight pause, just sufficient to indicate he was casting thoughts of that previous life aside. 'I came to Whitby and found you. I love you Kate Swan. Please marry me?'

'Are you absolutely sure, Malcolm?'

'Yes. Never doubt me.'

'Then, I will.'

His hands slipped from her shoulders to her waist and pulled her close to him. His kiss set the seal on his love, and Kate responded eagerly.

When Malcolm had picked up the reins, he waited before urging the horse forward. 'I suppose I will have to ask your father's permission?'

'That is the recognised procedure, but I say no; you will only meet with opposition and threats because I too walked out. Archie is the one to ask if we are to observe any form of etiquette. I would like that. And then, after you have seen him, we will announce it to Mrs Jordan before she hears it from anyone else.'

14

Archie's smile was broad, his handshake firm. 'Malcolm, it gives me great pleasure to say yes. All I ask is that you make my sister happy.'

'That will be my whole purpose in life, Mr Swan,' replied Malcolm, filled with euphoria upon receiving Archie's blessing.

'Mr Swan? I thought we would abandon formality once you and Kate...'

'It is difficult sometimes to forget you have become more than my employer.'

'I know, I know,' blustered Archie, 'but we are all friends here.' He slapped Malcolm on the shoulder. 'Now let's go and tell Kate and Rosemary of my decision.' They went through to the parlour where there were outbursts of excitement and joy when Archie told his sister and wife that he had approved Malcolm's request. Congratulations and kisses were exchanged all round and, when Rosemary and Archie tactfully left the room to organise celebratory drinks, Malcolm took Kate into his arms and they declared their love with a kiss that sealed their future.

After Rosemary and Archie returned and toasts had been drunk, Malcolm voiced a concern. 'I think I should inform my future father-in-law of our pending marriage.'

'I don't think that would be wise,' said Kate with concern as she visualised an adverse reaction from her father. She looked to her brother for support.

'Leave that to me,' he said.

'I couldn't let you stand that corner for me,' objected Malcolm.

'You can and you must,' Archie insisted.

'Archie is right,' agreed Rosemary.

'Very well, if you think it best,' Malcolm agreed.

'I'll organise a small dinner party,' added Rosemary. She glanced at Malcolm. 'You've met Samuel and Dorothea on two or three occasions.' Malcolm acknowledged that fact with a nod. 'I think they suspected that a closeness was developing between you two. I will invite your mother and father, Kate, and send the invitation with Archie when he goes to tell them the news. It might help break the ice.'

Though she doubted it would, Kate consented. 'As you wish.' Then she added, 'Could we invite Mrs Jordan? She's been more than an employer, she's been like a mother to me.'

'Of course,' Rosemary readily agreed. 'I'll write the invitations tomorrow after we have booked a room at The Angel.'

Two days later Archie and Kate picked up the invitations which would inform the recipients that the pleasure of their company was requested at a dinner party to be given by Mr and Mrs Archie Swan at The Angel Inn.

'What brings you here at this hour in the evening?' growled Titus when his son walked in.

'Sounds as if you haven't had a good day, Father,' Archie observed. He glanced at his

142

brother Samuel who raised his eyebrows, conveying agreement. 'I hope the news I bring you sweetens your mood.'

'Nothing could do that,' snorted Titus.

'I'll be going,' said Samuel hastily. 'I only called in with some shipping information for Father.'

'No need,' said Archie. 'I was going to call on you, too, so you may as well both hear the news now.'

'Get on with it!' snapped Titus.

'What is it?' asked his mother tentatively, hoping in vain that she might soothe troubled waters.

Archie knew he must plunge straight in. 'Kate is betrothed to be married.'

A moment of stunned silence was broken by their mixed reactions.

'Oh, my goodness!' There was surprise from Emma who was happy for her daughter but fearful of her husband's reaction.

'Good for Kate.' Samuel's voice was tinged with pleasure.

'I'm delighted,' cried Dorothea joyfully, already looking forward to telling her sister personally and at the same time wishing that Ben would set a final date for their marriage. Maybe this news would spur him on.

'What?' Titus exploded. 'That won't happen! I'll not approve it.'

'It has, Father,' said Archie, drawing himself up defiantly. 'I have given my approval.'

'You? How dare you?' Titus was on his feet, glaring at his son. 'It is my right...'

'You gave that up when you dismissed Kate from this house and severed her relationship with you. Your authority over her ended then!'

Titus's lips tightened, his eyes darkening with anger. 'I'll stop any prospect of marriage for her.'

'You'll do no such thing, Titus.' The words were quiet but they were full of significance. Titus looked aghast at his wife. His mouth opened, ready to blast her with scorn and fury. 'Don't!' said Emma, her eyes fixed firmly on him. 'I've had enough of witnessing behaviour from you I do not agree with. I should have stepped in before. I'll not sit back now and watch you try to ruin Kate's life again just because she would not marry Cyrus Garfield and line your pockets. You will *not* oppose this marriage.'

Titus was so shocked he could not speak; turmoil raged in his mind. Never had his wife spoken to him like this, never had he seen such defiance in her; she had always been compliant, bowing to his every word and whim. But now...! And in front of the whole family! He slammed his hands down hard on the arms of his chair, pushed himself to his feet and strode to the door in a fury.

Archie could almost hear his brother and sister silently cheering their mother. As surprised as he was by her defiance, he seized the opportunity to hand out the invitations. As he gave the first to his mother, he said over his shoulder, 'This includes you too, Father.'

Titus stopped with his hand on the door, knob. 'We will not be going!' he snarled, authority ringing in his voice.

'You please yourself but I will go.' Emma's voice, though low, was full of determination in spite of her shock at finding herself for the first time in her life resisting her husband's authority. She met his scowl. 'It will be your loss, Titus.'

The only reply she received was the slamming of the door.

Emma sank back in her chair with a sigh; opposing her husband had drained her. The future would never be the same. Words of praise started to pour out of her children. She held up her hands to stop them; she wanted none of their congratulations when she knew she had acted too late. 'Open the invitations,' she said quietly.

'A celebratory dinner at The Angel,' exclaimed Dorothea. 'How nice of you and Rosemary.'

'Alicia will love this,' commented Samuel. 'Thank you, brother, and thank Rosemary.'

'Who is this Malcolm McFadden?' Emma asked her son.

'A laird's son from Shetland,' he replied.

'So why is he here in Whitby, wanting to marry my daughter?'

Archie related the circumstances of Malcolm's arrival as he knew them and went on to tell of his position and work in the ship-building firm.

'You approve of him?' Firmly put, her question demanded a candid reply.

Archie knew his mother had Kate's future welfare at heart. 'I do, Mother. Kate is happy and in love.'

'Then I am satisfied,' she replied approvingly.

'Kate will be glad. And I know she would wish for Father to be the same.'

Resigned to her husband's opposition, Emma shrugged her shoulders.

Reaching Peak House, Kate called to Mrs Jordan that she was back and refreshed herself before returning to the drawing room.

'I have something to tell you,' she announced as she crossed to the sofa to sit beside her employer.

'And I you, my dear, but you first.'

'This is for you,' said Kate, handing over the sealed paper.

Mrs Jordan cast an enquiring glance at her but Kate said nothing. Breaking the seal, Mrs Jordan unfolded the paper and read quickly. A little bewildered, she looked up at Kate. 'An invitation to dine at The Angel with your brother and his wife. Is this somehow connected to the ship? Malcolm hasn't told me about it.'

Kate smiled as she shook her head. 'No. But he has asked me to marry him.'

Even though Mrs Jordan had begun to suspect that this would happen some day, she had not expected it to be so soon. It would nullify the test of their feelings that she had in mind. Or would it? The letter she had sent to her friend in Grasmere could still hold good... Besides, all the arrangements had been made ... Even as these thoughts ran through her mind, she composed herself and expressed delight.

'Kate, I am so pleased for you! You make a lovely couple. Malcolm is most charming and thoughtful. Now I don't wish to put a dampener on this occasion and your joy, but I must add a word of caution. Malcolm is a Shetlander. Would you want to live there, so far away from all you know, should he ever wish to return?'

'I love him, Mrs Jordan. I will go wherever he goes.'

She took Kate's hands. 'So be it. I hope your married life together will be as happy as mine was.'

'I'll see that it is.'

Their eyes locked in glances of mutual love and respect, then they flung their arms around each other.

As they parted, Kate said, 'Now it's your turn – you have something to tell me?'

Mrs Jordan nodded. 'I have, but my news is not as exciting as yours.'

'We shall see.'

'I have contacted a dear friend in Grasmere who has booked us rooms at a local inn of good standing for a stay of four weeks, beginning in two months' time.'

'Mrs Jordan, that is wonderful but...' Kate hesitated, obviously troubled.

'Yes?' she prompted.

'Malcolm and I had planned to marry in six weeks' time. That will give us the opportunity to have the banns read here, now that he is regarded as resident in the parish. We were going to announce the date at the dinner party.'

'So soon?' Mrs Jordan expressed surprise.

'There's no reason for haste,' Kate assured her. 'But I deemed it wise not to wait. I fear my father may try to interfere, and the longer we wait the more chance there is of that. I want to minimise his opportunity.'

'But he may be seeing things differently by now?'

'I doubt it. He made it plain I was an outcast when I defied him. And he's a stubborn man. If he accepts our marriage later on, I will be prepared to smooth things over. But I doubt he will.'

Mrs Jordan stopped herself from raising any further objections; she recalled her own happiness and the way she had married soon after the proposal. She did not wish to cast a shadow over Kate's engagement.

'Then I will reply to this invitation with great joy and look forward to meeting the rest of your family.' She left a little pause. 'We must make some plans regarding the visit to Grasmere. I must cancel ...'

'No, please don't. I'm sure we can work something out. I don't want to spoil your holiday now you have made all the arrangements. And I'm grateful to you for including me.'

'I will try and find a replacement for you, though it will be difficult. After all, I'll need to fill your position permanently, but to find someone like you will be well-nigh impossible.'

'You flatter me, Mrs Jordan.'

'I don't. I'm going to miss you. It's short notice to find someone who would be as amenable as you on holiday.'

'Then let me say now I will come with you and leave your employment when we return?'

'But what will Malcolm say? Will he agree to a separation so soon after the wedding?'

'Because it's you, Mrs Jordan, I'm sure he will. He gets on so well with you when he visits. Besides it will be a test of his love for me. But I won't know until the evening of the dinner party; I won't see him before then.'

'Do you think you'll get a chance to ask him?'

'I'll see that I do.'

Mrs Jordan smiled to herself. The test she had envisaged had come about, but in a way she had not expected.

As host and hostess, Archie and Rosemary arrived at The Angel early, and were assured by the landlord that everything was in hand for their private party. They saw that the table was elegantly set and confirmed that the menu was to their liking. An adjacent sitting room was also at their disposal. Samuel arrived with Alicia, and shortly afterwards Dorothea arrived with her mother.

'So Father is still stubbornly resisting making peace with Kate,' commented Archie.

'I'm afraid so,' replied Emma.

Archie detected a touch of sadness in her voice. 'I thought maybe after your...' He let his words hang in the air.

She gave a wan smile. 'I surprised you all, didn't I? I should have done it years ago then maybe...' The catch in her voice drowned the rest of her words, and then Emma changed the subject; nothing should be allowed to mar her daughter's evening. 'I'm looking forward to meeting this young man and Mrs Jordan.'

Though he had met everyone except Kate's mother, Malcolm waited nervously at the entrance to The Angel. He so wanted to make a good impression on Mrs Swan. He had arranged to meet Kate and Mrs Jordan, who would be arriving together, so that Kate could introduce him to her mother. He hoped her father would relent and accept the invitation, but was not filled with any expectation of that after what Archie had told him.

A trap drew up. Two stable-boys ran forward to take charge of it. Malcolm stepped forward, thankful for the activity to disguise his nervousness.

'Ladies.' He bowed gracefully. 'I hope your ride was comfortable.'

'I don't think we had time to consider our comfort, we chatted so much.' Mrs Jordan smiled at him.

'It was very enjoyable,' said Kate, excited at the prospect of the coming evening.

Malcolm escorted them into The Angel where their outdoor clothes were taken. The landlord led the way to the reserved room.

Greetings rang out when they walked in. Kate took Malcolm's hand and led him to her mother who, with her hands clasped lightly on her lap, was sitting in a wing-backed chair beside Dorothea.

'Kate!'

She took her mother's outstretched hand. 'It's been a long time, Mama.' She bent to kiss her mother.

'Too long.'

'I received news of you from Archie and Rosemary.' Kate hid her bemusement. This was not the cowed woman she had previously known. Even seated sedately in a chair, there was a new air of confidence about her. Kate had heard what had happened when Archie had presented the invitations but she had not expected to see such a marked change.

'And I of you.'

'Now we are together. And this is Malcolm.'

His eyes had never left Emma Swan. She was

not the meek person he had expected to see. Her eyes were lively and he knew he was under keen scrutiny as Emma sought to approve her daughter's choice.

'Mr McFadden.'

Malcolm took her proffered hand and felt a gentle pressure on his. He bowed. 'It is a pleasure to meet you, ma' am.'

'And I am pleased to meet you, Mr McFadden. By the end of the evening I hope you and I will know each other better. We shall seek to establish a good relationship, for the sake of my daughter's happiness.'

'Those are my sentiments too,' he replied. He left a slight pause and added, 'May I add, how elegant you look? The colours in your dress exactly complement your complexion and outshine the array of colours worn by the other ladies.'

Emma's eyes twinkled at the lavish praise. She had not enjoyed such a compliment for a long time. She smiled. 'You flatter me, Mr McFadden.'

'My observation was not intended as flattery. It is merely the truth, Mrs Swan.'

'I can tell you and I have much to discuss about my daughter and your future together. We will talk later, Mr McFadden. For now, I need to talk to Mrs Jordan.'

'Certainly, ma'am. But please call me Malcolm.'

Emma inclined her head in acknowledgement and smiled at him. 'Quite right, if you are to become my son-in-law.' She turned to Kate who had stood by enjoying these exchanges. She judged the transformation in her mother augured well for the future. 'Bring Mrs Jordan to meet me.'

A few moments later Kate was doing just that.

'Mrs Jordan, I need to thank you for being such a friend to my daughter at a time when she needed comfort and refuge and I was unable to give them to her. Though I had never met you, I carried a picture of you in my mind. I must say, Archie described you well.'

'Mrs Swan, Kate was there when I needed someone. I was lucky, and I am so grateful to her for all that she has done for me and for the friendship that has grown between us. I will be sorry to lose her, but what will be, will be. I pray for her happiness.'

An immediate bond was forged between the two older ladies and it strengthened as the evening progressed.

Malcolm leaned closer to Kate. 'Do I announce the intended time of our wedding now?'

'No.' She gave a slight shake of her head. 'I need to tell you something first.'

He looked puzzled but said no more.

The evening continued in a most convivial mood. As it wore on Kate tried to find an opportunity to speak to Malcolm alone. When she at last managed this and he recognised that the others, seeing them together, were allowing them a few minutes' privacy, he said, 'What is it you have to tell me?'

'Mrs Jordan has booked a four-week holiday for her and me in the Lake District, starting in six weeks' time.'

'That will be just a week after our wedding.' Malcolm frowned.

'Would you mind?'

'Well...'

'She has been so good to me, I feel I don't want to let her down. It would be difficult for her to find anyone else with whom she would feel at ease on holiday in the time available. I will be leaving her employment straight afterwards. To accompany her on this holiday would be a favour in return for all she has done for me.'

He still looked doubtful. Kate's heart sank. This was not what she had expected but she knew he had every right to object.

'Please, Malcolm. Understand.'

His lips tightened. 'I did not expect us to be parted so soon.'

'I know.' She left a charged silence.

At length he gave a little nod and whispered, 'I love you.'

She read this for agreement. 'Thank you,' she said. 'Let us have a quick word with Mrs Jordan first and then you can announce our intentions.'

Kate went over to Dorothea who was talking with Evelyn. 'May I steal Mrs Jordan?' she asked.

'Of course,' her sister replied.

Malcolm joined them and Kate informed her employer of their decision.

'I'm so grateful, Malcolm. I can leave the arrangements as they are then?'

'I would not have you forfeit your holiday for us, but I hope you won't mind if I intrude upon Kate's thoughts occasionally while she is with you?'

Evelyn smiled. 'You can occupy her thoughts all the time, if she so wishes.'

Malcolm was pleased to see the happiness shining in Kate's eyes. '*Now* you can make your announcement,' she told him.

He tapped on the table, bringing silence to the room. 'Kate and I wish to announce that we will be getting married in six weeks' time!'

For one moment there was silence, then the news sank in and everyone started to shout their congratulations at once.

15

When his Aunt Grizel had left the dining room, Angus looked hard at his father and took up the topic they had been discussing the previous evening. 'You know it makes sense,' he pointed out forcibly. 'We don't run this estate as a charity for the crofters. They are contributing less and less to our income. Other lairds have acknowledged this. You know there's talk of them taking their land back. After all, the crofters only have it on sufferance, and on condition that it contributes to the estate revenue.'

'Yes, Angus, I know all this. There's been talk of it going on for long enough, and it has intensified over the last two years.'

'And why is that?' Angus's voice sharpened as he answered his own question. 'Because every laird's income has dropped. Ours certainly has. It's all there in the figures I've drawn up.' He pointed to the folder he had laid on the table when he had first entered the dining room for breakfast. 'You'll

154

soon see it makes sense to turn all our land over to sheep. The price of wool will hold, whereas income from the crofters is volatile.'

'There is a human side to this,' Mungo pointed out.

'Don't start sympathising with the crofters' situation! Yes, there is a human side to it – our side. We are humans too; we have our own welfare to consider. I need to know this estate is on a sound footing when I follow you.'

Mungo nodded. 'I know, and I'll give it careful thought.'

In spite of that assurance, Angus was troubled by what he thought might lie behind the slight lift of his father's eyebrows that had followed his own words 'when I follow you'.

What did that involuntary action mean? Surely his father couldn't have any other ideas about the future of the estate? Malcolm had cut himself off when he had walked out. His father had disinherited his eldest son. Maybe I'm wrong, Angus sought to reassure himself. Maybe I'm imagining something that was not intended.

'Well, do it soon. It's the only way ahead. It needs to be dealt with,' he urged.

His father rose from his chair. 'I'll study your figures tomorrow. It's a fine morning, I'll go and look over the home farm now.'

'Do you want me to go with you?'

'No, I need to do this on my own.' Mungo was keen to get away from Angus who was continually pressing his views. He placed a bunch of keys on the table. 'Lock your figures in the desk, centre drawer, right-hand side.' He'd reached the door by the time he had finished issuing his instructions.

Angus shrugged his shoulders and tightened his lips in exasperation. Why was his father holding back from what was clearly the sensible course? In his prime he would have acted quickly and decisively. Why not now? Angus walked to the window and stood looking out thoughtfully. The grassy land fell away from the house, offering good grazing. In his mind's eye he could see it teeming with sheep – a fortune in revenue, year after year. And all of it would be his one day. He saw his father leave the house and stride away. He was soon lost to sight against the contours of the land. Angus stood for a few minutes, deep in thought, then turned away from the window, picked up the folder and the keys, and went to his father's study.

Reaching the desk, he realised Mungo hadn't shown him which key to use. He must have been too preoccupied. Angus gave a grunt of annoyance; he'd have to try all the keys until he found the right one. The fourth proved to be lucky, but when he opened the drawer he found it to be too full to accommodate the folder. His father must have been really distracted not to have remembered that. Ah, well, Angus thought, it shows I must have made my points forcibly enough. He went down on one knee and tried the corresponding drawer on the left-hand side. He was successful with the second key.

He opened the drawer and was in the act of putting the folder inside when the writing on a sheet of paper, folded around some other sheets, caught his eye. Bold lettering stated 'Malcolm/Angus'. He stared at it for a few moments. What was this about? Curious, he took the sheets out of the drawer and stood up. He placed them on the desk and carefully unfolded the paper that held them together. His eyes skimmed the first sheet and he realised he was looking at a codicil to his father's will. He started over again, reading more slowly, and with mounting satisfaction read that Malcolm was no longer heir to the estate and that from the date of this document he, Angus McFadden, was. He read on, taking in more details. He reached the last page – and froze. He stared in disbelief at the place where he expected to see his father's signature duly witnessed. It had never been signed! The significance of this burned into his mind. Malcolm was still the rightful heir!

Rage began to take hold of Angus. He slammed his fist down and cursed and cursed as a dark determination to tackle his father about this took over. He pressed his hands down hard on the desktop, staring down at the last page that had shocked him so deeply. All the work he had put into running the estate alongside his father could be for naught if the Prodigal Son returned! There was nothing for it but to confront his father; then ice-cold reason took over. If he did, Mungo would know he had seen the contents of this drawer. Something he was not meant to have seen. Angus's mind raced with all sorts of possibilities but he found nothing to answer his predicament. All he could do was bide his time and hope an opportunity would arise when he could confirm that his father had taken steps to transfer the inheritance to him. He would keep the folder he was meant to lock away until his father returned.

Angus had spent the afternoon with the estate factor, examining a section of the land that bordered on a five-mile stretch of coastline and was relaxing in the drawing room with his aunt when he heard his father return. Twenty minutes later, refreshed, Mungo joined them.

'Had a good day, Father?' Angus asked.

'Very. Most enlightening. There's restlessness among the crofters. They've started making demands to secure the tenure of their holdings.'

'I hope you did not give way, Father?'

'I certainly didn't. Their demands were far too wild.' Mungo scowled. 'Ruinous! You certainly make a strong case for turning the land over to sheep...'

Angus felt an upsurge of satisfaction. He felt like saying 'I told you so'. But instead he said, 'The figures I gave you...'

'Yes, yes, I said I will look at them tomorrow,' Mungo interrupted irritably.

'No, it's not that, Father. I couldn't get them into the drawer. It was too full.'

'It isn't. The centre drawer on the left-hand side.'

'You told me the right-hand side.'

Mungo's lips tightened in annoyance; Angus's statement had jogged his memory. He was irritated with himself for getting it wrong. 'So what did you do with them?'

'Put them safely in my room. I'll get them.' Angus left to do so.

As the door closed behind him, Mungo looked at his sister. 'I could have sworn I told him the left-hand side, but he'd no reason to get it wrong. Am I getting forgetful, Grizel?'

'Well, there has been the odd time ... but it's nothing to worry about, Mungo. We all do it. You have a lot on your mind, what with unrest among the crofters. Is it really serious?'

'When they hear what is happening on other estates it will be. And I think they know full well that their contributions to the estate are not as much as I need.'

'You've got to consider Angus in this. You can't leave him an inheritance that is going to be a cross to bear.'

Mungo nodded. 'I know.'

Angus returned then with the folder and the keys.

The next morning Mungo studied Angus's figures and analysis relating to the cash and kind that the crofters paid. Alongside, Angus had supplied an estimate of the monies the estate would have received over the same period if the land had been turned over to sheep. It made for interesting reading and Mungo admired the thoroughness with which his son had applied himself to the task. His estimate of the income they would have derived from sheep was not guesswork; notes stated the information was based on talks he had had with lairds in the south of Shetland.

As far as Mungo was concerned it was proof that they should turn all their land over to sheep; but there was no mention made of the effect on the crofters or what provision should be made for them. Mungo had mellowed a little in his attitude over the last two years. Losing Malcolm to the argument had made him look more closely at the

159

problem, but lately his attitude had hardened again and now, with this report and the hostility he had lately encountered from people in fear of losing their homes and means of existence, he had become convinced there was only one course of action left to him.

He rose from his desk and sought out Angus.

'I am away to Scalloway tomorrow. I will be back in two days. Arrange a meeting with the factor for the day after that, when we will discuss the eviction of the crofters.'

'You'll not regret it, Father.' Before his discovery Angus would have felt elated, but now he knew he would have to find some way of getting his father to sign the codicil relating to his inheritance. Otherwise all his hard work and planning would have been in vain.

Four days later, the factor, Dugan Macleod, came to the 'big house'. Though he had been to the laird's study on numerous occasions before, he never assumed the privilege of entering it unbidden but always waited as he did this day to be shown in. As usual he took the opportunity to sound out the reception that awaited him behind the study's closed door.

'What humour this morn, Unna?' he asked.

'Good, Mr Macleod,' the maid replied in deference to the big, broad-shouldered man who walked beside her. She was in awe of his red hair and beard.

Dugan gave a grunt of satisfaction. The laird in a good mood made for a more reasonable app-roach to issuing his orders, but Dugan's hopefulness wavered when he saw Angus sitting alongside his father. This meeting would probably not be as amiable as he had anticipated. Angus McFadden was full of his own importance, a trait that did not sit easily with the factor, who had, on a number of occasions, found himself in a dilemma when Angus assumed authority that was rightfully that of the laird alone. But he was the laird's son and Dugan walked the fine line skilfully. He had to look to the future and one day Angus would be the laird; the young man had made sure he knew that. How Dugan wished Malcolm had been able to accept the inevitable, but he had not. Now Dugan had his own future to consider.

He had known it would come one day so it was no real surprise when today the laird indicated a seat, told him to sit down and then announced, 'We must talk eviction, Macleod. We will take all the land back and turn it over to sheep.'

A blunt statement and to the point, but one that would have dire repercussions for the crofters. Dugan knew there would be trouble. Word of what was happening to the crofters in other parts of Shetland had been filtering through to the local people here and they had voiced their ire and opposition to Dugan, whose failure to agree only heightened their opposition.

'Yes, sir,' he said tonelessly.

'You will serve eviction notices on the crofters next week, informing them they're to be off my land within eight weeks.'

'A month, Father,' put in Angus.

Mungo glared at him. Dugan read in that stare the laird's fury at being contradicted in front of his factor, and knew Angus would feel the lash of his father's tongue once they were alone.

'Eight weeks, I said!' Mungo turned his eyes back to the factor. 'That will give them plenty of time to make their own arrangements to move. You can tell them if there are those who choose to emigrate, there is a brigantine, the *Hope*, leaving for Pictou, Nova Scotia, from Scalloway in eight weeks. The fare for a steerage passenger is seven guineas. I will pay half if they find the other.'

'Father!' Angus found the protest he was about to make cut short by a stern rebuke.

'This is not for you to decide!' He turned to the factor once more and there was still a rebuke to his son in the tone he used. 'Macleod, if the crofters don't comply with either of these alternatives they will be evicted and you will use all necessary force. You'll have men ready in case that is the course you have to take.'

'Yes, sir.'

'When you have some idea of the number of folk wishing to travel in the *Hope*, I will go to Scalloway again and make the final arrangements with the owners. At the moment she is at sea but will be back and ready for Nova Scotia at the time stated.' Mungo paused then added, 'Any questions, Macleod?'

'No, sir. I'll start making plans and will keep you informed.'

'Good. I hope this can be handled peacefully but...' Mungo let his voice trail away.

When the door closed behind the factor Angus started to rise from his chair.

'Sit!' His father's voice was so sharp it startled

162

Angus. He sank back on to his chair but even as he did so his mind was racing with fear of what was coming next. Mungo's eyes were fixed firmly on his son, boring into him so that he should have no doubt about the severity of his offence. 'Don't you ever again try to countermand my orders in front of the factor. *I* am the laird here.'

'And I will be one day!' Angus shot the words back belligerently at his father, seizing hopefully at this chance to make him deny that fact and reveal his own failure to sign the codicil. But the attempt failed.

'Then try and behave like it,' snapped Mungo.

'I do the work you ask of me. I always have the interests of the estate at heart.'

'Then stop carousing in Scalloway and Lerwick!'

Angus couldn't hide his surprise that his father knew where he spent his time away from the estate.

'Don't look so amazed. I hear talk whenever I'm visiting there, and it isn't all good. You should remember that such behaviour undermines your authority. I'm not denying you some freedom, but you have to be careful how you behave in company and what you say. There are those even among friends who will seize on anything they can turn to their own advantage.'

Though smarting at the criticism, Angus calmed himself and decided that he should play this situation carefully; he did not wish to scupper the chance of those documents being signed. 'Yes, Father, I take heed of what you are saying.'

'Good. Then that's the end of the matter. I suggest that as far as the eviction is concerned, over

163

the next month you quietly make an assessment of the crofts in terms of land that will become available to us, so we may work out how many additional sheep to obtain.'

'It shall be done, Father. And may I say, I think the decision you have made is the right one and will benefit the estate.'

Rowena straightened up from stacking the peat Jamie had brought. Her gaze fixed on a distant point. Two men on horseback had just topped the rise a mile away. With the Murray croft set some distance from the group of eight that made up one of the small communities on the McFadden estate, it was not often that riders passed this way. Rowena's curiosity was raised. Their leisurely pace brought them nearer. Then she recognised the red beard. 'Ma!' She scuttled towards the door of the croft. 'The factor! The factor!'

Her mother, a horn spoon in one hand, straightened up from over the iron cooking pot which hung from a wooden chain over the open peat fire in the middle of the room. 'Calm down, Rowena.'

'But it's the factor, Ma, and he has another man with him!'

Without a word, spoon still clutched in her right hand, Jessie hurried to the door. She took one step outside and shielded her eyes against the day's brightness. Rowena stood beside her. They remained there watching the riders who did not alter their pace.

There was something about their steady approach and the way they sat on their horses that seemed to presage bad news. Jessie wished Gordon had been here beside her, but then on second thoughts maybe it was better that he was not.

She recognised the man riding with Dugan Macleod and remembered that her husband had once had a run-in with him. On two occasions, knowing that Hayden Cameron was trying to line his own pockets, Gordon had refused to hand over part of his fishing catch to him. Irate at this defiance and accurate in his assessment of Gordon's intention, Cameron had physically punished the weaker man and left him in such a state that Jessie was convinced it had brought on her husband's early death, though she could not prove it.

She felt Cameron's cold eyes running over her now, and shivered. Rowena noticed, and slipped her hand into her mother's.

The horsemen reined their mounts to a halt, with Dugan edging his horse a little further forward to establish his authority.

He drew a sheet of paper from a pouch fastened round his waist and threw it on the ground in front of the two women. 'Notice to leave,' he growled. 'Be gone in eight weeks.'

The order was like a thunderclap of doom. Jessie felt numb. This had been her only home since marrying Gordon. To leave it would be like tearing her very heart out.

'Where shall I go? I have no one to turn to.'

'Find somewhere,' snapped Dugan.

'But...'

'Don't make life difficult for yourselves or for me.'

'What if we can't?' asked Rowena, her voice shaking.

'Then emigrate.'

'What?' Jessie gasped as the meaning of what he had said hit home. Leave her homeland, the only life she had ever known? Leave all that was familiar, for the unknown? And first a sea voyage of many days when until now the only thing the sea had meant to her were waves lapping on the shore or the fish her husband had brought home. Those visions faded as her mind carried her to the times she had seen huge waves crashing against the cliffs, sending spray flying high. Emigration might mean facing such mighty waves while closed in a tiny wooden ship. Jessie felt Rowena's grip tighten on her hand and sensed her fear too of what they might encounter. She squeezed her daughter's hand, hoping to instil some confidence into her.

'Emigrate!' Dugan's voice seemed to threaten them both. 'There's a ship called the *Hope* leaving for Canada from Scalloway in eight weeks' time.'

Jessie sneered her contempt as she said, '*Hope?* Who chose that ship for the emigrants? Is that supposed to encourage us to leave? What hope is there for us?'

'It gives you the chance of a new life in a new country. It's sailing to Pictou where there is a small Scottish community already established. The laird will pay half the passage fare of seven guineas, travelling steerage; you find the other half.'

'As if I could,' rasped Jessie.

'So there's nothing for us to do but stay here,' said Rowena, taking a defiant stance.

'Then you'll be forcibly evicted and put on board the ship with nothing paid and no guarantee of any comfort.' Dugan wheeled his horse and

166

rode away with Hayden beside him.

Jessie stared after them with hatred in her eyes as a feeling of hopelessness seeped into her very bones.

'Ma, what did he mean, with nothing paid there'll be no guarantee of any comfort?'

'I've heard tell of captains who'll take passengers who can't pay their half, for only the laird's payment – that's unofficial so no records are kept and the captain pockets the money to divide among the crew and himself. Receiving only half the usual fee means there's little comfort for that class of passenger.'

'What are we going to do, Ma?'

Jessie was silent. The riders disappeared over the hill. She shrugged her shoulders and turned into the croft. She stood just inside for a moment, looking round the room that soon would no longer be her home, then sank down on a chair and wept. Rowena dropped to her knees in front of her mother, took her hands in hers and cried with her. The tears reminded her of the chance she had lost when Malcolm walked away.

One day two weeks later Rowena rushed from the beach to the croft.

'Ma! Jamie tells me his father has heard that two factors and their henchmen in the south of the island have forcibly evicted the crofters on their lairds' orders and set fire to the crofts. Do you think it's true?'

'I can believe it, aye.'

'Can't we stop them if they try to do it here?' Rowena cried out in distress. 'They can't burn

167

our croft, Ma, they can't! It's our home.'

'I know it is, and as rough and as crude as it is, I've tried to make the best of it for us.'

'And you did, Ma, you did. We can't leave it, we can't!'

Jessie gave a resigned shrug of her shoulders. 'What will be, will be.'

As Kate drove into Whitby on her usual Wednesday visit, she wondered why Archie had summoned her to his office at eleven o'clock. The sound of saws and hammers resounded round the yard amidst the cries and shouts of the men working on Number One. It pleased her to hear of the success of Archie's enterprise and she knew she would be even more delighted when work started on the ship in which Mrs Jordan had invested.

As she pulled the trap to a halt, a boy who had obviously been told to be standing by stepped forward and steadied the horse.

'Good morning, miss,' he called brightly. 'Mr Swan is in his office.'

Kate nodded and responded to his greeting with a warm smile.

When she stepped inside the office she was surprised to see her younger brother there. 'Hello, Samuel.'

'Kate,' he said. 'You are looking radiant. Isn't she, Archie?'

'Indeed she is. That dress suits you.' He eyed the pale blue dress that flowed from her slender waist to her ankles. She wore a short over-tunic attractively embroidered at the neck and hem. It was open at the front, revealing the decoration on

168

the upper part of the dress.

'Now what's all this flattery for?' demanded Kate. She knew her brothers well enough to realise they were up to something.

'All in good time,' replied Archie with a conspiratorial wink at his brother.

'We have some news for you.' Samuel left a teasing pause then added, 'But you'll have to wait.'

'Until when?' Kate demanded sharply. 'I haven't time to be fooling around here.'

Archie raised an eyebrow and looked at his brother. 'Ah, well, if she thinks we are fooling around we'd better not go through with it.'

'Agreed, brother, agreed.' Samuel made as if to rise from his chair.

'Now, wait a minute,' put in Kate quickly.

'Ah, now you really are curious and want to know immediately,' put in Samuel, his eyes twinkling in a way that she knew indicated he was teasing her about something she would like.

Words of reproach sprang to her lips but were never uttered because, at that moment, there was a knock on the door, and after a very brief pause Malcolm walked in.

'Ah, sit here, Malcolm,' said Samuel, springing to his feet and pushing his chair closer to Kate. He then went behind Archie's desk to sit alongside his brother.

Malcolm shot an enquiring glance at Kate but all he received in reply was a shrug of her shoulders.

'This looks very formal,' she said, staring hard at her brothers and hoping their teasing was not going to continue, especially as Malcolm did not know them as well as she did.

'It is in a way,' said Archie. He pointed at some papers laid out on his desk. 'We want you to sign those.'

'I won't sign anything without knowing what I'm signing, and I don't suppose Malcolm will either. So stop playing around and tell us what...'

Archie held up his hand to stop her and looked at Samuel. 'She's getting on her high horse. I think we'd better tell them.'

Samuel nodded his approval.

'We have been wondering where you two will live when you get married. Kate, we know Father cut you off without a penny. We do not know Malcolm's circumstances, but we suspect he was in a similar position when he left Shetland and has only the wage I pay him to live on.' Seeing Malcolm was about to say something, Archie continued quickly, 'We aren't prying and we don't want to know. We aren't playing the prospective father-in-law, demanding to know how you will provide for your future wife.'

'I don't mind telling you, my father nullified my inheritance,' Malcolm replied.

'No matter,' went on Archie. 'Without any knowledge of that, Samuel and I have bought a property in Prince's Place off Spring Hill. We would like you to live in it rent-free.'

The momentary silence that fell over the room was charged with surprise and disbelief. Then a torrent of thanks poured from Kate and Malcolm. She jumped to her feet, rushed round the desk and hugged her brothers. Malcolm shook hands with his future brothers-in-law.

As the joy subsided Archie said, 'Let's finish the formalities. These documents state that the ownership is mine and Samuel's in equal part and that you two have the right to live there rent-free for as long as you will, unless asked to vacate the house by us. But that request must be made by both of us, neither one can do it alone unless death has reduced the ownership to one, then that person has full ownership of the property. You two have the right to leave whenever you like.' He paused then added, 'That is all. How does it sound to you? Is it agreeable?'

'It sounds wonderful! We were just getting around to thinking about where we should live. Naturally Malcolm will want to leave his lodgings and I will have to leave Mrs Jordan's employment when we return from the Lake District. This is just wonderful for us,' Kate enthused.

'It certainly is,' said Malcolm. 'We cannot thank you enough.'

Archie gave a dismissive wave of his hand.

'Does Father know?' asked Kate tentatively.

'No,' replied Archie. 'It has nothing to do with him. I did not want to incur his wrath, which I would certainly have done if I had told him. He'll hear sometime, but that can be dealt with when he does. By then it will be *fait accompli*.'

'Mother and Dorothea know and both heartily approve,' put in Samuel.

'And it goes without saying that Rosemary is more than delighted.'

'When can we see the property?' asked Kate.

Archie shoved two keys across his desk. 'Any time. Take a good look. If there is anything you

171

would like changed, tell Samuel and he'll see what can be done.' He then added with a little grin. 'Nothing too drastic, though.'

Kate picked up the keys. 'Come on, Malcolm, we'll go and have a look now.' For a second she curbed her enthusiasm. 'Can you spare him, Archie?'

Her brother laughed. 'What? I say no and spoil your day? Off with you.'

They stepped into the house in Prince's Place with hushed expectancy and curiosity. They went from room to room without speaking. Then, having decided that no alterations to the structure need be made, they walked round the house again, discussing each room and how they might furnish it, all simple, comfortable and cosy.

'It's perfect for us,' said Kate.

'We'll be so happy here,' said Malcolm, taking her into his arms. Their eyes met and held in a gaze that revealed their love for each other. Their lips met, sealing that love.

16

'The baking I've done for Mrs Miller is ready, Rowena,' said Jessie as she finished filling the second basket, a help for Mrs Miller who was feeling unwell.

'Right, Ma, I'll be away with it,' replied Rowena. She took her shawl from the peg near the door and swung it loosely over her shoulders, picked up the two baskets and left the croft, looking forward to the two-mile walk to their nearest neighbours.

Jessie stood at the door watching her until she disappeared from sight. She continued to stand there, trying to imprint on her mind forever the scene that lay before her. It had always been so familiar that she had taken it for granted, not really seeing it. Now that it would be snatched away from her, she regretted not appreciating it as she should have done.

Close to the croft, the plot from which Gordon had tried to wrest some sustenance was now showing signs of neglect. Soon it would revert to its natural wildness and seek to combine with the rough grassland that stretched away on all sides. That which Jessie was facing came to an end at the edge of the cliff half a mile away; beyond lay the sea. The vastness of the wide ocean stretched ... where? She did not know, nor did she want to, but the fates that were combining against her, undermining her will, seemed determined she should find out.

A tear ran down her cheek. She brushed it away, thankful that Rowena could not see it nor witness the melancholy mood settling over her.

Jessie had a strange feeling she wanted to get closer to the sea, to make a pact with it, that wherever it took her and Rowena, it would do so gently and in safety. She stepped beyond the doorway and, lost in thought, moved slowly towards the cliff edge. A gentle breeze plucked at her golden hair, falling free to her shoulders. She walked closer to the edge, gazing down at the ever-moving water breaking on the rocks before running effortlessly across them. She shivered at the memory of Gordon's fingers running smoothly over her skin before taking her with him to the depths of his love, where she had wanted to stay forever.

She stopped. The sea could take her now, gentle as it was, and envelop her in its depths where all care would be swept away. It would be easy. So easy...

'I wouldn't do that, Jessie,' a voice called to her.

Jessie started. She turned and saw Hayden Cameron swinging down from his horse. Annoyed that she had been so engrossed in her thoughts that she had not heard his approach, she immediately recalled the look he had given her when he had accompanied Dugan Macleod to serve notice on her.

'That would be a waste of a good woman,' he added, stepping close.

Jessie bristled. She looked to move away, but with the cliff edge behind her and the horse to the right there was only one way left open to her. As she stepped that way, Hayden seized her by the arm. She struggled against his grip, which he tightened.

Hayden laughed. 'Now, it wouldn't be very friendly of you to leave as soon as I arrive.' He reached out with his other hand and let his fingers run through her hair. 'Beautiful ... as golden as the sands.' She pulled her head away but his fingers turned it back so he could look into her eyes. 'I have a proposition to put to you.'

She looked at him with contempt. 'I want nothing from you.'

'Now come, Jessie, don't be so hard on me.

174

What I did to your husband, I had to do, you know that. He was not complying with the laird's fishing regulations.'

'He'd paid his dues. You were lining your own pockets.'

'So that's how you judge me?'

'No, not as a thief ... as a killer! You as good as killed Gordon. He was never the same man after what you took pleasure in doing.'

'Not the same man?' Hayden chuckled. 'Then maybe I'd better put that right for you.' He pulled her viciously towards him, overcome by lust, but Jessie met that move with defiance. 'Let me go!' She tried to pull free but his hold was too firm. He laughed, and she knew he was enjoying her resistance and would enjoy breaking it.

'Not yet,' he said. 'I said, I have a proposition to put to you.'

'Whatever it is, the answer's no!'

'You are going to hear it.' His arm tightened round her waist as if to emphasise his statement. 'I've always fancied you, Jessie Murray, and envied your man. You deserved better. Well, I can do that for you now, make you really come alive. Let me do that and I'll see you all right when the evictions are made – roof over your head, money in your pocket – and all you have to do is be there when I want you. And that could be a pleasure for you too.'

'A hell, you mean!' Even as she spoke, Jessie could hear Rowena's pleas: 'We can't leave it, Ma. We can't!' For a brief moment Jessie faltered but then she realised this man had more in mind than taking just her. The enormity of what her daughter might face also stunned her. She could not let that happen.

'A hell?' Hayden smiled. 'It won't be that, Jessie. I'll give you a sample now, to prove it.' His fingers came to rest at the neck of her dress.

Alarm coursed through every vein. Jessie struggled but it seemed useless. She heard her dress rip. His lips came towards her, but before they could touch her she spat viciously into his face. His immediate reaction was to fling her to the ground as he yelled, 'Bitch! Now you'll pay for it!'

But Jessie was free from his grip. She rolled quickly out of the way of the kick she saw coming towards her.

Hayden swore and grabbed at her but she had rolled further away. She heard his loud laugh of triumph. 'You can't do that again. Now you're mine!'

The note in his voice highlighted her predicament – she saw she was too close to the cliff edge. One false move and there would be no future left for her. Rowena... What would become of her? Hayden stepped closer. He loomed over her, feet astride in the pose of a conqueror. Jessie kicked out. Her heavy shoe caught his right shin. 'Bitch!' he yelled, and staggered at the pain. Jessie seized her chance. She lashed out at his other leg and was thankful to make solid contact. His yowl rent the sky. Jessie kicked again, but missed. Automatically he kicked back, but he was off balance. His foot met the earth on the very edge of the cliff. It fell away, carrying him with it. Jessie was aware only of flailing arms and legs and of an unearthly cry that spun down and down and down until it was silenced, leaving only the crash of the sea on the rocks far below.

She lay still in shock. Slowly her eyes focused on the vast expanse of peaceful blue and white above her and her mind grasped where she was. Then the nightmare of what had happened struck deep into her mind. She rolled over on to her front and stared over the cliff face. A figure with out-flung arms lay sprawled on the rocks below. There was no movement. How long she stayed there, wrapped in disbelief, she did not know. Tears started then and sobs racked her body which still shivered from shock until she felt the warmth of the sun dispel it. She pushed herself away from the cliff edge and sat up, realising she must take matters in hand. Hayden Cameron's body would be found. No one must know she had been here; there must not be a trace of evidence. His horse! She remembered it blocking her escape route; in the mêlée it must have run off. She scrambled to her feet. Some relief came to her then. It was champing grass a short distance away. She looked around – a piece of her dress lay on the ground. It must not be left here! She picked it up and stuffed it into her pocket. Another swift glance across the grass. Nothing more. She went over to the horse. There was nothing to be done but let it run free, with its empty saddle evidence that Cameron, noted for his ill treatment of beasts, had been thrown from it. She gave it a sharp tap; the horse whinnied and ran.

Holding her torn dress across her breasts, Jessie hurried home.

Once there she rinsed her face from the water in the butt and dried it off. She changed her dress and hid the torn one. With that done reaction set in. What faced her now? She sank on to a chair and with determination forced back the tears that threatened to flow. Rowena must not suspect there was anything amiss. Jessie took her knitting and sat outside to await her daughter's return.

An hour later she was surprised to see Mr Miller approaching with Rowena.

'Hello, Hugh,' Jessie greeted him. 'How's Martha? Sit yourself down.'

'She's still feeling unwell but not as bad as yesterday. She's grateful for the bread,' replied Hugh, sitting on a stone beside the croft door.

Rowena took the basket into the croft before she came back to sit down beside her mother.

'I came with Rowena because there is something Martha and I want you and your daughter to consider.'

Jessie stopped knitting. 'This sounds serious, Hugh?'

'Aye, I suppose it is. You've received notice to quit the same as us, no doubt?'

Jessie nodded.

'Have you decided what you are going to do?' he asked.

'It's difficult. This is our only home.'

'Aye, but you won't be able to stay here.'

'We've got to, Mr Miller,' burst out Rowena. 'We've nowhere else.'

Hugh gave a little smile. 'There are alternatives offered by the laird.'

Seeing Rowena about to speak again, Jessie intervened quickly. 'I've been thinking while you have been away, Rowena. We're going to have to take the passage to Canada.'

'But, Ma!' she protested. 'We can't leave...'

'We'll have to,' pointed out Jessie firmly. 'There's nothing else for it.' Though she could make no mention of what had happened on the cliffs earlier, she had to be firm on the point of emigrating for she saw it as a means of getting far away from the enquiry into Cameron's death. Out of sight, out of mind, she thought.

Hugh looked at Jessie. 'Martha and I have decided to take up the laird's offer of a passage to Canada. He pays half if we pay the rest.'

Jessie gave a weak smile. 'I'm afraid that won't be possible for us; we'll have to rely on the good nature of the captain.'

'You know what that means?' said Hugh.

'Aye, exploitation in the worst possible conditions so that he can line his pockets by carrying extra passengers, but if that has to be the way of it then so be it.' She silenced the protests against emigrating coming from Rowena with a withering look.

'Well, it won't have to be,' said Hugh. 'You'll travel steerage with us.'

Jessie looked puzzled.

'We will pay your halves,' he offered.

This unexpected suggestion was met by a silence filled with disbelief until Jessie spluttered, 'But...'

'We had enough put by for the family, but only just. A couple of days ago I gave my decision to Hayden Cameron, who will pass it on to Dugan Macleod, who will in turn inform the laird.'

179

The mention of Cameron caused a chill to fall over Jessie's spirits.

'When I gave this information to Cameron the blackguard made me an offer for my implements and boat. It was far below what they are worth, but it was certain money and as I might not be able to sell elsewhere, I took his offer. Notice of the sale was drawn up with each of us getting a copy, but I don't receive the money until the day before we sail. It will be just enough for you and Rowena.'

Jessie's mind was awhirl. The money wouldn't be there now. Hayden Cameron was dead at the bottom of the cliffs. But she could say nothing about that. Even though this dilemma occupied her mind, knowing that Hugh's offer to her could not be fulfilled, she found herself spluttering, 'But we cannot accept...'

'Yes, you can, Jessie. We'll say it is only a loan – you can pay me back whenever it is possible.'

'But that might take years...'

'It doesn't matter. Martha and I want you to accept.'

Tears came to Jessie's eyes. 'That is so good of you both.'

'Say nothing of it.' He stood up. 'Now you can make the necessary preparations.'

Wondering how things would turn out when the news broke about Hayden Cameron, Jessie watched him walk away. She could see it would negate her and Rowena's passage to Canada, but she could say nothing of that at this juncture and would have to accept whatever happened next.

'Ma, why must we go?' Rowena broke into her mother's thoughts with a question that had a plaintive ring to it.

Jessie knew why. 'Rowena, love, I think you have to accept that Malcolm is not coming back to Shetland.'

'He will, Ma. I know he will.'

'Well, we can't wait to see. Our future is mapped out.'

Even as she said this, Jessie wondered if it was. Had events conspired to keep them in Shetland?

Kate slipped her arm through Archie's on leaving the trap close to the ancient church on top of Whitby's East Cliff. He smiled at her. 'You look radiant,' he said.

'Thank you.'

'Ready?'

She nodded.

'Be happy.'

'I will.'

Dorothea, as Kate's only bridesmaid, was waiting at the door in a dress closely matching the bride's, though without a train or veil. Her smile not only carried her approval of the perfect picture her sister made but wished her every happiness for the future.

Malcolm, standing with Tom who was more than pleased to be best man, turned and had to hold back a gasp of delight on beholding the beauty who advanced slowly down the aisle to him.

As the vicar cleared his throat, Kate felt an irresistible urge to look back down the aisle. She did so with one swift glance but it was sufficient for her to glimpse someone familiar standing just

181

inside the church door.

The ceremony was short but meaningful, guiding the bride and groom towards happiness in their future life together.

When the newly married couple turned away from the altar to walk back down the aisle there was no one standing by the church door. Had she been mistaken earlier? Had hope played tricks with her imagination. Kate decided not to dwell on these thoughts and dispel the happiness of the day.

The guests followed the bride and groom in a procession of traps back to Mrs Jordan's house. She had insisted that, as Kate was living with her, the reception should be held there, and it appeared that her prayers for a fine day had been answered. She was content in the knowledge that the efficient Mrs Stabler would have the wedding breakfast ready on the lawn.

Everyone expressed their delight with Mrs Stabler's efforts and conversation flowed happily amongst family and guests until, as the sun moved lower in the sky, Kate and Malcolm made their round of thanks and goodbyes and climbed into their trap with a wealth of good wishes flowing around them.

There was laughter in their eyes and on their lips as they drove to the house in Prince's Place. They left the horse and trap secure, knowing that Tom would take care of it when he reached Whitby.

'Malcolm McFadden, you have made this day so wonderful.' Kate had slid her arms around him and nestled close, feeling the comfort and protection of his strong arms around her as they stood alone in the drawing room in Prince's Place.

'I am so pleased you decided against a big wedding,' he said with a grateful smile. 'I realise you did that for me.'

'Well, I knew you had no one to ask except Tom and his family, but you did share Mrs Jordan and my family.'

'I know. It's heart-warming how they have accepted me.'

'They could do no other with such a wonderful man as you. I only wish Father would meet you... I know he would be impressed. Today I thought Archie's efforts to arrange a meeting had been successful. I had a strange feeling, just as the ceremony was about to start. I glanced round and thought I saw Father standing at the back of the church. I hoped he'd be there at the end but when we came to leave the church he was nowhere to be seen.' She sighed. 'I could have been mistaken, it was only a fleeting glimpse, but I'm almost sure it was him. I must be thankful that he thought to come. I wish he had stayed.'

'Maybe it was his way of saying he forgives you.'

'I hope so, and that before long he will meet my new husband.'

'I'm sure he will. And I'm glad that he came today. I think it was a step towards reconciliation.'

Kate nodded. 'I believe that too. And I also believe we were right to choose not to go away now but to take our honeymoon after I come back from the Lake District.'

Malcolm nodded. 'It will be perfection. All the wedding guests gone and time alone with Mrs

McFadden.'

'Mrs McFadden.' Kate savoured the name quietly with a thoughtful expression on her face. After giving a little nod, she added, 'Yes, it sounds very good.'

He smiled, made no comment of his own but let his kiss say it all.

When their lips parted he gave a teasing frown and said, 'But the next four weeks without you will be so dull.'

'Then we'll make up for them before I go and after I get back.' Kate pulled him closer and lived up to her promise.

Dugan Macleod, ignoring the wind-driven rain that swept across the low-lying ground, rode fast to Garstan House. He went to the back door as usual and walked straight into the kitchen. His abrupt entry, coupled with his sombre expression, brought the preparations there to a halt. All eyes were directed at him.

'The laird ... I must see him immediately,' he demanded.

'I'll find him.' The butler was already scurrying towards the passage leading to the hall. In a few minutes he was back to inform the factor that the laird would see him in his study. Dugan nodded his thanks, swept his rain-soaked cape from his shoulders and cap from his head, dropped them on a chair and hurried from the kitchen.

'Trouble somewhere,' commented the cook turning her attention back to the meat pie she was preparing.

'Aye, and whatever it is, I wouldn't like to be on

the receiving end of Macleod's wrath.'

Mungo, seated behind his desk, frowned on seeing Dugan's serious expression. Something was very wrong. He glanced at Angus, who had turned from the window to face their visitor, and saw that he too anticipated trouble.

'Sir,' Macleod touched his forehead with his right forefinger, 'I've grave news. Hayden Cameron has been found dead at the bottom of West Cliffs.'

'What?' Mungo exclaimed.

'I hadn't seen him for two days, then a crofter brought Cameron's horse in. Said he'd found it roaming.'

'Did you believe him?'

'I had no reason not to. I organised a search party from among the estate employees. We found Cameron an hour ago at the bottom of the cliffs.'

'Accidental death or killed?' asked Mungo. 'I know he wasn't a popular man, especially among the crofters, but then neither are most of my estate employees.'

'Hard to tell, sir. The immediate supposition was that he was thrown from his horse, but he was a good rider, could handle any animal if not always considerate of its welfare. He could have been thrown... I had the men retrieve the body and take it into one of the barns; they are doing that now. I came here to inform you, only stopping on the way to examine the spot on the top of the cliffs where it's estimated he fell from.'

'And?' prompted Mungo.

'Difficult to draw a conclusion after this heavy

rain has swamped the ground. There was evidence of some of the earth at the edge of the cliff having given way, though why he should be as close to it we'll never know. The horse could have been frightened by the proximity of the drop and thrown its rider.'

A grunt came from Angus. 'Crofters most likely.'

'Could be,' Dugan half agreed.

'Had he any reason for being on that particular section of the cliffs?' asked Mungo.

'No. I had told him to investigate some trouble at one of the other settlements on the eastern side of the voe.'

'So there was no reason for him to go that way?'

'None, sir.'

'Nearest to those cliffs is the Miller settlement,' put in Angus. 'Some of the people there could have lured him to the cliffs to settle a score.'

'Any reason why anyone in that group should do that?' Mungo asked.

'They were hostile when we delivered the notices of eviction, and I heard that Cameron had a run-in with two of them afterwards.'

'Did you look into that?'

'I was about to set off when his horse was brought in.'

'Who brought it?'

'One of the crofters from the Miller settlement.'

'Then the answer's pretty obvious,' snorted Angus. 'Someone from that community lured him to those cliffs, tricked him somehow and pushed him off.'

'And we'll never know who. Crofters are a tight-lipped lot, loyal to each other if anyone is in

186

trouble,' mused Mungo. Then he added, 'Get them out a week early. Don't give them any warning. Let them witness the burning of their crofts and belongings, and let them know why.'

'Yes, sir,' Dugan confirmed, taking pleasure in the prospect.

The following morning the rain had gone. When Jessie stood at the door with Rowena she saw it as a sign that their lives were taking a turn for the better, especially with such good friends as Martha and Hugh Miller to help them. A new life, a new beginning with them as neighbours in Canada, might not be as bad as she had imagined. Even without the passage money they would have lent her, she felt that she and Rowena would manage the harsh crossing, knowing they would have such kind friends and neighbours in Canada. And maybe she would still see Rowena settled – Jamie would make her a good husband if only she would surrender her dreams of Malcolm. Distance might just do that.

'Ma, isn't that Mr and Mrs Miller?' Rowena's words, as she turned from hanging out some washing, broke into her mother's thoughts.

Jessie narrowed her eyes to focus on the two figures. 'Aye, it is. They don't often come together, and very rarely at this time of day.'

'Mrs Miller must be feeling better,' commented Rowena, dropping some pegs into the bag.

'I'm glad of that. She'll have a busy time sorting out what they can take to Canada. We'll have to get on with that too. Whatever you do, Rowena, take as little as possible. Remember, it will have to be carried.'

The girl did not comment and the two of them watched their friends draw nearer.

'Hello, you two,' Jessie called and stepped towards Martha with open arms. 'It's good to see you looking better.' They hugged. When they stepped back, Jessie saw that her friend's eyes were damp. 'Something's bothering you, Martha. What is it?' She cast Hugh an enquiring glance.

'Shall we sit down?' he said.

Jessie gestured to a couple of chairs and some flat stones near the door.

'I'm afraid we have some bad news,' he said.

Immediately Jessie's heart started to race. She guessed what was coming.

'Living as you do some distance from our croft you may not have heard... Hayden Cameron was found dead at the bottom of the cliffs somewhere along there.' He gestured in a direction Jessie knew well.

'What?' She forced herself to show utter surprise.

Rowena gasped.

'When? How?' Jessie asked.

'Nobody seems to know. We had the factor and his men call on us during yesterday's rain. Cameron's riderless horse wandered into our settlement the day before. Jamie took it to the factor, which started a search. They found Cameron yesterday at the bottom of the cliffs. Seems likely that his horse threw him, but I believe the factor is thinking he was pushed.'

'But...' started Jessie.

Anticipating what she was going to say, Hugh

added quickly, 'There were plenty who didn't like him, and when the notice of eviction was served he had several confrontations. There'll no doubt be further enquiries.' He paused and glanced at his wife who had taken a seat next to Jessie.

She reached out and took hold of her friend's hand. 'I'm sorry to say that we won't be able to help with your fare to Canada.'

Though this was what she had expected, Jessie showed the disappointment they'd expected to see.

'I'm sorry,' sighed Hugh. 'I'd an agreement to sell as I told you, but now there's no one to honour it so the money won't be there. I tried to sell the items elsewhere before going to Cameron but no one was interested. I'm so sorry.'

'It's not your fault, please don't feel bad about it,' she said. 'We'll just have to take our chance with the captain.'

When Martha and Hugh had left, Rowena said, 'Ma, maybe this is a sign that we shouldn't leave.'

'More likely a warning that we should. There'll be trouble over this,' Jessie warned her.

17

Lavinia hurried into the entrance hall of Garstan House. A door opened and her brother appeared.

'I thought I heard your voice. Did you have a pleasant time?' Angus enquired. He eyed his sister critically. 'Your time away has brought colour to your cheeks.'

'I certainly feel better for it, but eight weeks from home is too long. Mr and Mrs Chisholm couldn't have been nicer and it was good to see Fiona again after her time in England, but she was glad to be back in Shetland just as I am to be here. I couldn't imagine living anywhere else.' Lavinia started for the stairs. 'Anything happen while I've been away?' she asked over her shoulder, then added, 'I'll change from my travel clothes and then you can tell me.'

'I'll be in the drawing room. There is a great deal to tell you.'

'I'd better tell Father I'm back.' She started to turn away from the stairs and head for Mungo's study.

'Father's out. He'll be back early evening. Aunt Grizel is visiting the McBean family for a few days,' called Angus.

'Then I'll see you in a few minutes,' replied Lavinia.

She had just settled in a chair opposite her brother in the drawing room when Anna came in with a tea-tray set for one.

'The tea you ordered, sir,' she said, placing the tray on a low table next to Lavinia.

'That was thoughtful of you, Angus,' she said as the door closed behind the maid.

'Ever the thoughtful brother.'

'Trying to impress me or have you changed your colours?'

'I am as I have always been,' he replied, knowing full well that she would be right to contradict him.

190

'If this change is for the better, I like it,' said Lavinia. 'Now tell me what has been happening while I've been away?'

'Where to begin?' he mused.

'Heard anything of Malcolm?'

'Not a word. He's disappeared completely. You'd better get used to the idea that he'll never come back.'

Lavinia's lips set in a grim line. She didn't want to accept that she might never see her eldest brother again, but it was looking more and more likely. She poured her tea. 'And here?' she asked.

'The estate has been running as usual.'

'Good.'

'And Hayden Cameron was found dead at the bottom of the West Cliffs.'

'What?' The bald statement had shocked Lavinia.

'His horse wandered into the settlement known as Miller's. Jamie Miller took it to the factor. A search was made and Cameron's body was found on the rocks.'

'Thrown from his horse?'

'That's the accepted version.'

'But...' prompted Lavinia when her brother paused.

'I believe he was thrown over by someone.'

'Murdered?' She looked at him in disbelief.

'He was never popular with the crofters.'

'But you can't believe they'd kill him because of it?'

'He'd had trouble previously with two men from the settlement.'

'Over what? Surely nothing so drastic it would

191

lead to murder, which is what you are implying.'

Angus did not answer but drew a folded sheet of paper from his pocket and slid it across the table towards his sister. She looked at him with query in her eyes as she picked it up and unfolded it.

Lavinia read the eviction notice quickly, feeling a chill run through her body and devastation cloud her mind. Speechless, she stared at the notice with disbelief for a moment then raised her gaze to meet Angus's.

'So soon?'

'Yes.' He did not disclose that the evictions would actually take place, unknown to the crofters, a week earlier than was stated on the notice. He could see protests about to issue from Lavinia's lips, so added quickly, 'Don't think you can alter this. It's done. Appeal to Father all you will but it won't sway him, especially when there's suspicion surrounding Cameron's death.'

'So you think he was murdered because of this?'

'He was a good horseman. Murder seems the obvious explanation.'

Lavinia looked doubtful but said, 'You did not oppose this, I suppose?' She pointed to the notice.

'It would have been in vain. Father had figures comparing present income with that which would be obtained by turning the land over to sheep. His mind was made up. Opposition would have been useless.'

'Malcolm opposed it.'

'Aye, and look where it got him. I'm not going down the same path. Unlike him, I have the estate's survival at heart and believe me this is the best course for its future.'

'And yours, no doubt,' snapped Lavinia. She rose quickly from her chair and headed for the door. 'I'll see Father when he gets back.'

'It won't do you any good,' murmured Angus to himself as the door closed.

As anxious as she was to contact Rowena, Lavinia knew it was no use doing so until she had received the full facts from her father on his return that evening.

She was restless during the following hours as her mind ranged over and over what that stark notice of eviction meant for the crofters on the estate. How she wished Malcolm was still here; she needed support but feared there would be none forthcoming in this house. She would have to stand alone and believed she would get nowhere. Nevertheless, she had to try.

When Lavinia heard her father return, she hurried downstairs. He looked up from throwing off his redingote and hat when he heard her footsteps on the stairs.

'Lavinia! I'm pleased to see you back. I've missed my daughter.' Mungo smiled broadly and held out his arms to her. The gesture stemmed the tirade that was pent up inside her. This was not the moment; she must tread carefully if she was to make a good case for the crofters.

'It is good to be home,' she replied as her father hugged her.

'Tell me all about your time away when I come down. I'll be with you in a few minutes. Wait in my study; we won't be interrupted there until it's time to eat.' He kissed her on the forehead and hurried to the stairs.

She watched him go and her eyes dampened with tears of regret. He could be such a kind father, why couldn't he extend his generosity to others? Why was he so intransigent about the crofters and the future of the estate? Malcolm had left because of their opposing views. What might become of her? She quailed at the thought, and then rebuffed herself for cowardice. She must make a stand on behalf of the crofters who had befriended her brothers and herself.

'You had a splendid time, I hope?' asked Mungo as he crossed the room to the chair behind his desk.

Lavinia stood up and said, 'Angus showed me this.' She dropped the eviction notice in front of him. 'Are you going through with it?' she asked with an unmistakable note of challenge.

He looked up at her; any warmth that had been visible on his face had disappeared. 'Yes!' The firmness of his delivery warned her not to contest his decision.

'Why, Father? Why?'

'It makes financial sense.'

'Money! Is that all you can think of? People's lives are at stake … don't you ever think of them? Consider what is going to happen to them.'

'I'm giving them alternatives.'

'There is no alternative to losing their homes and livelihoods, slim as they are. You are only offering to pay half their fare to Canada to salve your own conscience! Many of them won't be able to afford the rest. So the choice is, travel in the worst conditions because the captain is getting paid no more than the half-fare you pay him, or stay here and become outcasts with nowhere to go and no future. Don't become a monster, Father. Angus told me about Cameron's death. It would seem to me that his murder could be laid indirectly at your door!'

Mungo sprang to his feet and glared at her across his desk. 'Don't you dare speak to me like that! There is no proof that it was murder so wipe that thought from your mind – and also any hope that I will change my mind. What's done is done. Don't dare to bring up this matter again.'

Lavinia was trembling as she snatched up the eviction notice from his desk and stormed from the room, slamming the door behind her. She raced up the stairs, flung herself on her bed and let the tears flow.

When eventually they subsided she realised this was getting her nowhere. She had to leave well alone or else do something constructive. If she didn't, wouldn't she be betraying Malcolm's trust? Hadn't she promised him she would look to the crofters? The gong announcing the evening meal resounded through the house. She pushed herself from the bed, dabbed her face with water from the ewer, straightened her hair and dress, and then went down to the dining room to what turned out to be a silent meal.

Revelling in the atmosphere, Angus smiled to himself. He could tell Lavinia had crossed their father, no doubt because of the eviction notice. Angus knew she was walking a very fine line with Mungo. One child had already been threatened with disinheritance. All that was required was a signature on that unsigned document in his father's desk.

'Going riding?' Angus asked the obvious at breakfast.

'Looks like it,' replied Lavinia, gesturing at her riding habit. 'Has Father gone already?' she asked, indicating the empty place at table.

'Yes. He told me last night he had decided he should visit Alistair McRae. Apparently he is carrying out evictions at the same time as us and is likely to use the same ship for those of his crofters wanting to go to Canada.'

'Wanting?' said Lavinia contemptuously. 'Forced into something they don't want, you mean.'

'I'm not prepared to argue that point, Lavinia. Father has made a decision and that's final. You know he won't budge.'

Their breakfast continued in silence. Lavinia made it a short one. Angus left the dining room a few minutes later. He reckoned he knew where his sister would be going.

Thankful that the day was fine and clear, he chose his route carefully and was pleased his surmise was right when he saw her heading for the Murray croft. He turned his horse on to a route hidden from the path to the croft, learned in childhood days when he wanted to spy on his siblings playing with Rowena. In a predetermined place he halted his horse, slid from the saddle and tethered the animal to a low shrub. He took a spyglass from his saddle-bag and hurried to a short incline he knew would give him a view of the croft. He trained the spyglass on it and clenched his fists in glee when he saw Rowena sitting outside peeling potatoes while her mother sat busily knitting. There was no sign of his sister. He awaited her arrival. Minutes later his whole body tensed. Lavinia! Now he must take in everything that happened. If it turned out as he expected then he had all the evidence he wanted and Lavinia too would have forfeited her right to any part of the estate.

Rowena looked up, dropped a half-peeled potato and her knife into the bowl of water, and jumped to her feet, shouting, 'It's Lavinia, Ma, Lavinia!' She ran towards the laird's daughter whom she had always counted as a friend.

Seeing Rowena running towards her, Lavinia waved. She pulled her horse to a halt and dropped from the saddle. The two friends hugged each other.

'It's so good to see you, Lavinia. You seem to have been away such a long time. I've missed you.'

'And I've missed you too.'

They fell into step and held hands as they headed towards the croft, Lavinia allowing her horse to follow at its own pace.

'Did you have a good time?' Rowena asked.

'Yes, but I'm glad to be back. I arrived home late yesterday afternoon.' They were nearing the croft. 'Hello, Mrs Murray,' Lavinia called.

'Nice to see you, Lavinia,' Jessie answered, wondering if she knew of the pending eviction.

The query in her mind was answered almost immediately, as if Lavinia had read the thought.

'Angus showed me the eviction notice as soon as I got back.' Her glance swung between mother and daughter as she sat down at the entrance to the croft on a large stone.

'Can you help us?' cried Rowena, desperation in her tone. 'Ask your father to let us stay?'

'I confronted him last night. I'm afraid I made no impression on him. In fact, I found myself running into serious trouble, but I will try again.'

'You mustn't,' said Jessie. 'No telling what your father's reaction might be if you do. We wouldn't want you to get into more trouble for our sake.'

'Have you thought about what you will do'?' Lavinia asked.

Jessie went on to tell her of the offer made by the Miller family and how that had fallen through. 'We've heard of captains taking passengers with only the laird's payment, but they show no consideration towards them because of the loss of the emigrant's contribution. We'll have to try to get our passage that way. There's nothing else we can do. We've nowhere to go if we stay here. We'll be all alone. Whereas if we go to Canada, we'll be with people we know. We're told that the Miller settlement will try to stay together. Better to face the unknown there than the unknown here.'

Lavinia screwed up her face. 'I've heard of lairds agreeing with captains to do this in order to get the crofters off their hands. I've been told the conditions are appalling. Steerage is bad enough, but that of non-paying emigrants is far, far worse. Are you definitely set on this course?'

'There's no other way.'

'Then you shall travel steerage.' As she was

saying this Lavinia stood up and fished in her pocket for her purse. She took some money from it and held it out to Jessie.

'Take this as a gift from me. It isn't sufficient for the two of you but I will bring the rest tomorrow.'

A bewildered expression crossed Jessie's face and then with a small shake of her head she said quietly, 'I can't take it, Lavinia.'

'Why not?' She did not wait for an answer but went on, 'You can and you will. I know the independent streak you have, Mrs Murray, but this is not charity. It is my parting gift to you, given with my love to you both and my grateful thanks for your kindness and friendship when I was young. They were happy times. Please take it.'

Jessie hesitated and then tentatively took the money. Tears filled her eyes and her voice was muffled as she made her thanks.

Rowena jumped to her feet. Tears of relief streamed down her cheeks as she hugged her mother.

'We'll be all right now,' Jessie told her. 'I know how much you want to stay, but you must have seen that was not going to be possible after we received the notice?'

Rowena gave a little nod of her head and in a low voice said, 'I know, Ma.' She released her hold on her mother and turned to look at Lavinia. 'We can never thank you enough, my dear, dear friend. I'm going to miss you so much.'

'And I you,' said Lavinia, holding out her hands to Rowena who clasped them to express all the affection she felt for the laird's daughter with whom she had shared much. Now they were to be torn apart and it would hurt.

Their embrace meant a great deal to them and each was determined to hold it in her memory for ever.

'I'll be back tomorrow,' promised Lavinia from the saddle before riding off.

Angus crept away until he knew he would be out of sight and then, straightening up, hurried to his horse. He rode at a steady pace to Garstan House, satisfied with the knowledge he had gained. He had witnessed his sister handing money over to Mrs Murray. And he had a very good idea why. He knew that since Malcolm had left, Lavinia had helped crofters within the Miller settlement when times had been hard, and had been especially helpful to Rowena and her mother. That had culminated in what he had just observed. If, as he surmised, that money was meant to pay their passage overseas, where had she obtained the amount required? Probably some of her holiday expenses left over. If he was right, there wouldn't be enough to pay for two half-fares. It would be worth keeping further watch on his sister.

So it was that the following day he once again witnessed her handing money to Mrs Murray and rode home in a mood of elation. He felt certain he knew how his father would deal with this information. Then his signature ... and all would be Angus's.

He curbed his impatience for five days before he sought out Dugan Macleod.

'Have the crofters decided which option they are going to take?' he enquired.

'Aye, those that can muster half the steerage fare to Canada. But that leaves more than half we'll have to force off. There's a disturbing undercurrent among them. Eviction day could turn ugly.'

'You have the men to deal with it?'

'Aye.'

'And they don't know eviction day is a week earlier?'

'No, sir.'

'Good.' Angus then asked casually, 'Let me see the list of those travelling steerage.'

'Yes, sir.' Dugan handed over a piece of paper.

Angus ran his eyes down the names. 'Jessie and Rowena Murray, mother and daughter.'

'Listed in the date order of payment,' Dugan offered without prompting.

Angus nodded. Rowena and her mother had handed their money over two days ago.

Lavinia noticed that Angus had cleared his plate with unusual relish. Now he laid down his knife and fork purposefully, as if something more than the food had pleased him.

'Father, while the three of us are together there is something I'd like to say.'

Mungo looked up from his plate. 'Get on with it then! What's this all about?' he snapped.

'Recently, on two consecutive days, I saw Lavinia handing over money to Jessie and Rowena Murray!'

'What?' Mungo exploded.

A chill swept through Lavinia at this unexpected revelation.

Angus, seeing that his arrow had struck home,

seized the moment. 'I then checked the emigrants' names; theirs were the most recent among them. Payment for their contribution to steerage accommodation was made just after Lavinia's second visit. So in this case it would appear that you are in fact paying *all* their fare, Father. After all, it is you who makes my sister her allowance.'

'You sneak!' Lavinia scolded him. 'Have you no generosity ... no compassion? You know as well as I that if a ship's master takes them with only Father's payment for recompense, their life on board will be intolerable.'

'And I know you have continually helped the crofters in all sorts of ways ever since Malcolm left.'

'What sort of a brother are you?' Her gaze was full of contempt. 'Spying on me! That money is mine. I can do what I like with it!'

'Oh, no, you can't!' Mungo's voice boomed off the walls and made the air between him and his daughter tremble. 'You can't use it to the detriment of the estate and you can't use it against *me* ... and that's what you have done! You've undermined my authority. You knew my policy relating to the crofters.'

'Yes, but you are wrong!' Lavinia replied defiantly. 'These people are human beings and you are casting them aside without a single thought for their welfare.'

'I'm paying half their fare to Canada!'

'Salving your conscience with a futile gesture when you know they can't pay the other half and so are condemned to a terrible passage. All you are doing is paying to get them off your land with-

202

out one thought for their future welfare. I chose to help them and I'd do it again. I'll not deny that ever since Malcolm left, I've been doing what he asked of me – looking after the crofters. We saw what was coming, and I have been putting aside money from my allowance to help any on our estate who knew they would want to emigrate when the time came. It is no use saying otherwise. This wretch of a brother...'

'Stop!' Mungo ordered her. 'Enough! I've heard enough. I can do nothing about what has been done; that money is lost to me. Lavinia, you have betrayed and opposed me.'

'Then change your policy, Father.'

'It is not economical to do so. Can't you understand that?'

'I see people being evicted because you want to put sheep on the land they work. It is wrong, Father. I'll always oppose your action and plead their case.'

'Then why don't you go and live with them?' put in Angus forcefully.

Lavinia rose from her chair, straightened her back and held her head up proudly as she replied: 'Maybe I'll do just that!' She headed for the door.

'Lavinia, don't...'

Not knowing whether this was an order or a plea from her father, she made no reply.

18

Lavinia's mind was in turmoil as she went to her room. She had put her arguments to her father but realised now she'd never change his mind. Malcolm had not prevailed against him so how could she hope to do so? Her elder brother had walked out in protest against their father's attitude to the crofters. She began to wonder about that; and with the memory came Angus's words: 'Why don't you go and live with them?' That leading question and her own reply rang in her mind. Maybe…

She sat down at her dressing table and looked at herself in the mirror. She saw a healthy young woman with her whole future before her.

'It's up to you what you do with it,' her image said.

'I know,' she answered herself. 'But what should I do? I promised Malcolm, but did he really know what he was asking? Did he know the choice that would be forced on me by Angus?' She sighed.

'It would be easy to stay,' the reflection in the mirror said.

'Very easy,' she agreed. 'But would I be able to live with myself if I did no more to help these people, whether it be here or where life takes them?' The enormity of those last four words struck her hard.

The reflection in the mirror said, 'It is your life. Be true to yourself.'

Lavinia rose from the stool, found a valise and, casting aside any sentimental attachment to her finery, quickly packed a bag with bare essentials. She knew if she left home hard times would face her; she would have to fend for herself, be a burden to nobody. Above all, she must travel light. She chose two plain dresses, her brown redingote, and her two favourite shawls. She discarded fancy footwear in favour of two pairs of stout but comfortable shoes. When she was satisfied that she had thought of everything, she fastened her bag, tested it for weight, and decided she might be better employing two bags to distribute the weight more evenly. Within a few minutes she was ready. Before she left her room she penned two notes, one to her father, the other to her aunt.

Dear Father,
I am sorry things have turned out this way but I must stand by my principles and they do not include injustice to the crofters. I will join them, as Angus suggested.
I thank you for your generosity in bringing me up.
Your loving daughter.

She read it over, signed it and sealed it. Then she wrote:

Dear Aunt Grizel,
When you return I will be gone, probably never to see you again. Father will explain what has happened. I must thank you for all you did for the three of us after Mother died. I am sorry the family has been split but you will be left with Angus who was always your

205

favourite, though you were kind enough never to overplay your preference. But that is the past. A new future awaits me.

Goodbye.

Lavinia

She read the note again and sealed it. Then she went to her aunt's room and laid it on her dressing table. She pushed the note to her father under his bedroom door.

Lavinia wanted no further partings so quietly left the house, pausing at the front door to impress the view on her mind for a final time. Her eyes settled on the road at the bottom of the hill. She saw it as leading to her future, and wondered what lay ahead for her.

Jessie shaded her eyes against the sun and concentrated on the figure that was walking towards the croft. Lavinia? No, it couldn't be; whoever it was they were carrying two bags. Lavinia had no need to be doing that. But... She frowned. Turning to the open door of the croft, she called out, 'Rowena, come here.'

Her daughter appeared, wiping her hands on her apron.

'Who's yon?' Jessie asked.

Rowena gazed into the distance and immediately said, 'Lavinia.' She glanced at her mother. 'She's carrying two bags and is dressed as if she's off somewhere.' Her curiosity roused, she ran without another word towards her friend.

'Lavinia, where are you going?' she asked in concern, eyeing the bags.

Lavinia dropped them on the ground and straightened up, easing her back. 'Will you and your mother give me shelter until we sail for Canada?' she asked.

'What on earth are you talking about?' asked a puzzled Rowena.

'I've left home.'

'What?' There was disbelief in her friend's reply.

'It's true,' replied Lavinia.

'Why? What's happened?'

'I think your mother should hear this.' Lavinia started to pick up her bags.

'I'll take one,' said Rowena, and took a bag from her friend. 'What's this all about?'

'You'll soon know.'

Jessie had watched the meeting of the two young women with curiosity and some speculation as she tried to interpret their actions. Now they drew near.

'Ma, Lavinia has left home and wants shelter,' cried Rowena, dropping the bag in front of her mother.

Jessie, bewildered by the statement, settled her eyes on Lavinia with an unspoken question.

Lavinia put her bag down. 'I'll explain, Mrs Murray.' She went on to tell them what had happened.

Jessie and Rowena listened intently without saying a word until she had finished.

Jessie, looking at her with contrition, said, 'Oh, Lavinia, I'm sorry if we are the cause of this trouble. I must go and see the laird and persuade him you are not to blame.'

'Mrs Murray, you will do no such thing. You

will not humiliate yourself in front of my father. Besides, it would be useless. I know he would not give way. Let what has happened be.' She saw Jessie was going to protest so went on quickly, 'I know my father, he won't reverse his judgement.' She left a slight pause to emphasise her next words. 'I won't go back, Mrs Murray. I won't! I'm prepared to stand by what I did. I have no regrets and I will take whatever life throws my way. Please, give me shelter now and let me be in your company on the way to Canada.'

Before Jessie could say anything, Rowena said, 'You've got to help, Ma. You've got to after all Lavinia has done for us.'

Jessie looked hard at the two young women. Then, with love and compassion in her eyes, held her arms out wide to them. Rowena and Lavinia shot a glance at each other, and with relief lighting up their faces they came to Jessie. As they held each other, each woman felt the bond of love strengthen between them. They were determined to make a good new life together.

When Mungo McFadden opened the door of his room later that morning his step faltered. He picked up the letter and broke its seal. Lavinia's words seared into his mind. He swung round, and with his anger up strode quickly along the corridor to his younger son's room. He rapped on the door and flung it open.

'Lavinia's gone because of that foolish remark of yours!' he barked. 'You find her, wherever she is, and bring her back. Tell her I forgive her her rebellion.'

'Yes, Father. Does this mean you are changing your mind about the evictions?'

'Of course not!' Mungo snapped. 'Just find Lavinia. Do you know where she will be?'

Angus felt sure he did, and in that moment saw he could make even more certain of his sister's defeat by telling the truth. 'I reckon she will have gone to the Murray croft.'

'Then go and get her back.'

'What if she refuses to come?'

'Do what you have to do!' Mungo swung round and stormed from the room.

Angus smiled with satisfaction at this turn of events. He turned to view himself in the mirror, made an adjustment to the set of his jacket, flicked a speck off his riding boot, and left the room.

The sound of a horse's hooves drew the attention of Rowena and Lavinia who were busy preparing to cook a rabbit which Jamie Miller had brought them earlier that morning. He had hidden his surprise upon seeing the laird's daughter there and learning that she was to accompany them to Canada. When he had left them the two young women laughed as they imagined him breaking that news among those who lived in the Miller settlement.

'Angus!' muttered Lavinia, recognising her brother.

'Will it mean trouble?' asked Rowena nervously.

Lavinia shrugged her shoulders. 'Who can tell with Angus? Why he should be here unless Father has sent him, I don't know.'

Her brother reined his horse in close to them. He cursed the animal and jerked hard on the reins as it tried to pull round. He took no notice of Rowena but cast an imperious glance at his sister. 'Father orders you to come home,' he said brusquely.

'Only if he changes his policy,' she replied, adopting a defiant stance.

'He won't do that,' snapped Angus, tugging at the horse which was still attempting to tug its head round.

'Then I shall stay here.'

Lavinia felt Rowena's touch on her arm and read in it a warning not to defy her father for her and her mother's sake.

'Be it on your head and those of the crofters,' said Angus. Without waiting for her reaction, he turned his mount and set it into an earth-pounding gallop along the path to Garstan House.

Rowena looked at her friend with a worried frown. 'Maybe you should go home.'

'I've made my decision. I'm going with you if Father doesn't change his mind about the eviction order.'

'But you don't know what lies ahead.'

'Nor do you.'

'It's different for me. Eviction means I have nowhere to go except a new country. You have a home.'

'Which I am choosing to leave of my own free will.' Lavinia took her friend's hand and looked at her with determination. 'I am going with you. We will be together, facing whatever happens.'

These words brought tears to Rowena's eyes. 'You are so strong. I'm thankful you'll be with me.'

When Jessie returned home from visiting the

Millers she was perturbed to hear that Lavinia had defied her father again. Fearing it might bring retribution down on them, she tried to dissuade her from the step she was taking, but her attempt was to no avail.

'Kate, I'm going to miss you,' said Malcolm, taking his wife into his arms.

'And I'll miss you too,' she replied, looking up at him with regret that she was leaving. 'It's not for long,' she added, trying to ease the pain of parting so soon after their wedding.

'Too long,' he whispered.

She kissed him and their lips kindled a passion that each intended the other to remember until their next meeting.

'Come, I'd better get you back to Mrs Jordan,' Malcolm said firmly. 'Have you everything you need?'

'Yes.' She gave a little laugh. 'I've checked so many times.'

Malcolm saw to the loading of the hired trap and soon they were heading out of Whitby for Peak House.

Malcolm kept the horse to an easy pace, as if he wanted to prolong the moment of parting as long as possible. Silence stretched between them; breaking it might release their pent-up emotions in a way they wanted to avoid.

As Malcolm brought the trap to a halt beside the carriage that was to take Mrs Jordan and Kate to Grasmere, George appeared.

'Good day, ma'am, sir,' he greeted them.

Kate felt a little surge of pleasure and importance at being addressed as 'ma'am' and acknowledged the greeting. She and Malcolm found Mrs Jordan in the drawing room.

She turned from the window to greet them. 'Ah, my dears,' she said, with a warm smile. 'I hope you have had a wonderful time?' Before they could reply, she gave a little laugh and added, 'That was a silly question. Of course you have.' They exchanged kisses then Mrs Jordan looked sorrowfully at Malcolm. 'I'm sorry to be stealing your new bride from you so soon.'

'Think no more of it. I hope you both have an enjoyable and relaxing time.'

'I'm sure we shall. And you ... what will you do?'

'Have no worries about me,' he replied. 'I have my work.'

'He's not telling you how he's going to be spoiled – Rosemary and Archie have invited him to dine with them. Tom's mother has also extended invitations to do so. With Tom away she'll be pleased to have Malcolm's company, though Tom should be home soon provided all has gone well in the Baltic.'

Realising that to prolong the parting would only add to the tension she could detect between the newly-weds, Mrs Jordan said, 'Then I think we should be on our way. You probably noticed George was already dressed for the journey. No doubt he will have all of our luggage stowed by now.'

When they went outside they found that was the case, and the cook and maids were there to receive any last-minute instructions and to say their goodbyes.

Kate had to make a fierce effort to hold back tears when Malcolm held her close for the final time. 'Don't worry about me,' he whispered. 'Enjoy yourself. I look forward to your return.'

George saw his two passengers were comfortably seated then climbed on to his box, picked up the reins and, with a call that the two horses recognised, set them on their journey.

As the coach rolled into motion, Kate's and Malcolm's eyes met and held, expressing all the love they felt for each other.

At that moment the *Lady Isobel* was cutting through a heavy sea, a day's sailing out of Lerwick, on her way to Whitby with a cargo of timber from the Baltic. As Tom Davis bent his head against the driving wind, he wondered how Malcolm would react to the news he was bringing about the crofters' plight in Shetland.

19

'Father, are we still planning the evictions a week early, without any forewarning for the crofters?' Angus asked.

Mungo scowled. 'Are you too having doubts about my decisions?' he snapped. 'Are you shirking your task?'

'No!' replied Angus emphatically. 'I was just making a final check.'

'Don't give me any reason to doubt you. You are the only child left to me.'

'I won't, Father. It will be done.'

Angus left the house and went to the stables where he ordered one of the grooms to saddle his favourite horse. After a hundred yards he put it into a gallop. With the speed, the pounding sound of its hooves and the rush of air, Angus felt an exhilaration that was enhanced by the thought that one day he would be laird here; this land would be his. He would see that it was highly profitable. At this moment he felt he was well on his way to achieving that goal.

Within the hour he had traced the factor who was surveying a tract of land that culminated in high cliffs.

'Good grazing?' queried Angus as he brought his horse, breathing heavily from the exertion, to a halt close to the man.

'Aye, it is that, sir.' Dugan was polite to him. He knew Angus liked it that way so he was willing to play humble servant. After all, the son of the laird was his own prospective employer.

'We'll soon be seeing it in use, Dugan. Assemble the men just out of sight on the east side of the Murray croft at six tomorrow morning. Not a word of what we are about, remember.'

'Aye, sir. Then are we on to the Miller settlement?'

'Yes.'

Dugan was about to point out a flaw in this plan. Although Angus had not mentioned fire, he was sure the young master would torch the Murray croft. Smoke from that would be a forewarning to the Miller settlement and present the crofters there with an opportunity to mount some form of resistance at the unexpected advancement of the eviction date. But Dugan kept his own counsel. He was not about to cross Angus and jeopardise his own position in the process.

Clouds driven by a steady wind scudded across the sky, competing with the early-morning light. Angus, anticipating the coming events that he would use to enhance his standing with his father, held his horse steady as he rode from Garstan House. He pulled his hat more firmly on to his head and fastened the top button of his coat. He had no time to admire the familiar landscape; his thoughts were elsewhere. A smile curved his lips; the crofters, believing they had another week to prepare for eviction, would get a shock this morning. He wheeled his horse away from the path to the Murray croft and headed for the prearranged rendezvous with Macleod and his men. As he neared the place he counted the shadowy figures; eleven – a full complement.

When they were aware of his approach the men stopped their quiet chatter. Some swung into their saddles, others stood by their horses. They touched their foreheads in a gesture of subservience which Angus acknowledged with a nod.

'All ready?' he asked as he stopped beside the factor.

'Aye, sir.'

'They know what to do?'

'They do.'

Angus raised his voice so all could hear. 'No one make a move until you receive my signal. Then waste no time in getting the crofters out.

215

Combat any resistance with force and destroy everything. Understood?'

Muttered 'ayes' came from the group.

'Good. Then let's do it.'

The group with Angus at its head headed for the Murray croft at a steady trot.

'What's that?' Rowena stopped stirring the porridge in the iron container hanging over the peat fire. She inclined her head, listening intently.

'Horses!' said Lavinia.

Jessie stepped over quickly to open the door. 'Oh, no!' The fear and distress in her voice sent shudders of anxiety coursing through the two younger women who moved hastily to stand beside her.

'What's happening?' gasped Rowena. 'Why are they here?'

'I don't like it,' said Jessie, taking hold of their hands in a futile impulse to protect them.

'It will be all right, Angus is with them,' said Lavinia, trying to find some comfort in the presence of her brother.

The horsemen pulled to a halt in front of them, presenting a menacing sight. Lavinia felt she knew what these men were thinking and, though that sent shudders of horror through her, she pinned her hopes on the belief that her brother would not let the situation deteriorate that far.

'You've got ten minutes to get your belongings and move out of here,' he called out.

'Is this eviction?' asked Jessie, a touch of defiance in her voice.

'Aye,' Angus replied.

'You are a week early. The notice was served for next week.'

'Well, it's been changed. It's *now*.'

'That's not right,' she protested. 'We can't get everything we need to take...'

'Then you'll have to leave it behind,' he broke in.

'Why weren't we told the eviction was to take place a week early?'

'So that you wouldn't have time to prepare – in punishment for Hayden Cameron's murder! Someone from the Miller settlement, of which you are regarded as a part, killed him.'

'His horse threw him,' Jessie contradicted.

'He was too good a horseman for that to happen. Someone killed him.'

Rowena felt her mother's grip tighten. In it she sensed trauma and knew that Jessie knew something about Cameron's death that no one else did. She fought to keep her shock from showing, but hoped the strengthening of her fingers on her mother's would prevent her from making any confession in a bid to stop the eviction. Rowena realised that it would not prevent the outcome, only delay it. She spoke up quickly to distract her mother. 'We took up the laird's offer of the assisted passage to Canada. What are we to do now?'

'Do what you like until sailing time. Fend for yourselves. Find shelter in the countryside.'

'There's little of that,' she snapped.

'Find an old building in Scalloway.' Angus turned his gaze on his sister, putting an end to any argument from Rowena and her mother. 'You, Lavinia, get yourself home!'

217

'Never!'

'Then be it on your own head!'

'Lavinia, don't...' began Jessie.

'I'm with you, Mrs Murray,' she replied firmly.

'Get your things!' ordered Angus.

The three women turned back into the croft.

'Thank goodness we got a few things ready,' said Jessie. 'Get what else you want to carry ... but be quick.'

When Jessie was out of earshot of Lavinia, Rowena came close to her. 'Mother, I sense you know something about Cameron's death. Please don't say anything! It will make no difference to what is happening to us.'

'I won't,' whispered Jessie. 'I didn't kill him, but there are those who would make out that I did.'

Rowena did not question her. If her mother wanted her to know more, she would be told when the time was right. She gave Jessie a quick kiss on the cheek and returned to the task of packing.

Angus eyed his men 'You know what to do so get on with it.' He strode into the croft. His figure seeming more menacing in the gloom. 'Time to get out!' he ordered.

The three women stuffed the last items hastily into their bags. Jessie paused and looked around the croft that had been her home since her marriage. Tears came to her eyes as they swept over the two chairs her husband had made, one for her and one for himself. How she wished she could take them, but that was impossible. She turned slowly towards the door.

Rowena, bag in hand, came to her and slipped

her hand into her mother's. 'I wish we could take...'

'Don't, Rowena,' said Jessie. 'Wishes like that will make parting from them much harder. Come.'

'Wait!' At the same moment as her cry, Rowena loosened her hand from her mother's and rushed to the bed she had occupied. She stooped, and a look of thankfulness crossed her face as she dragged a package from under it.

'Malcolm's drawings,' she gasped as she rejoined her mother. Then, hand in hand they moved to the door, ignoring Angus who stood close by.

Lavinia followed them, but as she reached her brother his iron grip on her arm stopped her. 'Don't be a fool, Lavinia. You can still go home.'

She looked at him with contempt. 'Forget it. You've endeavoured to persuade me, enough to salve your conscience and be able to tell Father you tried, so let go of my arm.'

'Fool,' he hissed. 'There's more to come.' He pushed her out of the door and strode past her, fury in every stride. 'All right, Dugan, you know what to do.'

'Aye, sir.' He made the prearranged signal and the men moved into action.

Four of them brushed past the three women without a word or sympathetic look. Helpless to do anything, Jessie, Rowena and Lavinia froze to the spot as they watched the horror unfold. Chairs, a table, cupboard, settle, were all smashed and thrown outside.

'No!' screamed Jessie, when she saw them carry her beloved spinning-wheel out and pitch it on the mounting heap to lie there in broken disarray.

She would have leaped at the perpetrator but Rowena, knowing it would be a useless gesture, held her tight.

'It's no good, Ma. We can't stop it.'

Lavinia, trembling with rage at what Angus was allowing to happen, placed what she hoped was a comforting hand on Mrs Murray's shoulder.

As much as they were experiencing an urge to run away, an uncontrollable desire to witness the final moments of the destruction was too strong to ignore.

A chest shattered when it was thrown out; pots and pans followed; blankets, straw bedding and timber from the box-bed were pitched on to the pile.

The four men came from the croft; Dugan moved in, to emerge a few moments later and call out, 'All clear, sir!'

'Good, go to it!' Angus shouted, his tone rich with satisfaction.

The men stripped the thatch away, loosened the main stones in the walls and cut the couples, allowing the roof to collapse and the walls to fall with a terrible deathly sounding crash, sending dust billowing across the whole scene. Then, to make sure nothing of any worth was left, Angus ordered the shattered remains be fired. As the smoke began to rise, he and Dugan and his men rode away in the direction of the Miller settlement.

Deep sobs racked Jessie's body as she sank to the ground, 'Oh, my God, what have I done? I could have stopped it!'

'Ma! What are you talking about?' screamed Rowena with tears streaming down her cheeks at

220

the sight of the only home she had known lying a broken, smoking ruin.

'I could have stopped it! Stopped it!' Jessie's voice rose hysterically. Her eyes widened, staring with horror at the two girls. She reached out and gripped Lavinia's arm. 'You know I could!'

Eyes red with tears, she stared back at Jessie. She shook her head and said with conviction, 'I don't!'

'You do! You do!' Jessie screamed at her.

Lavinia looked sharply at Rowena who reeled with shock when she saw in that bewildered expression the stirrings of doubt. The wild hysteria of Jessie's screams goaded Lavinia into action. She slapped Jessie sharply across the face. Jessie reeled, her right hand coming up to her cheek. Her screaming stopped instantly. Her eyes remained wide and staring, but now with shock at Lavinia's action. Finally she collapsed and sagged against Lavinia's shoulder. The younger woman held and soothed her. Lavinia's eyes met Rowena's and she was thankful when she saw that her friend understood why she had struck her mother. They remained like that until Jessie became more composed.

She brushed away the dampness from her cheeks, rubbed her eyes and looked at Lavinia with eyes that begged forgiveness. 'I'm sorry,' she said hoarsely, 'I did not know what I was saying.'

'Think nothing of it, Mrs Murray,' said Lavinia. 'I've already forgotten it.'

Rowena smiled her thanks.

The two girls helped Jessie to her feet. She looked at them thoughtfully for a brief moment then, her decision made, said, 'I must explain.'

'Are you sure you want to, Ma?' warned Rowena.

'Yes, I must. If don't there will be suspicion between us, and I don't want that.'

'There's no need,' Lavinia told her.

Jessie shook her head. 'No, I need to unburden myself.' She went on to tell them exactly what had happened with Cameron and how he came to be found dead at the bottom of the cliffs.

'You've nothing to blame yourself for, Mrs Murray,' said Lavinia, when she had finished.

'Not for what happened to Cameron, but I have for what followed. It was thought someone on your father's estate had murdered him. When no one confessed, he brought the eviction date forward without telling us. You've seen what happened here. Now it will happen at Miller's. If I had spoken up, explained what had happened, the evictions might have been averted.'

'They wouldn't, Mrs Murray. Remember, the orders were given before Cameron's death. If you had said what really happened, I don't think you would have been believed. You would only have brought down retribution on yourself, and who knows what that would have led to? Maybe execution. Say no more about it, Mrs Murray. It's a secret between the three of us that none of us will break.' Lavinia held out her hands for Jessie and Rowena to take in an unbreakable bond of friendship.

Jessie's gaze moved across the desolation and ruin around them, wreathed in smoke driven by the Shetland wind. She tightened her lips, straight-

222

ened her spine determinedly and said, 'It is no good standing here feeling sorry for ourselves. There's a new life to be made.'

'Ma, where are we going to find shelter tonight?' asked Rowena, perturbed by the prospect of a night spent huddled together without protection in a safe haven.

'We'll go to the Millers,' replied Jessie, but even as she offered this solution had little hope they would find help there; she was sure the men who had plundered and destroyed her home had left in the direction of Miller's settlement.

Her worst fears were proved correct when they topped the rise half a mile away and saw smoke rising from several fires that could only be coming from Miller's settlement.

'Ma!' Rowena's cry was full of alarm.

'Oh, God!' Dark despair settled on Lavinia. She choked with emotion. What had her father set in motion? The decision must have come from him, but no doubt Angus was revelling in carrying it out mercilessly.

'Be strong, both of you,' said Jessie, and then started forward.

Lavinia and Rowena were only a step behind her.

A running figure broke out of the hollow ahead.

'Jamie,' Rowena cried.

Panting heavily, he stopped in front of them. 'Thank ... goodness ... you ... you're all right.' He drew a deep breath. Relief shone from his eyes. 'We saw smoke. Ma told me to see if you were all right. I was halfway to you when I saw the horsemen, and hid. I saw them heading for us, didn't

223

know what to do but...' He paused.

'Now there's smoke coming from your settlement,' Jessie finished for him. 'You fear the worst. Come on.' She started off.

'I'll take this, Mrs Murray,' Jamie said, reaching for one of her bags.

They hurried on without a word, each lost in their own anxiety, drawn by the billowing smoke which must signify the end for the Miller settlement.

When the horrific meaning of what lay before his eyes made its full impact, Jamie let out a wail that rent the sky and tore at the minds of the others. Eager to know what had happened to his family, he started a clumsy, staggering run that became easier when he dropped Jessie's bag. Lavinia grabbed it and they hastened towards the ruins of what had once been a poor but happy community.

They moved past smouldering houses, piles of broken furniture, burned cloth, heaps of stones that once were walls. Mothers held babies in a comforting embrace while trying to calm bewildered children, who were wailing with the shock of what they had witnessed. Women tried to staunch the blood of battered men; some were howling in despair, others cursing the laird and the perpetrators of his orders.

'What's the laird's bitch doing here?' A shout from someone brought murmurs of agreement from others.

Jessie bristled. 'Curb your tongue, whoever you are. And that goes for all of you. Hear this – Lavinia McFadden is one of us. Thrown out by her father for pleading our cause, she came to me

224

as a friend. She sails with us to Canada. Accept that, accept *her* ... or answer to me.'

Jessie had quickly realised that she had to exert some authority otherwise these folk would kick against their fate and vent their feelings on an innocent girl.

'Over here!' came a cry. Rowena had seen Jamie reach his mother. She was kneeling beside her husband who was lying on the ground, his back against one crumbled wall of their croft. Blood flowed from a cut on his forehead, an eye was blackening and one arm hung limp.

Jessie immediately went to help. She sank to her knees, saying, 'Martha, let me.' She eased the cloth from her friend's fingers. 'I'll be gentle, Hugh.'

He nodded and Martha looked at her appreciatively from red-rimmed eyes that also revealed the shock she had been through. 'Jamie found you then?' As if the mention of his name had triggered a thought she looked round for him and said, 'Jamie, you and Lizzy see to the weans.'

Brother and sister instantly checked three of their bewildered siblings, hanging around the ruins that had been their home, and told them to stay there; then they went in search of the other two who had wandered off in the upheaval. They were joined by Rowena and Lavinia.

'We saw smoke, did it happen to you?' Martha asked her friend.

'Aye, it did.'

'We protested they were a week too soon with their eviction orders but Angus McFadden said it was to happen now unless someone owned up to the murder of Hayden Cameron. Everyone made

225

angry complaint, pointing out vigorously that they knew nothing about it, but that wasn't good enough. Some of our men tried to retaliate but they weren't a match for the laird's men who were ready for anything we could do.'

Jessie felt a prick of conscience as she heard this but, heeding Lavinia's earlier reasoning, held her tongue. To reveal now what she knew could only make the situation worse. 'The blood has stopped, Hugh.' As she was speaking Jessie lifted the hem of her dress and tore a strip off her petticoat to make a bandage which she secured round his head. 'Now the arm ... can you bend it?'

He did so but with some pain, which worsened when she pressed it. 'I think it's only bad bruising. I don't believe anything is broken.'

'I rode a blow from a piece of fencing before felling my attacker with a punch to the jaw, then someone else sent me reeling with the blow that caused that gash.'

'It's a bad one but it'll heal,' Jessie reassured him. 'We need you right for Canada. But first we have to think what to do in the days until we sail.'

'Where have those kids got to?' said Martha, exasperated that her two youngest had wandered off again.

'They'll be back,' said Jessie. No sooner were the words out of her mouth than Jamie, Lizzy, Rowena and Lavinia appeared with the two children.

'All right,' said Martha. 'We are going to start moving from here. Get whatever you want to take, but remember – you'll have to carry it.'

All around the ruins of what had but a short time ago been a living, vibrant community, people gathered their essentials or scratted for some last item that held precious memories. Bags were crammed with what had been salvaged; women wept, regretful at having to leave behind what had once been essential to their lives; men, racked with anger at the laird and the bullies who had so ruthlessly carried out his orders, cursed and swore revenge even though they knew there was no chance of fulfilling it. They were doomed to a life in exile.

Those families who had chosen to stay in Shetland, now with no roof over their heads, condemned to find shelter where they could and live on the hope of finding new employment, straggled away, wondering if they had done right in not seeking a new life in Canada. Those who had chosen the shipboard route from Shetland, realising that they could help each other on their walk to Scalloway, gathered together. When the last family declared they were ready, they started on their journey into the unknown.

20

'Are you comfortable, Mrs Jordan?' Kate asked in concern once the coach had settled after George had urged the horses up a rough slope.

'Yes, my dear,' she replied, with laughter in her eyes. 'It's rather fun ... a splendid start to our holiday. The road will improve after we get off these hills. And we'll certainly appreciate our comfortable beds in York.'

Kate was pleased by Mrs Jordan's attitude; she had been a little apprehensive about the exigencies of the journey for her employer, but so far Mrs Jordan had made light of them. They settled into spasmodic chatter, observing things along the way, anticipating what was to come. They paused for refreshment in Pickering after which they made good time to York where George skilfully manoeuvred the coach through the busy streets to Etteridge's Hotel in Lendal, noted for its comfort and its provision of horses for private carriages.

The following morning they were relieved to find the weather was fine and were given local information that it would remain that way, certainly until they crossed the Pennines, after which, they were told, 'A Yorkshireman can't be responsible for what the Lancastrians might have in store for you.'

'Whatever it is,' said Mrs Jordan as she and Kate settled in the carriage, 'we'll have to put up with it, but we won't let it spoil our day.'

She had instructed George to take them on a picturesque route and, although it was not the easiest of roads, his choice proved to be most attractive, leading them through pleasant farmland in the valleys between dramatic, soaring hills.

Kate loved it and let her imagination run riot until finally it settled on visualising herself roaming these hills with Malcolm beside her.

The crofters from the Miller settlement matched their pace to the slowest and, when faced with a first cold night in the open, huddled together for warmth, urging each other to bear up and summon all their strength to battle the troubles that were sure to lie ahead. They found comfort in their fellowship. But after two nights of little sleep, when the wind strengthened and driving rain soaked them, came the realisation that survival meant everyone thinking of themselves, or at best drawing together as a family and closing ranks against other people who had once been close. Those who had food, blankets and shawls guarded them with fierce antagonism against those who tried to take them. Curses and blasphemies replaced sympathy and blessings; bitterness exiled gratitude; happiness was drowned in a morass of general despondency. The group separated and straggled into smaller units and no longer thought of the general welfare. Survival of their own was all that mattered.

'Ma, what's happening to us all?' cried Rowena.

'Oh, Rowena love, I don't know,' came the plaintive answer. 'But don't let us get embroiled in any discord. People can be thoughtlessly cruel and act in ways they once would have abhorred when they are pushed to the limit.' As she was speaking, she was fishing in a bag for some biscuits.

'Put them away,' said Lavinia. 'They'll keep better than this bread I picked up.'

'But it's yours,' said Rowena.

Lavinia shook her head. 'No, it's ours.'

They broke the bread equally between them and slaked their thirst at a speeding burn, bounding along on its bed of stones.

As she straightened up from the bank, Jessie eyed the evening sky. 'I don't like this. We're going to get a storm. Let's find some sort of shelter.'

Lavinia looked around. 'Follow me,' she said.

Neither Jessie nor Rowena questioned her.

She led them away from the burn, pausing only to glance back and see if they were being followed. Seeing other families were still spread out along the burn or wearily following its course, she nodded with satisfaction. They topped a rise, dropped into a hollow and followed it for about half a mile to where it opened out into a small circular sward of heather and stunted grass. Stones were scattered across the ground and, though time had seen most of them overgrown, several appeared previously to have formed a wall around a dip in the ground that might once have been some sort of dwelling.

'Maybe we can shelter here?' said Lavinia.

Jessie had already been surveying the prospects. 'We certainly can,' she said. 'You seemed to know it was here, Lavinia, what's it been?'

'When we came to the burn I thought the landscape was familiar but I couldn't remember why I should think so. Then, as I cupped my hands to take some water, I recalled doing just that when I was a child. Then I remembered that Father was with me, and he brought me here and told me it was a dwelling from very far-off days.'

'We can get down behind those stones over there.' Rowena pointed them out.

'Come on,' said Jessie, 'let's see what we can do before the rain comes.'

They worked quickly, placing some more stones to make the back-rest more comfortable and gathering heather to form a bed. Once they were satisfied, they had some biscuit, then, with the rain starting, settled down, huddled close together for warmth, drew their shawls over their heads and spread the blanket Jessie had snatched from their home before the fire had taken the rest of their belongings.

The wind rose and the rain lashed down. They huddled closer, thankful to have each other.

When they met at breakfast after their final night's stop before reaching their destination, Mrs Jordan greeted Kate with a cheery, 'Good morning, I hope you slept well?'

'I did, Mrs Jordan, thank you. Every bed has been most comfortable, but this last one here in Kirkby Kendal was the best.'

'Good. If the accommodation at The Travellers' Rest in Grasmere, where my friend has booked us rooms, is as good, we will be most fortunate.'

'You haven't stayed here before then?' Kate enquired.

'No. I've always stayed with my friend, but this time it was not possible.'

'Oh, I hope I was not the reason for that?' replied Kate, feeling that she might be intruding on a friendship.

'No, no, my dear. Her husband is not in good health.'

'I'm sorry to hear that. I hope it isn't serious?'

'I don't think so but it is disturbing. We will find out tomorrow.'

'Is he a farmer?'

'Oh, no.' Mrs Jordan gave a little smile. 'He is a writer. He found inspiration here when he and his wife visited five years ago. They had a reasonable private income together with some returns from his writing and so they decided to settle here. I believe that recently he has turned to writing poetry. It seems this area of the Lake District is attracting poets. I think you will see why as we drive to Grasmere today.'

'If it is any advance on the scenery we have passed so far, I will be very impressed,' said Kate. 'I particularly liked Bedale and the country between Leyburn and Hawes, and it was a treat to see the falls at Aysgarth.'

'We have been very fortunate with the weather, with only a little rain that first day,' commented Mrs Jordan. 'I do hope it continues fine today for your first sight of the Lake District.'

Kate sat back and enjoyed the kaleidoscopic colours of the soaring hills surrounding them. She was so glad Mrs Jordan had insisted she bring her paints and brushes which she had not used for some time; this countryside seemed to insist that she should apply her skills again, limited though they were. But she was even more in awe as they descended from Ings towards the shining water ahead, stretching out of sight to left and right.

'The lake is Windermere,' Mrs Jordan informed her. 'And at the other side are the Claife Heights and beyond that the Furness Fells.'

'It's glorious,' gasped Kate. 'I must paint it. I'm so glad you persuaded me to bring my paper and watercolours.'

'Ah, wait until you see Rydal Water and Grasmere,' returned Mrs Jordan, with an air of mystery in her tone. Wanting the scenery to speak for itself she would not be drawn further.

Kate saw why. Though the scene was on a smaller scale from that of Windermere, it glistened like a jewel, intimate in its attraction, filled with exquisite details that had seemed lost in the vastness of Windermere. She waxed enthusiastic about it and knew she was lucky to be seeing it for the first time on a day of sunshine, blue sky and cotton-wool clouds. Some day she must bring Malcolm here.

The landlord and his wife at The Travellers' Rest greeted them with such warmth that they immediately felt at home.

As soon as she was alone in her room, Kate flung herself on the bed. Laughter came to her lips; this one would certainly match that in which she had slept last night. Without doubt this was going to be a most comfortable stay in an area of beauty that would remain in her mind forever.

Three weary bodies, shoulders sagging, hair dishevelled, legs aching, halted on a rise and looked across East Voe towards a tiny town of grey-stone buildings and a ruined castle that, in the fading light, did nothing for their hopes. A few small fishing vessels lay forlornly in the harbour but there was no sailing vessel that looked as if it could battle the Atlantic waves and convey her passengers across thousands of miles of stormy water.

'What now, Ma?' Rowena's voice carried despair. 'This looks hopeless.'

Lavinia moved closer to her and put an arm round her shoulders, hoping she could encourage her friend to stay hopeful.

233

Jessie, drained by fatigue, knew she had to be strong for the other two. She tightened her lips, determined to ward off any feelings of despair that would only make a bad situation worse. 'We've to go down there and find shelter until the ship comes in.'

'And when will that be, Ma?'

'Who knows? Come on.'

Jessie started down the slope in the gathering dusk. The other two followed. She became more alert as she led them past the first of the houses and then on towards the harbour area, where she felt sure there would be some building where they might find shelter. She was thankful that the few people who were about seemed bent on reaching their own destinations before darkness settled over the town, and took little notice of them. A small building that had lost most of its roof, standing back about a hundred yards from the harbour, looked the most likely place to offer them some shelter. Jessie squeezed round a door hanging from one hinge and paused to let her sight adjust to the gloom. As soon as it had she saw by the faint light coming from a broken window an uneven stone floor on which were scattered some old nets and a quantity of sacks. She turned to the others. 'In here.' When they joined her she said, 'We'll make do with this tonight. The remaining part of the roof can keep the rain off and the sacks might help keep us warm. Let's see what we can do.'

They set about trying to make things as comfortable as they could for their night's stay and in doing so disturbed a rat or two, shuddering at the prospect of having the creatures running around them during the night.

When she was satisfied that they had done what they could, Jessie said, 'Wait here, I'll be back in a few minutes.' She started for the door.

'Ma! Where are you going?' Rowena's voice carried the unspoken words, 'Don't leave me.'

'She won't be long,' Lavinia said.

'How do you know?' snapped Rowena.

Lavinia, recognising that her friend was close to breaking point, said gently, 'She said so. Come on. Help me find a couple more dry sacks.'

Ten minutes later, Rowena was growing tetchy. 'Where is she? She should have been back by now. I'm going to look for her!' She started for the door but Lavinia grabbed her arm.

'You can't, you don't know where she's gone.'

'I'm going!' She tried to shake off Lavinia's grip but it had tightened. 'Let go!' Wild-eyed, she screamed defiance. 'Just because you're a laird's daughter, you think you can boss me about!'

'Rowena!' The word came like a whiplash from the doorway.

'Ma!' Relief filled her answering cry.

Jessie's face was filled with thunder. 'Tell Lavinia you're sorry.' Still Rowena hesitated. 'Go on, do it!'

The crisp authority in the order jolted Rowena into realising what she had done. She turned to Lavinia. 'I'm so sorry.' Tears welled in her eyes. 'Please forgive me. I didn't mean anything...'

Before she could finish the sentence, Lavinia enfolded her in her arms and said soothingly, 'I know you didn't. Forget it.'

Jessie had joined them. Now she said, 'We must

235

always stick together and never fall out. It is the only way we will get through this.' She left a little pause then added, 'Let's have something to eat.' She opened the shawl she had tied into a bundle, revealing a loaf of bread, some slices of meat, a cake and three apples.

Both girls were wide-eyed.

'Where did you get these?' gasped Rowena.

'Ask no questions, girl, get no lies. Just eat and be thankful we have this and we are together.'

'Are we to stay here until the ship comes in?' asked Lavinia.

'I think so,' Jessie replied, then added with a wry smile, 'unless we are evicted again.'

'Davis!' The First Mate's voice rang out across the deck of the *Lady Isobel* as ropes were tossed on to the Whitby quay to stevedores eager to get the ship tied up.

'Aye-aye, sir.' Tom was across the deck in a few quick strides.

'Davis,' said the well-built mate who carried an air of authority, 'Captain wants to see you, right away.'

'Aye-aye, sir.' Tom spun round and in a matter of moments was beside the captain who was supervising the final docking of the ship. 'You wanted me, sir.'

'Aye.' Captain Williams eyed him in friendly fashion. 'I know you were disturbed by something you heard in Shetland. Your attitudes altered after we had left the islands, though your work as a crewman was not affected. I concluded it must be a private matter. You're a friend of McFadden, the

Shetlander, aren't you? Does what you heard there concern him?'

'You are right, sir. I must see him as soon as possible once I get ashore.'

The captain had been eyeing Tom closely, noticing his reaction when his friend's name was mentioned. 'Then get ashore now. You are excused duty,' he said.

'Thank you, sir.' Tom started to turn away, hardly believing his luck, but the captain stopped him.

'Report to me this evening instead.'

'Aye-aye, sir.'

Tom hurried to Swan's yard. He paused to take in the busy scene around the two ships in different stages of construction, but could see nothing of Malcolm. His swift steps took him to the office where, much to his relief, he found his friend in discussion with Archie.

'Tom!' They were both instantly on their feet to welcome him.

'When did you get back?' asked Malcolm, shaking his hand.

'Just now.' Tom glanced at Archie. 'Sorry to disturb you, Mr Swan, but I have news which I thought Malcolm should hear as soon as possible. Captain Williams allowed me ashore early to tell him.' He looked his friend in the eye. 'I'm afraid it's bad news.' Tom left only the slightest pause but in that brief moment saw anxiety cloud Malcolm's expression. 'When we were in Lerwick we heard rumours of trouble in the north. Thinking it might be in your home area, I made enquiries. It seems

237

your father has evicted his crofters.'

'Damn!' Malcolm's face looked pale with shock.

Tom continued, 'Badly handled, I heard, with little consideration shown for the crofters.'

With his thoughts immediately flashing to Rowena, Malcolm asked, 'What's happened to them?'

'Can't be certain of that,' replied Tom. 'Some were said to be fending for themselves as best they could. Others, I was told, had chosen to take passage to Canada when a ship, the *Hope*, became available.'

'Has that happened yet?'

'Not when I left Shetland. There were rumours of a delay.' Tom hesitated. Malcolm saw that his friend was troubled.

'There's something else, isn't there?' he pressed, his tone revealing he feared worse news was coming.

'It was being said that the laird had turned his own daughter out.'

'What?' Malcolm felt his world crumbling about him. 'Lavinia? Oh, no!'

'Because she sympathised with and helped the crofters,' finished Tom.

'She did that because *I* asked her to keep an eye on them and to help if she could.' Malcolm clenched his fists and shook them in frustration. 'Goodness knows what she will do...'

Archie saw his distress. 'Will she stay with the crofters?'

'More than likely, unless she begs Father ... no, she'll never do that! My sister may appear gentle and easygoing, but she has a spine and mind of pure steel. So it's a life of poverty in Shetland or the unknown in Canada for her.' As he spoke the last sentence Malcolm realised he was also summing up Rowena's fate. 'I've got to find out, I've got to help,' he exclaimed.

'That means immediate passage to Shetland,' said Archie.

'Aye, but there's my work ... you made me foreman. I can't just walk away from Mrs Jordan's ship.'

'There is nothing that can't be handled by us,' said Archie. 'You choose the best man from your team to take over until you return, which shouldn't be long. I will keep an eye myself on the ship's progress; we'll not let Mrs Jordan down. I know how much she is looking forward to seeing her ship completed and launched. Don't worry about progress here, we'll keep it going.'

'Thanks, Archie. Once I find my sister we can come back to Whitby immediately.' He did not mention Rowena even though in his own mind Malcolm acknowledged he must take care of her as well. 'The immediate problem is getting to Shetland.'

'Then we'll see Sam Beadmore. Come on,' said Archie, stepping out from behind his desk.

The brisk pace he set as he left the shipyard was matched by Malcolm's and Tom's. They crossed the bridge to the East Side and entered the offices of Beadmore & Son in Church Street, beside the quay along the riverbank.

Tom hesitated; as a mere seaman he had never before entered the sanctum of Beadmore's.

Archie glanced round at him. 'Come on, Tom,

Mr Beadmore might want to hear what you have to say.' He nodded and followed the others in.

The clerk announced them and, when the initial greetings were over, Archie came straight to the point.

'Have you a ship calling at Shetland soon, Sam?'

He looked surprised by the question. 'Aye, the *Guiding Star* will be away to the Baltic. What's your interest?'

'Tom here...' The pause Archie left encouraged a comment.

'Aye, I know Davis. Good seaman.'

'Captain Williams allowed him ashore immediately the *Lady Isobel* was tied up. He had important news for my brother-in-law Malcolm regarding family matters in Shetland.'

Sam immediately realised where this was heading. 'And you want me to allow him passage on the *Guiding Star* on her way to the Baltic?'

'You understand me precisely.'

'Bad, is it, Malcolm?' asked Sam.

'How bad I don't know, but Tom heard that my father has evicted all crofters from his estate, and my sister has become embroiled in upholding their case against Father. I fear she and the crofters, with whom I once had close contact, need my help. From what Tom heard it's likely they'll be shipped to Canada soon. I need to get to Shetland quickly.'

'I thought you might help,' put in Archie.

'We've been good friends, Archie, and are always straight with each other, so the answer is yes,' said Sam.

The relief that flowed from the three men was

palpable. Both Malcolm and Archie poured out their thanks.

Sam Beadmore rose from his chair. 'I'll see Captain Bradshaw now and issue new orders. I suggest you come with me, Malcolm, and we'll get his ideas on the situation.'

Once outside Tom hurried away to rejoin his ship for the evening watch. Sam and Malcolm parted from Archie and were soon aware of plenty of activity around the *Guiding Star*. Orders were being yelled, cargo stacked, the noise resonating along the quay; foremen urged their gangs on to greater effort; waggoners cursed their horses into obedience as they manoeuvred their vehicles into position to be unloaded; the whole area teemed with the labour that added to the port's general prosperity.

Sam led the way up the gangway and on to the deck where he had seen Captain Bradshaw supervising the loading operation.

'All going according to plan, Captain?' he asked.

'Aye, sir, smoothly so far.'

'Will you be away tomorrow?'

'We should make the evening tide.'

'Good, make sure you do. Mr Malcolm McFadden needs to be in Shetland as soon as possible. You have my permission to call there on your way to the Baltic.'

'Yes, sir.'

'If you need to hire more stevedores to get away on time, do so.'

'Very good, sir. I doubt we'll have to do that, but I'll bear it in mind.'

Sam turned back to Malcolm. 'Then I'll leave

you to make ready whatever you have to.'

'Mr Beadmore, I cannot thank you enough for what you are doing for me. I will be forever grateful,' he said.

'Think nothing of it. I only hope you will be on time and able to help those poor people.'

'Thank you. I'll do my best.' Malcolm gave a shake of his head. 'I've just got to succeed! I must.' He turned to Captain Bradshaw then. 'When would you like me on board?'

'Early evening tomorrow.'

'I'll be here. And thank you for your help.'

'Malcolm, Kate isn't here now but I know she would want me to say for her, "Do what you have to do." Remember, you are one of us now and we will all support you, whatever happens.' Archie extended his hand, and when Malcolm took it he felt his brother-in-law's reassuring grip echo his words.

Malcolm turned up the collar of his coat against the cold freshening wind as he said, 'I'll be back as soon as I can. It shouldn't take me long to find out what has happened and the possible consequences. I should be home before Kate is back from the Lake District.'

Archie nodded, slapped him on the back and said, 'Safe voyage.'

Malcolm gave a small smile, picked his bag off the quay and walked up the gangway to the deck of the *Guiding Star*. No sooner was he aboard than the gangway was hauled on to the deck and secured.

He remained at the rail while the ship was

manoeuvred away from the quay. He raised his hand in farewell to Archie and stayed where he was until the ship cleared the twin piers and took to the sea.

21

Time seemed to stand still for Malcolm, who was eager to be back on his native soil and to find out what had happened to Lavinia and Rowena. He hoped he would not be too late to take them back with him to Whitby, into the security of the new life he had found there.

When the *Guiding Star* sailed into Bressay Sound, with grey clouds in the late-afternoon sky threatening rain if the wind dropped, Captain Bradshaw had a boat-crew standing by to strike out for the harbourside as soon as the ship anchored. Malcolm made his thanks and goodbyes to the captain and was instantly in the boat, ready to take to the water. Strong arms propelled them quickly to the quay at Lerwick harbour. Malcolm called out his grateful thanks to the crew, clambered up the stone steps at the quayside, and hurried into the town.

Impatient to be on his way to Garstan House, he found a stableman willing to sell him a horse and saddle. As he busied himself, Rob the stableman asked casually, 'Here on business, sir?' The man was wondering why Malcolm McFadden was back in Shetland. There might be an opportunity to line his own pockets with this information, if he did not reveal that he recognised Angus's brother.

Malcolm seized on the opening but disguised his Shetland accent and played down his reply. 'Aye, I deal in cattle and sheep. I have good stocks fattening in the Lowlands. Thought there might be a market for them in Shetland.'

'Could be you've come at the right time, sir.'

'Why is that?'

'Crofters hereabouts are being evicted and the land cleared for sheep. More money in that it seems than the pittance the lairds say they get from their tenants.'

Malcolm nodded. 'Aye, there's money in sheep.'

'Maybe you would do well to go to the McFadden Estate.'

'Where is that?'

'It's twenty miles or so up north. Rumours have been coming through. It seems evictions have been started recently and there's been trouble in one of the townships on the estate.' The stableman warmed to his tale. 'I've heard tell that one of the laird's men was found dead at the bottom of some high cliffs. Was it murder? Well, the laird accused the crofters of a particular township, but no one owned up so he brought forward the evictions by a week without warning. The crofters weren't ready so there was trouble ... quite bad, so we hear. And I've heard the laird's daughter was unable to use her influence to stop it. It's said she fell out with her father over the clearances and he kicked her out too.'

'And she went to the crofters?' Malcolm suggested.

'That's what I've heard.'

'So what happened to them?' he asked cautiously.

'Left to fend for themselves. I've heard some are due to ship out to Canada from Scalloway on the *Hope*, leaving on this evening's tide. There you are, sir, everything ready for you.'

Malcolm nodded. 'Thanks.' He paid the stableman, led the horse outside with comforting words and swung himself into the saddle. Even as he was doing this, he was pondering what he had learned. If crofters were leaving for Canada, and his sister and Rowena and her mother were among them, he had better be away to Scalloway rather than his old home, and hope he was there before the *Hope* sailed.

Angus was about to step out of the doorway of a notorious whisky house and brothel but drew back into the shadows on hearing the sound of a horse's hooves. The rider passed close by. Angus froze in disbelief, doubting his own eyesight. It couldn't be...? No! Malcolm couldn't be in Shetland. But...? Once again doubt assailed his mind. He stared after the retreating man. There was something about that figure ... about the way he sat his horse ... that could not be disguised by his heavy clothing.

Angus stood reasoning out the possibilities of why his brother could be back in Shetland. Where had he been these past years? Had he heard of the evictions? Had he regretted leaving and returned to make peace with his father? That question reverberated the loudest in Angus's mind. If that were so, he realised, he could say goodbye to the McFadden Estate – the document relating to the change of heir still lay in the drawer unsigned!

The rider was lost to view. Angus hurried in the opposite direction until he came to the last house in the street. He hammered on the door. There was no immediate answer. He cursed with frustration and hammered again, this time keeping up the pounding until an upstairs window rattled open.

'What the hell...?'

The objection was cut short by Angus's sharp voice. 'Get down here, Alan Duguid, and bring your bone-headed brother Colin with you. NOW!'

The close-cropped head that had appeared under the raised sash disappeared. The window was slammed shut so that Angus did not hear the curses being rained down on his head by the two brothers and the girls who occupied their beds.

A few minutes later the bolts were drawn back on the front door to reveal a couple of burly, muscular men whose mean eyes and scarred features imparted an unspoken warning to any who crossed their path.

But Angus knew how to handle them. 'Come with me.'

Neither brother questioned the order; having worked for him before they knew better. They would be told in good time why they were wanted, and they knew that whatever it was they would be well paid for it.

Angus hurried them to the stable and told them to wait outside.

'Good evening, Mr McFadden.' Rob touched his forehead. He was a young man who had left a lonely life on the island of Papa Stour to take over the stable only a year ago and had quickly learned it was a good thing to keep on the right side of Angus McFadden whenever he was in Lerwick.

'Rob,' began Angus amiably, 'did a rider leave here a short while ago?'

'Yes, sir. He bought a horse from me.'

'That seems to indicate he'll be in Shetland for some time.'

'Most likely. He came in on the ship that's in Bressay Sound. I hear it's on its way to the Baltic. It's a Whitby ship.'

'Did you know the man?'

'No, sir,' lied Bob. He was shocked to realise Angus must know of his brother's return, but with that knowledge he saw there might be opportunities to drive a hard bargain with Angus in the future.

'Did he say what he was doing in Shetland?'

'Yes, said he was looking to sell sheep.'

'Any word about where he was going?'

'Never said. He was polite but a man of few words. I know no more about him.'

'That's all right, Rob. Now, I want to hire two horses for the Duguid brothers. Get them ready quickly while I have a word with them outside. Then, when they leave, get my own horse ready. I'll be away earlier than I intended.'

'Very good, sir.'

Angus left the stable. Even as he had been speaking to Rob his mind had been turning over what he would do if he were in Malcolm's place.

247

Whitby? He could have got Shetland news from a ship calling there ... suppose he had and the news concerned the clearances taking place on the McFadden Estate? Malcolm would surmise Rowena was involved. Remembering how he had been sweet on her, Angus could readily understand why his brother was in Shetland – to find and help her. His first enquiries would be about the crofters from the McFadden Estate. On learning that many of them were emigrating to Canada and that the *Hope* would be leaving Scalloway tomorrow, he would more than likely make straight there rather than go to Garstan House to see their father.

Angus eyed the Duguids. 'You remember my brother Malcolm?'

'Aye.'

'You'd recognise him again?'

'Aye.'

'I believe he's back in Shetland and heading for Scalloway and the *Hope*, the ship bound for Canada tomorrow. He must not get on board nor make contact with any of the crofters.'

Both men nodded.

'And once the ship has sailed, we let him go?'

Remembering that unsigned document, Angus answered emphatically, 'No. Get rid of him for good. You'll be well paid to do it.'

Once clear of Lerwick, Malcolm put his horse to the gallop and prepared himself to face the unknown. He was presuming Lavinia, Rowena and her mother were still alive though filled with horror at the thought of what might have happened to them during the violent eviction the

248

stableman had mentioned. If they were indeed alive, any one of them might oppose his plan to take them to a new life in Whitby. Surely she would rather face a new life there with his help than start again thousands of miles away in an unknown country, with no settled future? He thrust aside the questions he was unable to answer. First he had to find the women.

'There he is!' called Alan Duguid, bringing his horse to a halt at the top of a rise.

'Let's take him,' said Colin.

'No!' rapped Alan. 'We can't take him by surprise out here. And if we did, what are we going to do with the body? Far better to set about him in the warren of streets in Scalloway.'

'But...'

Alan cut his brother's objection short. 'Don't start trying to plan things in your numb-headed way, just do as I say.'

Colin gave a surly grunt; he didn't like being continually reminded that his brother had the sharper brain.

'The *Hope!*' The name swept through Scalloway's brokendown hovels where the crofters had sought shelter while waiting the ship's arrival. Ignoring the early hour, when daylight was just beginning to oust the night, they streamed into the open, anxious to see the ship that would take them to what they hoped would be a better life in Canada.

Jessie, Rowena and Lavinia, awakened from a shallow sleep by the disturbance, grabbed their belongings and, pleased to be away from the

249

stinking rubbish and filth that had accumulated in the streets, joined the throng heading for the quay where they had been told the *Hope* would tie up. After the degradation they had recently suffered there was a new hopefulness and excitement in the air. It overrode any hostility to the bumping and shoving generated by the hordes of people all heading for the quay.

'Rowena!' A hand grabbed her arm.

The moment of shock was banished by her recognition of the man's voice. 'Jamie!' she gasped with delight. 'I'm so pleased to see you again.'

'And I you.' He grinned. 'We wondered what had happened to you after we were separated?'

'Where's...' She did not have time to finish her sentence; the rest of the Miller family were there, showing relief and pleasure that the two families were reunited again.

'We must stick together, get berths near each other on board,' urged Jessie.

'Keep close,' called Martha to her younger children.

'Here, take my hand,' Lavinia offered to the youngest, overpowered by the crush, who was glad to do so.

Other people made contact again with friends and acquaintances but, apart from in a few cases like theirs, there was not the same camaraderie between the former crofters that they had once experienced. In the days following the evictions, most had developed an 'every man for himself' attitude, which they would need to put behind them if they were to survive in the unknown Canadian settlement. But, for the time being, they were concerned only with getting aboard the *Hope* and crossing the Atlantic. Some of the older and less robust had already succumbed to the conditions they had faced while getting to Scalloway. Now the next stage was before them; setting sail could not be far away.

Once the ship was tied up, the captain immediately set his crew to assisting the port authorities in sorting out the passengers and directing them to the quarters they would occupy. The crew had little sympathy for them and hurried them on with hard blows, curses and profanities, pushing the slow ones and not giving the old or infirm a second thought.

'Pick your places for the voyage and keep to 'em,' they yelled above the protests of those who travelled on no more than the laird's payment. The conditions in which they were to survive were truly primitive. Crowded together in the hold, the space allocated to each passenger was barely big enough to lie down in. They were faced with insanitary hygiene arrangements: a few buckets ill concealed behind torn curtains in one corner of the hold, to be emptied overboard daily on a rota system organised by one of them, who would be appointed by the captain. Those who had thought ahead and brought food on board were the lucky ones, at least until that ran out; those who had not were told they could purchase food from the avaricious captain, but that turned out to be a monotonous diet of poor quality, barely enough to sustain life. Even before they sailed the crofters realised they would be facing a grim crossing, without even considering the tribulations Nature could throw at them with storms and heavy seas.

Those who had contributed to their passage found their conditions a little better, with three tiers of bunks arranged around the walls of the top section of a separate hold, the other tiers being filled with all manner of goods bound for the ship's destination of Pictou in Eastern Canada. They were thankful the ventilation here was better and the facilities less distasteful than those in the lower reaches of the ship. They even found that slightly better food could come their way from the captain – but at a price. Families had to sleep together as best they could in the bunks allocated to them. Jessie, Rowena and Lavinia were embarrassed by their good fortune in being given a bunk each, especially when it brought hostile and jealous looks from those sharing the hold with them. Though she never voiced the thought, Lavinia wondered if Angus or her father, as a parting gesture, had slipped the captain some money to ensure them this advantage. The Miller family succeeded in getting bunks next to theirs, and between them the two families made themselves as comfortable as possible.

They were informed that the captain would allow all passengers on deck for leaving port, but when the ship was clear of the harbour they would have to return to their quarters. He would then visit each section in turn and announce his orders for the voyage.

With sailing time drawing near, the crofters left their bunks and went up on deck to crowd the rail from where they would have their last glimpse of their homeland.

Anxious to get to the quay, Malcolm was unaware of the two riders matching his pace, who only closed the gap between them when the throng of people began to thicken as they neared the quay.

Frustrated by these human obstacles and realising he would make better progress on foot, Malcolm slid from the saddle and quickly tied his horse to a nearby rail.

'Come on.' Alan dropped from his own mount, making his order crisp. Colin followed him without question. 'Quick! We'll take him now, one on each side, into the first alley.'

Colin knew exactly what his brother wanted him to do, having used similar tactics in Lerwick whenever they had a score to settle. They fell into step, pushing their way through the gathering crowd, until they were within touching distance of their quarry.

Malcolm eyed the crowd. It was going to be difficult getting near enough the quayside to attempt to identify any of the folk crowding the rail of the *Hope*, but get there he must, and hope that at least one of the three people he sought was at the rail. His attention was so fixed on what he wanted to achieve that he was unaware of the two men, one on either side of him, until he felt their tight grip on his arms. Alarmed, he shot hostile glances at them but they took no notice. Before Malcolm could utter a word of protest, he was hustled into an alley. A sharp push sent him crashing into the wall on the right. Before he had time to raise an arm in self-defence a blow took him hard on the cheek and another crashed into his stomach, doubling him up. A fist against the back of his neck sent him pitching to the ground. He gasped for air, tried to call out, but it was no good. In any case, he would not have been heard above the noise that rose from the quayside where orders were shouted to get the ship cast off and the crowd of onlookers called out their good wishes to passengers bound for a new life far away. A sailing that carried evicted crofters always brought out sympathisers to wish them well.

Kicks rained down on Malcolm. He tried to roll away but his attackers were merciless. Eventually he succumbed. For him, all hurt had stopped, all noise had ceased.

'All right,' panted Alan. 'Into the harbour with him. There's to be no evidence. Act drunk.'

They hauled Malcolm to his feet. With one man on either side, arms round him, they staggered back to the quay. As they moved among the crowd they received curses for their cumbersome steps and laughter at their drunken antics. Gradually they moved further and further along the quay, beyond the bow of the ship, away from the crowds.

Alan looked back. He reckoned with people's attention focused on the *Hope*, no one would be taking any notice of three drunks disappearing into the gloom. 'A bit further,' he said. Then, after another fifty yards, 'Ship is on her way. This'll do.' He fished a purse from Malcolm's pocket. 'Proof enough for Angus McFadden.'

'Aye,' agreed Colin.

'Let's be rid,' said his brother. They staggered to the edge of the quay where, with one swift push, Malcolm was sent plummeting into the murky water that quickly closed over his head. He sank from sight like a stone.

'Job done,' said Alan.

'And further payment waiting,' laughed Colin. 'Easy money!'

22

As the ship slipped away from the quay some passengers began to move back from the rail, though most chose to watch what they would always regard as their homeland slide away into the gathering darkness.

'I'll get the little ones settled,' said Martha to her husband. 'You see to the others.' She glanced round the deck. 'I don't know where they are ... exploring, no doubt, maybe with Lizzy. See they don't get into mischief.'

Hugh nodded. 'I'll find them, don't worry.'

'I'll be down shortly to give you a hand, Martha,' Jessie offered.

'Thanks,' she replied.

Jessie, feeling a yearning to have her last glimpse of Shetland on her own, moved to a space further along the rail, leaving Rowena, Lavinia and Jamie standing together. Jessie hoped that this might be the beginning of a closer relationship between her daughter and the Millers' son.

He was somewhere cold, wet and dark... A glimmer of realisation told Malcolm he was somewhere he shouldn't be. Automatically he kicked out. Everything was a blur; nothing made sense to his bewildered mind. He broke water but still everything was confusion. Why was he wet and so cold? Where was he? He reached up to clear his eyes, but his arms ached and the effort was almost too much. Feebly, he brushed water from them and was aware of a huge shape close by. Panic started up in him. What was it? He turned in the water, instinctively keeping himself afloat. Pain stabbed at him from more than one place in his body; his head throbbed. The shape drew closer. Something in his mind said 'ship' and he knew then he was in danger. He shook his head, trying to clear his mind. His attention fixed on the moving wall of wood. Something dangled down it. Was it meant for him? He reached up. The wall bore down on him. His hand closed round the rope, and he knew he must hang on or perish.

Two of the crew had come forward on the captain's orders to wind in the rope that had been left dangling over the side after the ship had cast off. One of them grasped it and was startled to feel the tension in it.

'Joe! Rope's snagged,' he called to his mate.

Joe looked over the rail. 'Snagged be damned, there's summat on the end.' He grabbed the rope. 'Haul away!'

The two men pulled, then, puzzled by the weight on the rope, they called for help. Another crewman ran to their aid.

The commotion drew the attention of the

passengers still on deck and they began to crowd around the crewmen to see what was happening.

'Stand back! Stand back!' This sharp order came from the captain who hurried to find out what was causing the disturbance. The crowd made way for him. 'What is it?' he demanded.

'Looks like someone hanging on to the rope,' replied Joe.

'What?' he snapped in disbelief, and peered over the rail. 'Get him on board, damned quick!' He assessed every movement as the person was brought slowly and carefully upwards. It seemed an eternity before the captain could reach out and grasp him. Another crew member appeared, gripped the man's clothing, and together with the captain hauled the man on to the deck where he lay gasping for breath.

It took only one glance for the captain to see that the man had suffered some severe injuries and needed immediate attention.

'Anyone know if he's one of the passengers?' he called.

There was no answer.

'Well, he'll have to be one now, there's no turning back, but he needs looking after and he'll need a bunk.'

There was no immediate response. Many of the passengers, not wanting to become involved, began to disperse.

'I'll see to him,' called out Jessie from the back of the crowd. 'We can give him one of our bunks.'

'Thank you, ma'am,' the captain replied.

Having recognised Jessie's voice, Rowena, Lavinia and Jamie waited until there was more room on deck as the other passengers went below and Jessie was able to come forward.

'Jamie, give me a hand,' she called as she dropped on one knee beside the injured man. 'Good grief!' she gasped then in disbelief, the expression in her eyes betraying bewilderment as she looked up at the two young women standing beside Jamie.

'What is it, Ma?' asked Rowena, but her voice faded away as her gaze settled on the man lying on the deck. 'Malcolm!' she breathed.

Lavinia too was numbed by the sight of her brother. Questions teemed in her mind. 'What...? How...?' Wanting reassurance that she was not hallucinating, she sought Rowena's hand with hers. 'Malcolm?'

There was no response from him.

They knelt down beside him, each with mixed emotions.

Lavinia wondered, Is my brother really here or is he a figment of my imagination? She reached out and touched him. He really was lying on the deck of the ship taking them to Canada. But how? Where had he been? Not a word from him had she heard since he had walked out of their home, yet seemingly he had never left Shetland. 'Malcolm?' There was no response, just a vacant look when his eyes rested on her. No sign of recognition. Then, aware of his bruised and bleeding face, she wondered what other injuries he had suffered and feared the worst. Someone must have inflicted those wounds on him and pitched him into the dock afterwards. But who and why?

Rowena moaned, 'Malcolm! Malcolm!' Tears

streamed down her face, masking the horror she felt at the sight of his wounds. Her love, the man she had never expected to see again, was here. Where had he been? How had he come to be plucked from the harbour, bruised and battered, to lie on the deck of the *Hope?* How she wished she had never driven him away. If only... 'Malcolm!' He showed no sign of recognition. He did not know her. She felt an arrow pierce her heart and she cried out again. She recognised the touch of her mother's hand on her shoulder, conveying comfort and understanding, endeavouring to lend her strength for what might lie ahead: a future living in the shadow of a man who did not recognise her.

'You know this man?' The captain's authoritative demand jolted the three women to attention.

'Yes,' answered Jessie for them all.

'If he's with you, what's he doing in the water? Drunk, no doubt.'

'He's not drunk,' said Lavinia sharply, in a tone that surprised the man. 'He's not with us, but he is my eldest brother.'

'Then what is he doing on the deck of my ship?'

'I don't know. But look at his face ... what else has been done to him?' She saw that the captain was about to remonstrate with her so said quickly, 'He must have been attacked and thrown into the water. He's lucky to be alive. Thank goodness that rope was hanging over the side and he managed to grab it.'

'All right, young woman, he's on board now. I can't turn back, so he's bound for Canada with us. You look after him.' The ship's master bent down and, while making a pretence of examining Malcolm, whispered to Lavinia, 'I know who you are. Your brother Angus paid extra for your three bunks. As the other lady has implied, I'm sure two of you can manage in one of them. Now see to him and make sure he's no more trouble.' With that, he turned and walked away.

The other folk who had hung around slowly went below, the excitement over. The three women were left to sort out the situation to the best of their ability.

Only Jamie, stunned by the sight of Malcolm McFadden, his thoughts in confusion as he recalled Rowena's deep friendship with the laird's son, lingered. 'Miss McFadden, if I can help...?'

Seeing the bewilderment on the faces of Rowena and Lavinia, Jessie seized on this offer. 'Thanks, Jamie. We must get him below deck and out of these wet clothes before he catches his death of cold.' She reached down to Malcolm. 'Come on, get up.'

He looked at her without recognition, which sent alarm through her, even though he had understood her order and was struggling to get to his feet. Jamie grasped him under one arm and helped him up. Malcolm, wincing from the burning pain around his ribs, swayed but Jamie steadied him.

'Come on, lassies,' said Jessie crisply.

Her sharpness jolted them into action. Seeing Malcolm's legs begin to give way, Lavinia took hold of his other arm and she and Jamie helped him across the deck.

Still reeling from the unexpected apparition, Rowena slid her hand into her mother's. 'I knew he would come back,' she whispered.

'Aye, he has.' But Jessie's thoughts were troubled. Had Malcolm suffered a loss of memory? If so, how would Rowena react if he never recovered enough to recognise her? What might that do to her when her joy at his return was so cruelly deceived? Jessie knew there was going to be more to cope with and she herself was going to have to be stronger than ever on this voyage to Canada.

Curious as to what had happened, other passengers stared at them or cast sympathetic glances their way as they entered their living section, but then swiftly returned to making their own bunks and the area allotted to them as comfortable as possible.

Martha came over to them. Even though she knew Malcolm, she automatically asked, 'Jessie, is it really...?'

'Aye, and he doesn't look too good. I'll be able to tell better when we get him into a bunk. He's taken a bad beating by the look of his face and the way he holds himself, but he'll survive.' Then she added quietly for only Martha to hear, 'He doesn't seem to know us.'

Her friend nodded her understanding and said, 'If there's anything I can do, just call. I'm sorry I can't accommodate him.'

'Thanks. I wouldn't expect you to, you haven't the room with your family.' Jessie gave a wan smile.

'Ma,' Jamie spoke up, 'I can sleep on the floor.'

'No, no, Jamie,' Jessie quickly refused. 'You'll do no such thing. Malcolm can have Rowena's bunk. She and I will manage in one.' Seeing protests coming from Jamie, she added, 'That's the end of the matter.' Then, for Rowena's benefit, 'You're a good, kind lad, Jamie.'

Accepting the decision, he nodded. 'He'll need some clothes; I have a spare set he can have until his are dried.' He and his mother headed off to help Hugh who was having trouble calming two of the children.

'Thank goodness we aren't travelling in the worst conditions. At least here we have some degree of privacy; these curtains, as full of holes as they are, will draw across the bunks,' Jessie said.

When Jamie returned with the clothes he'd found, she had got Lavinia and Rowena arranging the drawn curtains as best they could. Satisfied, she told them to find some food and explore the facilities for cooking. Then she turned to Malcolm, who was without any apparent comprehension of what was happening. 'Malcolm,' she said gently, 'Jamie will help me get you out of your wet clothes and into this bunk so I can treat your cuts and bruises.'

'Mrs Murray, I can see to him,' Jamie said hurriedly.

Sensing his embarrassment, she smiled to herself as she said, 'Oh, Jamie, I've seen it all before. There's no need for you to be embarrassed.' Without waiting, she started to remove Malcolm's clothing.

Jamie blushed deep red but soon lost his shyness as they stripped Malcolm and Jessie started to examine him.

'Those are nasty bruises on his legs but they'll clear as will his black eyes. That's a horrible gash on his head ... we'll have to watch that carefully after we get it cleaned up. I don't like these bruises on his ribs either. I think he's been kicked viciously.' She felt around them and was disturbed when Malcolm winced with pain even though her touch was gentle. 'I don't think any are broken, but he'll have to take extra care for a while.'

Jamie had taken all this in. 'Let me help when it's necessary, Mrs Murray.' He blushed again. 'You know what I mean?'

'Of course I do, lad, and I appreciate your offer. I won't forget.'

He nodded. 'What about dressing him now?' he asked.

'I think it might be best if we leave him still. Lay your jersey and a blanket over him to keep him warm until we see how he gets on.' She had noted that, while he appeared to be taking this all in, Malcolm had still said nothing. She glanced at Jamie again. 'Now we'll see if we can learn any-thing from him.' She turned to the injured man then hesitated a moment, trying to decide on her best tactics. 'Malcolm. Is that your name?' He looked at her with no expression in his eyes but seemed to be struggling to say something. 'You don't know?'

He shook his head.

'Then we will call you Malcolm.'

He gave a small smile and nodded.

Though Jessie knew his surname she did not want to prompt him; she needed to know if the attack had truly caused a loss of memory in him. 'Who are you?' she asked. He did not reply. 'Your surname?'

'Malcolm. You called me Malcolm.'

'Yes, I know, but I want to know your full name.'

He appeared to be struggling to find an answer. Then he muttered something but she did not catch the word. 'Yes, go on. Malcolm who?' she urged.

'Er ... er ... Swan.' He smiled as if delighted that he had remembered. Suddenly the smile vanished; he reached up and touched his own face.

Though he had given a name, Jessie knew it was the wrong one. 'You say you are called Swan?'

'Yes.'

Where on earth had he plucked that from? She was puzzled but did not want to contradict him for fear he might think she did not believe him, be offended and clam up altogether.

'Did it hurt when you touched your face?' she asked.

He nodded.

'How did you get hurt?'

He shook his head.

'You don't know?'

He shook his head again.

Jessie looked at Jamie.

He asked, 'Malcolm, do you live in Scalloway?'

Again he shook his head, leaving them uncertain as to whether he meant no or that he didn't know.

Jamie was about to put another question to him when they heard Rowena call, 'We're back.' He turned to Mrs Murray and lowered his voice so that she almost didn't hear him; she could only take this as a sign that he wanted to say something without Malcolm hearing. She leaned closer to Jamie who said, 'If we bring Lavinia and Rowena in, it might jolt his memory.'

'It's worth a try,' Jessie agreed. She stepped from behind the curtain and saw the anxious expressions on the girls' faces.

'He will be all right, as far as I can tell, but he will need rest. I am also concerned about his memory. He didn't know his first name so I said we'd call him Malcolm. When I asked if he had another name, he struggled for a while then blurted out "Swan".'

'But that's ridiculous!' protested Lavinia.

'Ma, why should he say that?' asked Rowena, her eyes filling with tears.

'That is what he told us. Does the name Swan mean anything to either of you?'

They both shook their heads.

'Right. Then we'll see if the sight of you has any effect on him; see if he knows you. Be warned, he is not a pretty sight – though better than when he was hauled out of the water.' She ushered them next to the bunk.

Lavinia concealed her shock and said, 'Hello, Malcolm.'

'Hello,' he replied, but showed no sign of knowing she was his sister.

Disturbed by the fact that he had not recognised her, she bit her lip to hold back tears.

'Malcolm.' Rowena whispered his name, convinced he would smile back at her once he recognised her.

But, blank-faced, all he said was, 'Hello.'

She reached out and touched his hand, but it

had no effect on him. Silent tears streamed down her cheeks and silent words screamed in her mind. Oh, why did I send you away? Why? She looked at her mother, and the pleading in her voice as she asked, 'What can we do now, Ma?' tore at her mother's heart.

Jessie realised with regret how different things might have been if she had supported her daughter's wish to be with Malcolm, no matter what.

'All we can do is hope and pray that his memory returns.' As she spoke Jessie held out her arms to Rowena and Lavinia. They came into them, finding comfort there against the shock of Malcolm's condition.

Jamie watched, wanting to help them, wanting to bring them comfort – especially Rowena. In that moment he knew he really did love her, and in that same moment realised he might have to sacrifice that love if Malcolm McFadden ever regained his memory.

23

Four days out from Scalloway Lavinia and Rowena, having found their sea-legs, returned from a walk on the section of the deck allocated by the captain for the use of what he called cabin passengers, those who had paid towards their fare and were housed in better conditions. Once inside they discovered that Malcolm was missing.

'Ma told him never to leave here unless someone was with him,' exclaimed Rowena. 'We'd better find him.'

'Let's see if Jamie's seen him.'

'Not since breakfast,' he told them. 'You stay in your area in case he returns. I'll go and look for him. It will be better if I go alone in case he's wandered into parts it would be wiser for you not to see.'

They looked at him with curiosity but did not question his words: the discovery of Malcolm was of prime importance now.

Jamie hurriedly searched each deck until, not having gained sight of the sick man, he knew he must venture into the crowded steerage area with its unpalatable conditions. As he stepped inside he sensed hostile looks shot in his direction and realised these people were very protective of what they had, even though they were living in a squalor that was growing worse each day. The hold was dank, with little air or daylight. To escape these conditions and the unsavoury smells below, many of the steerage passengers spent most of their time on the section of deck allotted to them, even when the weather turned foul. This in turn did nothing for their health, which in many cases was beginning to suffer.

Jamie searched in the gloom. His intrusion upon what the steerage passengers regarded as their privacy, though they had precious little of that, brought many abusive remarks in his direction. About to give up, he heard, amongst the mixture of loud conversation and raucous arguments, a louder sound coupled with threats coming from one corner of the hold. Suspicious, he moved closer and found two men standing threateningly over a cowering Malcolm. In no uncertain manner, Jamie yanked one of the men round and drove his fist into his face, sending him sprawling on to a bunk, bringing fresh yells of abuse from its two occupants. But they were lost to Jamie who was dodging the unwanted attention of the second man. As he spun away from him, Jamie flailed with his right arm, catching the man on the side of his head. He staggered backwards and Jamie gave him no time to recover. Knowing the man would be out cold for a while, he grabbed Malcolm and propelled him towards the makeshift gangway, out of the hold and up on deck.

'Mrs Murray told you not to wander,' he snapped.

'I'm all right. I can't stay caged up,' countered Malcolm.

Jamie bit his tongue; he did not want to provoke Malcolm now. 'Rowena and Lavinia were worried about you, and no doubt Mrs Murray too if she's returned from purchasing food. And rightly so. Going where you did brought you trouble. You were lucky I came along when I did. Now, let's get back.' He hustled Malcolm as quickly as he could back to their own deck.

Lavinia and Rowena showed immense relief when they saw the men.

'Where have you been, Malcolm?'

'Where did you find him?'

'He was in steerage,' replied Jamie.

'Why did you go there, Malcolm?' Jessie asked. 'I told you not to wander until you were fully recovered.'

'I felt well and thought I could look round the ship on my own,' he said, with some contrition.

'You aren't that well yet, Malcolm,' said Jessie gently. 'Please don't wander off again.'

'I won't, Mrs Murray.'

It pleased her that he was still remembering their names even though they themselves obviously meant little to him. She watched him go as he walked over to the rail and leaned against it.

'If only he could remember who we are,' said Rowena quietly to her mother.

'He may one day, love,' Jessie answered soothingly. 'I've heard tell of people who, for no apparent reason at all, suddenly get their memory back.'

'I hope that happens to Malcolm.'

'Trust in God, dear.'

Malcolm stared at the water running along the side of the ship, churning like his thoughts. What am I doing in this place? How did I get here? He shivered as he sensed heavy wet clothes weighing down his limbs, but when he ran his fingers over his jacket it was dry. He shook his head, trying to clear the fog of uncertainty from his mind, but it would not move and questions to which he could find no answer nagged at him. Who were these people with whom he was sharing living space? He knew them by name but nothing of their lives except that they referred to their previous existence in Shetland. Where was that? It meant nothing to him. And where had he come from? All attempts to penetrate the fog that clouded his mind came to nothing. His previous life remained such a tantalising mystery to him that he began to try and ignore all the questions that haunted him, but he could never stop yearning to know who he really was.

Mrs Murray, Rowena and Lavinia were always cagey whenever he brought up the question of his identity, saying that they had only known him since he had come on board the *Hope*. They were always kind and solicitous towards him; he liked them and hoped he could stay with them when they got to Pictou. That name had meant nothing to him either but it was where they told him they were going; a place in Eastern Canada, a small settlement inhabited mainly by Scots, which had been their main reason for choosing it. He was relieved when they intimated that they expected him to remain with them there; it cemented his relationship with them and with the Miller family more closely.

The conditions in which they were living were far from easy but they made the best of what they had. The shock of what he had seen when he had wandered below decks remained with Malcolm. When he tried to question Jamie about why those other people were living in such horrible squalor, he was cautious in his replies. Rowena and Lavinia, afraid of disturbing Malcolm's state of mind, refused to talk about it either, and Mrs Murray would only say, 'The conditions on board this ship are no concern of ours. The captain is in charge.'

The ship's master tolerated the raucous behaviour in steerage, which was often enlivened with music from violin and concertina, and was thankful it did not spill over into cabin class, though even there the passengers made the most of any diversion that could help to ease the boredom and harshness of the voyage, illness took its toll. After five days out, every new day saw bodies committed to the sea, with little distinction between classes. Everyone suffered in the poor conditions, and as the eighteen-day crossing of the Atlantic progressed, the shortage of food became evident. It was the main cause of unrest. At times matters were brought to open insurrection by one group of steerage passengers, but the captain and his marines kept strict control and every new outburst was dampened down before it had time to burst into dangerous revolt.

With conditions on board the *Hope* deteriorating further with each passing day, despondency began to creep in. Jessie found her self-imposed task of keeping Rowena's and Lavinia's hopes buoyant becoming a strain, especially as she knew Rowena still dreamed of a life with Malcolm. Her daughter tried to hide her increasing despair that her relationship with him remained nothing more than friendly; that he showed no sign of wanting it to be anything else. She could only dream of the love they had shared in Shetland.

They were standing at the rail together when the cry, 'Land ahoy! Land ahoy!' rang out across the ship, bringing other passengers rushing on to the deck to get their first sight of what they regarded as the 'Promised Land', even though they knew nothing of this new country or the people who awaited them there.

'I'm glad the voyage is nearly over,' said Rowena with deep relief.

'So am I,' agreed Malcolm. 'I'm tired of being confined.'

'You'll have plenty of space when we disembark.'

'This is Pictou, where we are going to settle?' he asked when they caught their first glimpse of the small township.

'Yes. About fifty of us. The rest go on to somewhere on the American coast.'

'I don't know why I'm on this ship. I don't even remember coming on board. I don't know where I'm supposed to be going either,' said Malcolm with a puzzled frown.

'You're with us,' replied Rowena, alarmed by his words and disturbed expression. Surely he couldn't be thinking of going elsewhere? 'Remember, we agreed you would stay with us?'

He looked puzzled for a moment then he nodded. After a moment's thought, he asked, 'Why are you here?'

'We had to leave Shetland.'

'Why?'

She hesitated. How much should she tell him? She had to be careful; one wrong word could tip the delicate balance of his mind.

'The laird wanted the land so we had to leave.'

'Did you want to?'

'No.'

'Then the laird was cruel to turn you out. I wish I had been there to help you.'

Rowena's heart missed a beat. Was he close to recollection? 'I wish you had too,' she replied.

'Well, maybe I can be in Pictou.'

'I'd like that very much.'

They lapsed into silence again amongst the

excitement audible among the other passengers as Pictou drew nearer and nearer.

'It doesn't look very big,' commented Malcolm.

'No, but from what we were told back in Shetland, it is a place looking to grow.'

'Well, the inhabitants seem a friendly lot if this welcome is anything to go by,' he said. Rowena was pleased that a note of enthusiasm had come into his voice. She hoped it would remain there and that here, in Pictou, a full recovery of his memory would bring them happiness together.

Once the *Hope* had been sighted, Pictou people left their work and flocked to the beach to satisfy their curiosity about the newcomers they hoped would settle among them. Knowing the conditions they would have endured during their eighteen days at sea, they came with offers of food and drink as well as words of welcome.

The captain anchored off-shore, deeming it wiser to use longboats to ferry ashore those disembarking here. Those remaining on board were either envious of the passengers reaching their destination or pleased they themselves were moving further south to the American coast, but they appreciated the new food supplies that were being taken on board.

The small community in Pictou, hoping to ease the trauma the newcomers had experienced on being uprooted from their homes, welcomed them in the friendliest of ways. Temporary accommodation, in log cabins of various sizes, kept available for newly arrived emigrants, was quickly allocated by two of the town's elders. Basic fur-

273

niture kept in store for the same purpose was made available until the new arrivals were able to obtain their own.

'Malcolm, you'll be with us,' said Jessie.

'Won't I be better with some of the men?' he suggested.

'You've been with us on the voyage so we'll continue like that. And your bruises are still rather ugly. I'd like to keep an eye on them,' insisted Jessie.

They were housed in a log cabin with three bedrooms and helped by some of the friendly community to furnish them. While this was going on people were setting up tables in the open and laying out all kinds of food, which was constantly replenished, in a welcoming party for the new settlers.

'If my first impressions continue to be fulfilled, I am pleased we chose Pictou,' said Jessie when they returned to their cabin. 'I think we can make a good new life here.'

'I like it,' agreed Lavinia. 'A far cry from Shetland but not unlike it in some ways, at least the little we've seen of it.'

'They are a friendly lot,' agreed Malcolm. 'They wanted to know what skills I had, and when I told them I was a joiner and had worked on building ships, I was given the names of two men to contact and told I'd be welcomed with open arms.'

The three women exchanged quick glances. As a boy he had helped Rowena's father construct a boat and keep it in good repair, but this was the first they knew of Malcolm being a joiner. They immediately wondered where he had learned that trade.

Rowena longed for his mind to clear and his memory to return; if only it would life would be so much better and Pictou would be an even happier place for them. Even if Malcolm's mind did not clear, she hoped he would nevertheless become interested in her, for she knew she could love him for the person he was now.

Two days later they watched the *Hope* sail. Many of the new settlers had to fight off feelings of isolation as the ship that was their last link with home passed from sight. Knowing this from their own experience and wanting to focus the minds of the new arrivals, the elders called a meeting. A brief speech of welcome was given by the senior man who then announced that land was available for those who wanted it, the holdings to be dependent on the purpose for which they were used.

After consultation with the others, Jessie took a lot in her own name and was pleased that Martha persuaded her husband to do the same on an adjoining plot. They both planned the houses they would build, and when the time came to start work they were overwhelmed by the help they received from the whole community. It was the same for all the newcomers, and was seen as a means of integrating them swiftly into life in Pictou.

After this was achieved, Jamie announced he had obtained work with a man and his two sons who needed an extra pair of hands to expand their fishing enterprise. His father Hugh found employment with a farmer who had invested in land and needed others to work it.

Everyone worked hard to get their new home to their liking, but throughout this time Jessie's thoughts kept turning to earning an income, not only to provide for their everyday needs but also to pay for the land and the house she had bought, on generous terms and repayment time, from the local banking system implemented by the early settlers.

One morning a month later she was sitting at breakfast with Rowena and Lavinia when Malcolm rushed in. 'Sorry I'm late. I slept in. All the thinking I've been doing must have tired me.'

'Thinking?' queried Rowena, hoping that he had recalled something of his true identity.

Malcolm had settled into Pictou life seemingly with ease, despite the fact he still couldn't remember his past nor how he came to be on a ship destined for Canada. This was the life he was in now, and this was how it would be.

'Aye, it might surprise you but that is what kept me awake. I'm going to take up an offer I was made in the boat-building yard. I heard they were seeking more joiners so I went along. They tested my skill with the plane and saw, and were satisfied. I start tomorrow morning.'

'Where did you learn to be a joiner?' asked Rowena cautiously, hoping she might jog his memory.

Malcolm looked puzzled. 'Learn?' He frowned and shook his head. 'I don't remember. It just seemed natural to me to apply at the shipyard.'

Realising her daughter and Lavinia might push too hard to widen the chink in his memory, Jessie said quickly, 'That's wonderful, Malcolm. I hope it satisfies you.'

'Oh, it will, Mrs Murray. I like working with wood.'

Lavinia and Rowena wondered if this was another small step on the way to full recollection.

Jessie noted that and worried about the complications a complete recovery might bring, for she knew of Jamie's continuing interest in her daughter.

'I'll be able to provide for us,' said Malcolm, his words breaking into Jessie's thoughts.

'You can't do that,' she said. 'You can pay something, yes, that will be fine, but not our entire upkeep. I've been giving our means of income some thought and I've come up with an idea. I think there is an opening here for a bakery. I've made some enquiries and apparently there used to be one until a short time ago. It only closed because the husband died and his widow, who had kept the bakery, went to live with her daughter in Montreal. What do you think?' she asked, casting a glance at Rowena and Lavinia.

'I think that's a splendid idea, Mrs Murray,' said Lavinia. 'I've been wondering what I could do. I can't sit around being idle. But I will have to rely on you to teach me.'

'Good.' Jessie smiled. 'Rowena?'

'Yes, of course, you know my baking.'

'Then that is settled.'

'Good,' said Malcolm with enthusiasm. 'Then I'll be able to enjoy your baking again!'

Jessie exchanged startled glances with Rowena and Lavinia. Did his remark indicate some further trace of remembrance? Malcolm had always enthused about her baking whenever he'd visited the croft in Shetland; she had done little of it since arriving in Pictou, there had been other things to see to. Yet he had used the word 'again'. What deep memory lay behind it?

No one spoke, but there was new hope in three of the people around the table.

24

'What would you like to do for your last day here?' Mrs Jordan asked Kate at breakfast.

'I think it is I who should be asking you that question,' she returned.

'All right, but you answer my question first.' Mrs Jordan raised her finger in reproof, indicating that that was the way it must be.

Kate smiled. 'Very well, but whatever I answer must not affect your plans. I will fall in with whatever you want to do. The weather looks set to be fine so I would like to finish my painting of Rydal Water. It's a gentle walk to the place from which I chose to make my study. Rydal Water, with its backdrop of rising hills giving way to mountains, makes for a fascinating subject. Besides it now holds some special memories for me. And before you mention a chaperone, I will be perfectly all right on my own. It's not as if I will be anywhere isolated. Besides, I don't want you to feel tied by me. I'm sure when you were young there were times when you wanted to be on your own.'

Memories made Mrs Jordan's eyes twinkle. 'All

right, but do not stray!'

'I won't.'

'I will visit my friend this afternoon while you enjoy your walk and your painting. You can call for me there on your return. Then we'll come back here and enjoy our last evening meal in The Travellers' Rest.'

Kate knew there was no more to be said; their day was planned.

'Tomorrow we'll start our journey home, and hopefully the weather will be kind for our passage over the Pennines. But whatever it is like, you'll have Dorothea's wedding to look forward to.'

Kate nodded. 'I shall.' Her joy in this acknowledgement was touched with a hint of sadness when she added, 'I only wish I was to be Matron of Honour, but I agreed with Dorothea it might have led to trouble for her with Father, and wouldn't want to spoil the day for her and Ben.'

'You were right, my dear,' Mrs Jordan agreed. 'But you never know, this wedding could be the means of bringing you and him closer again.'

'It's unlikely,' said Kate softly. 'Father didn't like my defiance of his wishes, and he has never shown any approval of my marrying Malcolm.'

'But he did make an appearance, albeit briefly, on your wedding day.'

Kate shrugged her shoulders as if dismissing that observation. 'He has never tried to find out anything about my husband. Whenever Archie has tried to raise the subject, Father has always cut him short.' She left a short, thoughtful pause then added, 'Mrs Jordan, please let us drop the subject.'

Her friend leaned across the table and patted

her hand. 'Of course. I'm sorry I brought it up.'

'You didn't,' said Kate. 'It just arose.' She then took the opportunity to add, 'Mrs Jordan, I must thank you, though words seem inadequate, for what has been a wonderful holiday. The beauty of this area is almost overwhelming.'

Mrs Jordan gave a wave of her hand, dismissing Kate's thanks, but said, 'It has been a great pleasure for me too. And I owe you special thanks because I know how much you have missed Malcolm, especially so soon after your wedding.'

'We have a lifetime in which to make up for lost moments together, but coming here at this particular time in our lives has shown me how much he means to me. Grasmere will always hold a special place in my heart. I must bring Malcolm here one day to share it with me.'

As she painted near the lake that afternoon, Kate's thoughts kept drifting to what would be their honeymoon and to her future with the man she loved.

Reaching the Yorkshire coast, three days later, they drove straight to Peak House where they were given a warm welcome by Mrs Stabler, Enid and Lily, who had all the preparations made for their return.

'George, get things sorted out and then you can drive Mrs McFadden into Whitby. See her safely home.'

'Certainly, ma'am.'

When Kate had seen Mrs Jordan settled in, she enjoyed a cup of tea with her before leaving for her own house in Whitby.

'I'll see you tomorrow afternoon, Kate, when we'll think about your replacement. I'd like you to help me with that.'

'I will, Mrs Jordan. You have been extremely kind to me. I don't know what I would have done if I hadn't found you when things went wrong for me.'

'You were a godsend to me too.'

'George, go via the shipyard, I'll give my husband a surprise,' said Kate as they neared Whitby.

He guided the horse to Swan's where, as Kate was dismounting from the carriage, Archie stepped out of the office and held out his arms.

'I saw you coming,' he said, his expression wreathed in a welcoming smile.

'It's good to see you, Archie,' she replied as she hugged him. Then, glancing around, she added, 'Where's Malcolm?'

'Not here, I'm afraid.'

The smile left Kate's face as she asked, 'Why? Where is he? Ill?'

'No. As far as I know he is well.'

'As far as you know? What do you mean?'

'He had to return to Shetland.'

'What?' Astonishment filled her exclamation.

'He had bad news and felt he should go.'

'Bad news? Archie, tell me!'

'The crofters on the McFadden Estate were being evicted. He felt a strong desire to know what was happening and to see if he could help them. Apparently he was close to some of them.'

'When was this?'

'Four days after you left for the Lake District.'

'But that means he's been away a month!'

281

Alarm was rising in Kate's voice; she recalled Malcolm once mentioning a girl he had lost at home.

'He said he hoped to be back before your return.'

'Then why isn't he? Have you heard from him?'

'No, but there is no reason why I should have done. Now don't take on, Kate. I'm sure there'll be a good reason keeping him in Shetland. He'll know when you are due back and will send word then.'

She nodded. 'I suppose so, but this isn't at all the way I imagined my homecoming.'

'I know. I suggest I come with you, to leave your luggage, and then you can come home with me. Rosemary will be pleased to see you, and this way you won't be on your own on your first night back.' Kate hesitated, confused by Malcolm's absence. 'Come on, it would be for the best.'

'All right.'

'I'll get my things,' said Archie. 'I'll only be a moment, George,' he added as he turned to the office. By the time he had returned Kate was seated comfortably in the carriage and George, holding the horse steady, was ready to leave as soon as Archie was seated.

Reaching the house in Prince's Place, they deposited Kate's luggage in the care of the maid. Kate's disappointment that Malcolm was not there to share her homecoming was almost overwhelming, but she was determined not to show that to anyone and left the house without further comment. She responded to her brother's queries about her holiday in a light-hearted way.

Arriving at Archie and Rosemary's house, she dismissed George with thanks for all he had done to make the holiday comfortable and easy for her. Rosemary was more than delighted to see her sister-in-law and effusive in her support of Archie's suggestion that Kate should stay with them until they knew more about Malcolm's situation.

'I'm sure it won't be long before he's back. He knows when you were due,' Rosemary tried to reassure her. 'You must stay with us until he does.'

'That is so kind but I want to be in our own house when he does.'

'But you can't be ...' began Archie, only to be cut short by Rosemary.

'That is entirely understandable. Kate must decide for herself.' She turned back to her sister-in-law. 'Stay as long as you want.'

At night Kate's troubled thoughts kept sleep at bay. How serious had the news been to take Malcolm to Shetland and keep him there so long? Hadn't he once mentioned a girl with whom he had been involved there? Had he returned because of her? Surely concern for the crofters in general wouldn't have kept him away for so long? Such thoughts led to others, more troubling still. Has he tired of me so soon? Didn't I come up to expectations? Doesn't he love me any more? Those finally brought tears and she wept.

When she voiced her concerns about Malcolm's lengthy absence and the need to know more, Archie told her, 'You have just voiced what Rosemary and I discussed last night. We understand your desire for information, but it means waiting

283

for a ship from Shetland to put in at Whitby.'

'We don't know when that will be and it may not bring the news we seek,' Kate protested. 'I can't wait. I'll have to go to Shetland myself.'

'That presents further problems,' said Rosemary. 'We've thought about those and Archie thinks he has a solution.'

Kate turned to him with hope in her heart and curiosity in her eyes.

'You need transport to Shetland and you cannot go alone,' said her brother.

'You are making it sound impossible!' cried Kate.

'Hear me out,' he urged. 'Rosemary and I have thought this through carefully, but our solution needs not only your approval but agreement from Dorothea and Ben.'

'Why from them?'

'If you are prepared to wait until after their wedding, I will put a proposition to them: that they honeymoon with a voyage to Shetland, and allow you to accompany them. If they agree, I will charter the *Lady Isobel* from Sam Beadmore to take the three of you to Shetland.'

Kate was rendered speechless by this generous offer and it took a few moments for its significance to sink in. 'Archie, this is too wonderful for words,' she enthused. 'Of course I accept. I only hope Dorothea and Ben will agree.'

'I'm sure they will,' said Rosemary. 'I know it means waiting fifteen days but that might well be the right thing to do. Malcolm knew when you were due back; he may be on his way home. If you left now, you could pass him and never know.'

'Rosemary's right,' said Archie. 'If you receive no news before the wedding, then I agree you should go.'

'As much as I would like to go sooner, I understand all you say. I'm overwhelmed by your generosity, Archie, and by your thoughtful kindness, Rosemary,' Kate told them.

'Stay one more night,' said her brother. 'I will see Ben tomorrow and ask him to bring Dorothea here at two o'clock.'

'If Father hears about this meeting and knows it concerns me,' said Kate with a worried frown, 'he may stop them from coming.'

'He won't know, because I won't tell Ben what it is about, only that it is important.'

The following day, as the hands on the clock neared two o'clock, Kate could not hide her nervousness. 'I wish Archie would get here. I hope nothing has gone wrong.'

'He'll be here,' said Rosemary reassuringly.

No sooner were the words out of her mouth than there was a knock on the door and Polly announced that Miss Swan and Mr Crichton had called.

After greetings were made, Dorothea looked askance at Kate. 'Archie's acting very mysteriously. He contacted Ben with a request for him to bring me here at this time, saying it could not be refused. He didn't say you would be here but as you are it seems you are also involved. What is going on, Kate?'

She feigned ignorance. Ben tried to calm Dorothea's impatience while Rosemary, who would

285

give nothing away, distracted them with offers of wine.

Five minutes later Archie bustled in with apologies for not being at home when they arrived.

'Well, now you are, tell us what this is all about,' chided Dorothea. 'We have much to do with the wedding drawing closer.'

'I know,' said Archie, 'but what I have to say is connected to that.'

'What on earth are you talking about?' snapped Dorothea, shooting a glance at Ben who responded by means of a quick grimace that he was only as wise as she.

'Just calm down and hear me out.' Archie paused to accept the glass of wine Rosemary had poured for him, then said directly to Dorothea and Ben, 'How would you like to spend your honeymoon sailing on the *Lady Isobel?*'

'What?' said Dorothea in a tone that dismissed his query as foolishness.

'You know we've got our honeymoon arranged,' said Ben.

'Yes,' returned Archie, 'and I also know it can be easily changed.'

'I don't understand all this,' snapped Dorothea.

'You will if you'll let me explain,' replied her brother.

'Get on with it then. Ben and I haven't time to listen to twiddle-twaddle.'

'This is not twiddle-twaddle.' Archie's rejoinder was sharp. 'It is a serious proposition. Now let me explain...' When he had finished, a stunned silence filled the room. Dorothea and Ben were taken aback by what it meant, not only for them but for

286

Kate. Stiff with anxiety, she clung to the hope that they would agree to her brother's suggestion.

The hush was broken by Ben. 'Dorothea, I think we should help your sister and honeymoon on the *Lady Isobel;* it will be a wonderful experience and a marvellous opportunity for us to see something of Shetland, but I will fall in with any decision you make.'

She hesitated.

Kate held her breath.

'What will Father think if we change our plan?' Dorothea asked.

'There is no need for him to know until the last minute. In fact, probably not until you have sailed,' said Rosemary. 'Kate can slip quietly away from the reception and go to the *Lady Isobel*. I will distract your father's attention while you and Ben go to the ship. Archie will have briefed Captain Williams about what he wants him to do. He will have the ship ready to sail in mid-stream as soon as you are aboard. Archie will have timed how long it will take you to reach the quay from the reception and, when he judges you will be there, he will make an announcement telling everyone that if they want to see you leave on your honeymoon, they must go to the quay where you will be boarding the *Lady Isobel* in mid-stream.'

'Then and only then will I offer an explanation to Father,' Archie rounded off Rosemary's explanation.

'That sounds reasonable enough to me,' said Ben, who had listened intently to the plan. 'It could work and your father could do nothing to stop us. Kate would then be on her way to Shet-

287

land.' His eyes brightened at the thought of the subterfuge. 'How does it sound to you, Dorothea?'

She held back her reply in thoughtful consideration. Kate knew only one word now stood between disappointment and elation for her. She fixed her gaze on Dorothea, willing her sister to agree.

Dorothea came over to her and took Kate's hands in hers. 'For a sister I love dearly, who deserves every happiness with Malcolm, I will agree to this.'

The relief that everyone felt filled the room. They all started to speak at once but to the two sisters all that mattered were their embrace and Kate's whispered, 'Thank you. I will always love you for this.'

The next days were long for Kate; she hoped each one would see Malcolm come back into her life. When it didn't happen she wished the day would speed by. More and more she believed that the answer to his prolonged absence lay in Shetland, but she had to curb her impatience until the wedding was over.

At one time she had thought of absenting herself from the ceremony because it would mean coming face to face with her father, but she knew Dorothea and Ben would be disappointed by that and she did owe them her gratitude for changing their honeymoon plans for her sake.

Now, on the day of the wedding, she was finding it hard to control her nerves. Plans for getting away to Shetland had been meticulously laid by Archie, but there were aspects he couldn't control and the most difficult of these was outmanoeuvring her father at the ceremony. Kate's luggage and that of Dorothea and Ben had been taken aboard the *Lady Isobel* the day before. Good weather would make things easier and she was convinced her prayers for a fine day had been answered when she looked out of her bedroom window that morning.

She went to the church in good time so that she could find an inconspicuous seat, though she knew she could not hide completely. The church began to fill up with guests, some of whom raised their eyebrows in surprise on seeing her; others whispered with their escorts and some gave her a smile and a wave of their hand.

She watched her mother, elegant in a pale pink chiffon dress, walk sedately down the aisle without looking about her. Her heart warmed to the sight of Dorothea, so pretty in a white lace dress spreading wide from its slim waist almost to the ground; the puff sleeves were elbow-length and the rounded neck-line dipped from the shoulders. Her dark hair fell in ringlets to the nape of her neck from the top of her head, where a cascade of lace was held firmly but allowed to fall freely to below her waist. She wore short white gloves and carried a small posy of red roses.

At the steps to the chancel, Ben watched with adoration in his eyes as his bride advanced sedately towards him on her father's arm. Kate could not help but admire her father, too, impeccably dressed and walking so proudly beside his lovely daughter. For one moment she was touched by the thought of what she had missed without him by her side at her wedding to Malcolm, but for that she blamed her father for stubbornly insisting she should marry the man of his choice, not hers.

Archie and Samuel acknowledged her with small gestures of their head, indicating that all was well for the escape to Shetland. Even so Kate felt more and more nervous as the minutes ticked away.

The ceremony over, guests followed the wedding party outside where, after greetings and well wishes were made, they boarded the carriages waiting to take them to the Swans' house on the West Cliff where, with the weather so favourable, a magnificent reception had been arranged outside.

Kate kept as low a profile as possible, this was the bride's day, but it was impossible for her to avoid old friends. As she mingled, she managed to receive a quick word of reassurance that all was set for the moment they had decided on for her to slip away and go to the ship. That moment was fast approaching and she was keying herself up to make her excuses to the friend to whom she was talking when a voice she recognised sent a chill through her.

'Kate.'

'Mr Swan.' Kate saw her friend smile as she added, 'It has been wonderful day.' And then she took her leave, as Kate's father said, 'If you'll excuse me, I must have a word with my daughter.'

Kate turned round slowly. 'Father. It is good to see you looking so well.'

His eyes expressed no thanks for this and his voice was cold as he said, 'I am surprised to see you here.'

'Dorothea's my sister. I saw no reason not to be here,' Kate replied calmly.

Titus grunted. 'Be that as it may.' His eyes darted towards the guests, adding further emphasis to his rudeness as he said, 'I don't see your...' he left a slight hesitation as if the word he was about to say was dirt in his mouth '...husband.'

'He was called away to Shetland, but I have no doubt you already knew that. You have eyes and ears in many places.'

Titus gave a cold smile. 'And he's been away longer than expected. Maybe he's not coming back. If not you may regret not following my plans for your happiness.'

Kate bristled at the insinuation that Malcolm had walked out of their marriage. 'Happiness with Cyrus? Don't be ridiculous, Father. You only wanted that marriage for your own ends.'

'Believe what you like.' Titus's eyes darkened. 'But don't come running to me when you find you have to try and earn a living again.'

'There will be no danger of that. Malcolm will soon be back to take his place in Archie's shipbuilding business.'

'Archie knows I don't approve of him employing that man, but there is nothing I can do about it. His business is his own.'

'I don't know why you are still dead set against my marriage, except that you did not like my defying you and still don't. I thought when I saw you in church on my wedding day that you were offering forgiveness, but the fact that you did not wait to meet Malcolm and give us your blessing was a clear enough sign that your were still bitter.

I'm sorry to find you still are. Now ... I must go and have a word with Mother.' Kate turned away abruptly.

Titus scowled and stared after her. He watched disapprovingly as mother and daughter embraced and made what he saw as some pleasant exchanges. As he moved among the guests, Rosemary busily engaged him in conversation. His thoughts would have been elsewhere if he had known Archie and Samuel were watching his every move.

Conscious of the time, Archie signalled to Kate.

Seeing her brother's sign, she took leave of her mother and casually made her way from the house. Once certain she was out of sight, she made her way to the *Lady Isobel*.

Alert to what was happening, Dorothea and Ben slipped away from their guests on the excuse that they needed to change before leaving for their honeymoon.

Samuel used the back stairs to reach the married couple. Once they were ready, he escorted them down the same stairs and out of the rear of the house to a horse and trap held waiting by a stableman from The White Horse, hired to transport them to the *Lady Isobel*.

Goodbyes were hastily made and once the trap was moving off Samuel returned to the house, his arrival being a signal to Archie that so far all had gone according to plan. Now it was up to him to get his timing right.

Two sailors had been waiting on the quay to escort Kate down a flight of steps to a rowing boat tied there. They took her quickly to the *Lady Isobel*, moored in mid-river. Helped on board, she was duly welcomed by Captain Williams. As he escorted her across the deck, she saw the boat returning to the quay to await the arrival of the newly-weds. A few moments later she was shown the cabin she would occupy, which was normally used by the First Mate.

'He's found a bunk elsewhere,' Captain Williams explained 'We are not employing a full crew for this short voyage so we have some spare bunks. Your sister and her husband will occupy my cabin.'

'That is extremely kind of you, Captain Williams. I know they will appreciate it.'

'It was the least I could do. I think we have considered everything that will make this voyage as pleasant as possible for you and the newly-weds. The only thing we can't control is the weather, but signs are that it should be a good voyage.' Kate saw in his eyes the look of a man who had viewed far horizons in all sorts of weather, someone able to make present judgements founded on a wealth of knowledge; she was pleased he had predicted good weather.

'Ma'am, your valises are there. Make yourself comfortable, then maybe you'd like to be on deck to greet your sister and her husband? As soon as they are on board we will cast off, as per instructions from your brother.'

'Thank you, Captain Williams, I will be on deck in a few minutes.'

He paused at the door of her cabin. 'Oh, by the way, Tom Davis is one of my crew. He was particularly friendly with your husband when he first came to Whitby, I believe. I'm sure he'd be glad to talk to you. Now, I must see that everything is ready for sailing immediately the happy couple are on board.'

Kate gave a shiver of anxiety when she stepped out on deck. She hoped nothing had happened to upset Archie's plan since she had left for the ship. Time seemed to weigh down heavily on her as she waited to welcome Dorothea and her new husband.

'Quiet, everyone! Quiet!' Archie's voice rang out, silencing the guests. 'I have an announcement to make. If you want to see Dorothea and Ben off on their honeymoon, you must get yourselves off to the quays. They are sailing on the *Lady Isobel!*'

Gasps of surprise rippled through the guests and then everyone seemed to move at once.

Kate felt a surge of relief at the sight of a trap approaching the quay. She watched as Dorothea and Ben were helped on board the rowing boat. Strong arms propelled it quickly to the ship where the new arrivals were helped aboard. The sisters flung their arms around each other in a gesture of love and confidence that all would be well. Kate turned to Ben, ignored the formality of his hand held out towards her, brushed it aside and hugged him. 'Thank you for what you are doing for me.'

'Dorothea is happy to help, and if she is happy then so am I. I hope you are happy too.'

'That goes without saying,' replied Kate with

every ounce of gratitude she could muster. 'Now I'll go below deck and leave centre-stage to you two.'

'No,' said Dorothea crisply, 'you are part of this, you must stay on deck.'

The captain's orders rang out. The anchor was hauled and the ropes, from the pilot boats that were to steer the *Lady Isobel* under the opened bridge and into the sea, straightened and took the strain.

'Here they come!' Ben shouted, pointing to the surge of people rushing along the quay.

'Archie's timing was impeccable!' laughed Kate.

'There's Mama, in that second trap!' Dorothea called out.

'Driven by Father,' commented Kate. Even from this distance she could feel his hostility towards the subterfuge that had outwitted him. The words she added under her breath were filled with delight. 'Mama must have insisted he bring her to the quay, and she got her way for once.'

Well wishes, cries of 'Good luck!' and best wishes for the future were shouted across the water to the young couple starting out on their future life in this unexpected way. The sight of Kate on deck caused some surprise but the on-lookers' good wishes spilled over to her, too, when explanations were given and they learned she was setting out to find her husband.

25

With Shetland coming into sight, Kate, Dorothea and Ben, eager to see this unfamiliar land, came on deck. None was more eager than Kate. This was Malcolm's land; this was where she would find him; soon they would be in each other's arms again.

'It looks a bit grim,' commented Dorothea, eyeing Lerwick's grey-stone buildings as the captain manoeuvred the *Lady Isobel* into a suitable position to anchor in Bressay Sound.

'The glowering clouds don't help,' said Kate. 'It will be a different story in the sunshine.'

Dorothea, thinking it only natural that her sister should try to see the sight as an enticing prospect, did not reply; her own opinion was that the town would hardly be enhanced by sunshine.

'Sir, ma'am.' The captain's voice had them turning away from the rail. 'I understood from Mr Swan that you do not know Mr McFadden's destination.'

'That is true, Captain Williams,' replied Kate. 'We shall make enquiries with what little knowledge we have.'

'Then, as it is late in the day, may I suggest that you stay on board tonight and begin your quest in the morning?'

'But, Captain Williams, I...'

'Kate, I know what you are going to say,'

Dorothea interrupted, 'but I think it would be wise to heed the captain's advice. After all, we do not know this country or where we might have to go.'

Seeing Kate's disappointment, Ben said, 'I agree. What I will do now is go ashore and make some enquiries about the McFaddens. That could give us a good start in the morning.'

'Splendid,' Dorothea approved.

Her enthusiasm for Ben's suggestion made it impossible for Kate to disagree and she had to admit to herself that there was sense in it. 'Very well, but first thing in the morning we act on what you learn.'

'Good,' said Captain Williams. 'Might I urge you to make the *Lady Isobel* your base for as long as your enquiries keep you in Lerwick, and thereafter whenever necessary. Mr Swan told me I was to stay in Shetland for as long as you need me to do so.' He glanced enquiringly at Ben, for he did not know what the young man's commitments were in Whitby.

'That is my understanding too,' confirmed Ben.

'Good.' The captain gave a nod of satisfaction. 'Mr Crichton, I will order a boat ready now. The two men I will assign to take you ashore know Lerwick from calling here on their whaling voyages to the Arctic. I would advise you to make full use of their knowledge. There are some unsavoury places here that are best avoided.'

Ben smiled. 'I understand, and thank you for the warning.'

Ten minutes later the boat had been lowered and was waiting at the side of the ship.

'Take care,' whispered Dorothea as she hugged

her husband.

'Be careful,' echoed Kate. 'And thank you.'

'I hope I'll soon be back with good news,' he replied.

With that he was over the side and climbing down the rope ladder. As soon as he was in the boat, the two sailors pushed away from the ship, dipped their oars and rowed in unison to the nearest quay.

The sisters watched until they could no longer see the men and then decided that, as a chill had crept into the wind, it would be wiser to wait below decks, having the captain's reassurance that he would call them as soon as the boat's return was sighted.

It was an uneasy three hours for the sisters. Though neither of them voiced their thoughts when the oil lamps were lit and twilight began to fade from the sky, anxiety became etched a little deeper into their expressions.

Kate started. 'What's that?'

'What?' asked Dorothea.

'Across the deck. Footsteps?'

Dorothea gave a little shake of her head.

'Ahoy!'

The shout was faint but it caused both young women to look up. Neither of them spoke as they jumped to their feet, grabbed shawls and hurried out on deck. A lantern held high revealed several figures at the rail, one of whom was Captain Williams.

'Peters!'

'Aye-aye, sir?'

'Away and tell...' Half turning, he saw Kate and Dorothea. 'Ah, ladies, I was just sending Peters to tell you Mr Crichton is back. Belay there, Peters.'

'Aye-aye, sir.'

A space at the rail was made for them and they watched anxiously as Ben climbed the rope ladder.

As he stepped on to the deck Kate could not restrain herself. 'Any success?'

'Some.' He gave her a reassuring smile. 'Give me a few moments to change and then come to our cabin. Captain Williams, I think you should hear this too.'

'Very well, sir.'

Kate wanted more information now but with the captain complying with Ben's request she could do no other than rein in her impatience.

A few minutes later she was knocking on the door of the cabin occupied by her sister and brother-in-law. As she was stepping inside she saw Captain Williams hurrying to join them.

'You learned something?' Kate pressed eagerly, her eyes fixed on Ben.

'Yes. The name McFadden is a fairly common one in Shetland, but when I mentioned the laird and his son Malcolm I found people reluctant to talk to me. It was as if they knew something but did not want to impart it to strangers. I was glad I had those two crew members with me. Not only did they know their way around Lerwick but they finally latched on to some contacts they thought might talk.'

'And did they?' pressed Kate.

'I learned that Malcolm is the eldest son of a

laird called Mungo McFadden who owns a considerable acreage in the north of Shetland. I was told Malcolm left home after a dispute with his father over his policy, of clearing the crofters and turning his land over to sheep.'

'That must be why Malcolm came to Whitby,' said Kate.

'Seems to be,' agreed Ben. 'He was known to have gone to Lerwick, and others were able to verify that he signed on to help bring a damaged whaler back to Whitby.'

'The *Lady Isobel*,' gasped Dorothea.

'But that was before we knew him,' said Kate. 'What about his return here?'

Ben gave a little shake of his head. 'No one had any information about that. He was seen coming ashore, but no one saw him after that. Or at least, if they did, no one is talking.'

'Someone must have done!' Kate protested.

'The people I talked to seemed reliable. There was no reason for them to say they hadn't seen him if they had.'

'What about a stableman? Malcolm would require some means of transport.'

'The one we met denied having seen him.'

'You can't have talked to everyone,' countered Kate, desperation creeping into her voice.

'Of course not, but...'

'Where is the most likely place for him to go?' she interrupted, a tremor in her voice. She didn't wait for an answer. 'To his home ... to see his father!'

'But would he? Remember, they had had a quarrel,' pointed out Ben.

'It's worth a try,' agreed Dorothea. 'Did you find out where his father lives?'

'Yes, Garstan House which stands on a peninsula in the north. A helpful fellow drew me a map of where it is and the best way there. It was rather a rough drawing but it will help. I made enquiries about hiring a horse and trap. The stableman can oblige.'

'Then we'll go tomorrow,' said Kate enthusiastically 'Now you know our plans, Captain Williams, I hope we will not hold up your return too long.'

'Mrs McFadden, I'm here to follow your wishes.'

Rob had been surprised by the young Englishman's enquiry, but was even more surprised when Ben entered his stable again the following morning accompanied by two smart young ladies.

'I enquired yesterday about hiring a horse and trap. Can you do that for us now?'

'Yes, sir,' Rob replied. Then, with his curiosity aroused and desirous of eliciting more information about these well-to-do customers, added, 'For how long, sir?' Rob had found that having such information, particularly about strangers, could often come in useful.

'That is unclear,' replied Ben, 'but we are willing to pay well.'

Rob nodded thoughtfully, then let an expression of doubt cross his face. 'I always like to know how long I will be without my property.'

'Rightly so,' agreed Ben. 'I'm not sure exactly where this business will take us, but we first need to go to Garstan House.'

'Ah, to see Mr McFadden, no doubt?'

'That's right,' agreed Ben, though something made him hold back from mentioning Malcolm. 'We hope our business won't take us more than a few days. So, the trap?'

'It is all cleaned down, sir. I'll soon have the horse between the shafts.'

He was true to his word, and when he led the horse and trap out, Ben expressed thanks at Rob's thoughtfulness in also providing cushions and rugs.

'I thought it would be more comfortable for the young ladies, sir.'

'What are the roads like in Shetland?' Ben enquired as he climbed on to the driver's seat.

'The main ones are only fair, the rest not good. Beware of pot-holes.'

Ben nodded his thanks and took up the reins. Rob watched the trap move easily away and knew he was seeing a man who was used to guiding a horse. He pursed his lips thoughtfully and gave a little nod of satisfaction. He might be able to make more than a coin or two out of the knowledge he had gained. He was sure Angus McFadden would not know of these people who had only arrived in Shetland late yesterday afternoon and now had business at Garstan House. If he had known, he would either be at Garstan House awaiting their arrival or he'd have met them yesterday when the ship dropped anchor in Bressay Sound. Besides, Rob knew where Angus McFadden had been last night and that he generally continued with his nightly pleasures until noon. He was not prepared to risk Angus's wrath by interrupting him now.

It was an hour after noon when he walked into the stable.

'G'day, sir.' Rob touched his forehead deferentially.

'Good day to you, Rob,' replied Angus breezily. 'I have a feeling it's going to be a good day for me. I'll recoup my losses today, so keep my horse for one more night.'

'Well, sir...'

'What's this, Rob?' Angus snapped. 'You look doubtful. Think I'll lose and not be able to pay you?'

'I think you'll not be sitting at the card table.'

'What the devil do you mean?' Irritation rose in Angus's voice. He frowned. 'I see. You know something I don't. Oh, blast you!' he added, realising why the man was holding back. 'You're an extortionist, if you know what that means.' As he was speaking Angus had been fishing in his waistcoat pocket. He flicked a coin through the air, which Rob caught deftly, but snorted with derision.

Tight-lipped, Angus fished two more coins from his pocket.

'Come on, out with it,' he snapped. 'What have you for me?'

'See that craft in Bressay Sound?'

'The ship? Yes.'

'Seen it afore, have ye?'

Angus scowled. 'Damn you! Cut out the guessing games or you'll feel the lash of my whip.'

'You'll hear nothing from me if you try that.'

'Oh, get on, get on!' Angus held out the coins. Rob decided it was best to do so now he'd had his bit of fun.

'It's a Whitby ship and it has brought three English people, a young man and two young women. They hired a trap from me and the young man informed me they had business at Garstan House and might not be back for four days.'

'Get any names, Rob?' asked Angus, eager for more information.

'No. But I thought even their presence would interest you.'

'It certainly does,' he replied. 'Saddle my horse now! I'll win my money back another day.'

'The house itself doesn't look very imposing but I suppose to the McFaddens it does, standing on that hill,' commented Dorothea as the trap neared the bottom of the track leading up to the house.

'I think it could be very comfortable inside,' said Kate loyally.

'It will certainly command some striking views, situated as it is on this narrow spur of land between two voes,' pointed out Ben.

'I wonder what reception we'll meet with?' said Dorothea.

'More to the point, will Malcolm be there? And what explanation for his absence will he have for us?' said Kate, trying to hide the tremor in her voice.

'Nervous?' asked Dorothea.

Kate nodded. 'A little.'

Ben drew the trap to a halt in front of the four steps leading up to the front door. He helped his wife and sister-in-law from the trap and up to the house. 'Ready?' he mouthed. Receiving a nod

304

from both of them, he grasped the large brass knocker and rapped hard on the door.

The few moments they waited seemed endless to Kate and the pit of her stomach began to feel numb. Then the door opened and a maid stood before them, surprise in her eyes and query in her expression.

'This is Garstan House, the McFadden residence?' Ben enquired.

'Yes, sir,' came the reply from the maid, whose glance kept darting from one stranger to the next.

'We would like to see Mr McFadden,' said Ben.

'Which one?' the maid asked.

'Mr Malcolm McFadden,' interposed Kate quickly. Her heart was racing. Was Malcolm really here?

'Oh, ma'am, Mr Malcolm McFadden left Garstan House some time ago. It's said he went to England.'

Kate's hopes fell. She inferred from that that her husband had not come to Garstan House when he'd returned to Shetland, and felt her hopes shattering.

Sensing her despondency, Ben asked quickly, 'Then may we see the laird?'

'I will see, sir. May I say who is calling?'

'Tell him Mrs McFadden and friends.'

The girl stood there speechless, staring at the three strangers with disbelief in her eyes.

'Mrs Malcolm McFadden and friends,' repeated Ben.

The maid scurried away and returned a few minutes later with a smart, middle-aged woman who held herself with an air of some authority.

There was a kindliness about her too, particularly evident in the bright eyes that at this moment surveyed the three young people with frank curiosity.

'Ma'am,' the maid spoke, 'these are the people I told you about.'

'Thank you, Jenny.'

Kate was struck by the gentle lilt in the lady's voice; it reminded her of Malcolm's. Kate's pulse quickened. She had a strange sensation that he was nearby, yet the maid had indicated it was not so. A shiver ran down Kate's spine.

'Good day, ma'am,' said Ben.

The lady inclined her head in reply and at the same time said quickly, before he could add more, 'Jenny told me Mrs McFadden and friends were here and that you had asked for Malcolm? It is obvious you are not from these parts and therefore I conclude ...' she glanced quickly from Dorothea to Kate '...that one of you...' She left her surmise hanging in the air.

Kate spoke up. 'I am Mrs Malcolm McFadden,' she said.

'And I am his Aunt Grizel.' Then she added, 'I think you had better come in.'

26

Grizel ushered them into a comfortably furnished medium-sized room. Four armchairs were set in an arc facing the fireplace. The wallpaper was patterned with faded roses. Above a mahogany sideboard hung a portrait of a fine-looking bewhiskered man whose eyes seemed to be assessing the onlookers. Three attractive seascapes were positioned on the other walls, one situated between two large windows that gave a view over a well-kept garden.

As they entered the room, Ben said, 'I must introduce myself and my wife. Ben Crichton and my wife Dorothea who is Kate's sister.'

Grizel acknowledged them politely and, once she had seen them settled comfortably, said, 'We will come to the reason for your visit in one moment. First let me explain. As I said, I am Malcolm's aunt, Mrs Grizel Robertson – his father is my brother. I am a widow, childless, and came here when my sister-in-law died, to help run this house for my brother and his young family, so naturally they are very dear to me.' She looked at Kate. 'You say you married Malcolm?'

'That is so, Mrs Robertson. We were married in Whitby.'

'And what is the reason for your visit here?'

'To try and find my husband.'

'Find Malcolm?' Grizel looked puzzled.

'Yes.' Kate went on to explain how she had returned from holiday to find that he had left Whitby for Shetland and had not returned within the time expected. 'In fact, Mrs Robertson, it has now reached the stage where I am deeply worried and concerned.'

'Do you know why he returned to Shetland?' Grizel asked.

'He had heard that the crofters here had been evicted and hoped to help them by coming back.

307

Realising that the eviction must have been ordered by the laird, we thought Malcolm might have come here to plead their case with his father.'

Grizel shook her head.

'I can say with certainty that Malcolm did not come here. I am almost certain that if he had I would have known. I should add that no news of his being back in Shetland has reached us here.'

A pall of despondency settled over Kate. She instinctively liked this woman and felt sure that she was not hiding anything from them. In fact, she was not disguising the worry their query had aroused in her.

Grizel rose slowly from her chair, saying, 'I think you had better see my brother, though I doubt if he knows any more than I, but he should meet you. After all, you are his daughter-in-law. If you will excuse me, I will fetch him.'

Kate experienced a mixture of gratitude and panic; she was grateful that Mrs Robertson appeared to have accepted her story and uneasy at having to meet Malcolm's father.

Apprehension mounted as the minutes ticked away. Nobody spoke as they all tried to control their feelings of unease about the approaching confrontation.

The door opened then and Grizel walked in followed by a man who looked much younger than any of them had expected. But the real shock that Kate experienced was how closely he resembled Malcolm. This could almost be a more mature version of him standing before them now.

'May I present my brother Mungo, Malcolm's father,' Grizel said. She turned to him and introduced each of them in turn, leaving Kate until last. 'And the young lady I believe is Malcolm's wife.'

That Grizel should be so decisive about this sent a wave of relief through Kate; it surely must have swept away any doubt from Mr McFadden's mind. Her stomach tightened when he did not speak but stood with his eyes fixed on her. Blue like Malcolm's, they gave nothing away.

Finally he stepped forward, both hands extended. She took them and felt their warmth. With his eyes still fixed on her, he said, 'My son has good taste.'

Kate blushed. 'You said "has". Does that mean you know he is alive?'

'I have no idea if he is alive or dead,' Mungo replied, then added, 'Should we sit down?' When they had all done so, he continued. 'The last time I saw Malcolm was when he walked out of this house after a disagreement with me. I had no knowledge of his whereabouts after that. There were rumours he had signed on to help sail a damaged whaler to Whitby. They would seem to be true now that you bring proof that he was there. Do you know what led him to leave Whitby?'

'I was away at the time but my brother Archie, with whom Malcolm worked in my brother's ship-building business, told me Malcolm had received news from Shetland about the crofters' precarious situation, and said he had to go and see if he could help them.'

Mungo sighed as if deeply troubled. 'Malcolm felt very strongly about possible evictions of my tenants and left before the clearances were instigated. Receiving news of what was happening could have brought him back to Shetland. If he did return, he did not visit here. Nor have I heard of anyone seeing him.' He left a slight pause. 'I'm sorry to say that there were also rumours about that same time that he was dead, though where they came from no one seemed to know.'

Cold fingers tightened on Kate's heart. They threatened to overwhelm her but she managed to hold them at bay. Her throat constricted but she had to ask the question. 'How did you hear this?'

'My other son, Angus, heard that a body had been lifted from the harbour in Scalloway by a ship leaving for Canada. People put two and two together and made five, one speculation leading to another.'

'Wouldn't the captain have turned back?' Ben asked.

Mungo gave a little shake of his head. 'That would have taken time and further delay in Scalloway. There would be nothing gained. Far easier to commit the body to the ocean once the ship was well clear of the land. I'm not saying it was Malcolm, if indeed there was a body, but if he did return to Shetland because of the clearances, it would all have happened at about the same time.'

At that moment the door to the room swung open.

Mungo looked annoyed by the interruption but dismissed his frown when he saw his younger son. 'Ah, Angus, come and meet Mrs McFadden and her friends.'

Angus looked at him with feigned bewilderment in his eyes. He had ridden hard from Lerwick, hoping to reach Garstan House before

310

the strangers who had arrived on the ship from Whitby, but his horse had gone lame and it had taken him some time to find another. He had cursed his misfortune but, on reaching the house, realised it had been to his benefit. He had heard voices, seen the door ajar and stood there to listen. Now, having overheard what his father had said, he could take up whatever course the conversation followed.

'Mrs McFadden?' Angus feigned incomprehension.

Explanations were made which he appeared to accept without question, and when his father mentioned the rumours about the body in Scalloway, Angus gave a feasible explanation of how he had heard them and then expressed his belief that, even if they were true, the body was not Malcolm's.

'Then where is he? People don't just disappear!' cried Kate.

Angus shrugged his shoulders. He thought he had said enough already; he did not want to become trapped into making a careless observation.

'We could speculate for ever,' Mungo pointed out, 'and draw no nearer solving what remains a mystery.' He looked at Kate. 'I am so sorry, my dear. I know you must have come to Shetland in high hopes of being reunited with your husband. I regret that I have no uplifting news for you.' He turned to Grizel. 'Our visitors can't return to Lerwick today. Can we accommodate them for the night?'

'Of course.'

'It is very kind of you,' put in Dorothea, 'but we

311

cannot impose on your hospitality.'

'It will be no imposition,' insisted Mungo. 'I will not listen to a refusal. After all, you are family now and I should like to get to know you better. Is your time here restricted?'

'No,' replied Kate. 'My brother put a ship at our disposal for as long as we like; we weren't sure how long my search for Malcolm would last, although we hoped we would find him here. But the *Lady Isobel is* a working ship, so if we add sailing days to a week, I think we will have had her long enough.'

'I agree with my sister,' said Dorothea. 'We appreciate your kindness and hospitality, but I think it would be better if we returned to the ship.'

'A week?' said Mungo thoughtfully. 'Why not stay here for that time? Give us a chance to get to know Malcolm's wife better.'

His widow, Angus thought to himself, and went on to wonder if Kate's presence here could offer any threat to what he regarded as his inheritance; with Malcolm dead all would be his, but with Kate now on the scene he would be far happier if that still unsigned document could be made binding.

'Do,' put in Grizel enthusiastically. 'It will give us a great deal of pleasure.'

'Kate,' said Dorothea, 'why don't you stay? Ben and I will return to the ship tomorrow and come for you a week today?'

She hesitated. 'I do feel close to Malcolm here ... in fact, visiting this house has brought me the strongest conviction that he is still alive. Maybe if I stayed I could learn more.'

'It is only natural for you, as his wife, to feel

312

that way,' Angus pointed out. 'Because of what you have told us we know that he came back to Shetland, but if he is alive why hasn't he visited us? Why hasn't he been here? Why hasn't he been seen?'

'Has anyone questioned the crofters?' Kate asked. 'He supposedly came to try and help them.'

'He would have been too late, they would have gone already,' said Angus, a sharp edge to his voice.

'Gone? Where?' asked Kate.

'They all shipped out ... some to Canada, others to America.'

Realising the direction of Kate's thoughts, Dorothea asked, 'Could Malcolm have gone with them?'

'Oh, no!' cried Kate, distress in her voice and in her eyes. 'Why would he?'

'He couldn't,' said Mungo. 'Places on the ship for my crofters were strictly allocated. The captain would have known if anyone else was among them and would have notified me to ask for my contribution to their passage.'

'Then Malcolm must still be in Shetland,' said Kate. 'Mr McFadden, if I may take advantage of your generous offer, I would like to stay.'

Realising there was a reason behind Kate's acceptance, Dorothea said, 'Ben and I are not throwing your generosity in your face, Mr McFadden, but I think it would be pleasanter for you to have Kate's company on her own.'

'As you wish,' replied Mungo. 'But come ready to stay the night when you return for her.'

'And we won't take no for an answer that time,'

313

put in Grizel, who was already relishing the prospect of the time she would have with her nephew's wife.

'Kate, your stay at Garstan House is settled,' said Mungo with obvious delight. 'My carriage is at your disposal tomorrow, to fetch whatever you need from the ship.'

'That is very kind. I thank you,' she said.

Grizel was pleased for her brother. She knew what the separation from Malcolm had cost him, and now he had the company of a daughter-in-law. 'We must make the meal this evening special,' she suggested.

'Splendid,' her brother agreed.

'I will see Cook immediately.' Grizel rose from her chair.

'Angus, the best wine we have!' Mungo instructed.

'That has been a splendid meal.' Ben's appraisal was echoed by Dorothea and Kate. 'The fish from your own waters, no doubt?'

'Indeed,' replied Mungo.

'Not without some illegal competition from our neighbours down the coast,' put in Angus.

'This is neither the time nor the place,' Mungo admonished him.

Angus scowled at the rebuke, but it did not stop him from saying, 'You could have had the matter resolved by now if you had listened to me.'

'We have guests!' cut in Grizel to put an end to the discussion. 'This is not a matter to be aired at a family celebration.' Then, as she rose gracefully from her chair, she added, 'Ladies, shall we leave

314

the gentlemen to their cigars and port?'

Kate and Dorothea left the table and followed her from the dining room to the cosy room they had been shown into on their arrival.

When they were settled, Kate directed her gaze at Grizel. 'Mrs Robertson, I would be extremely grateful if you could explain something to me. Why did Malcolm return to Shetland because of the crofters? Hearing that might help give me an insight into a side of my husband I didn't know?'

'I take it that you heard nothing from him about the policy of clearing the land for sheep?'

'Nothing,' Kate agreed.

Grizel explained why the local lairds evicted their tenants from the land.

'And this was carried out throughout Shetland too?' asked Dorothea.

'Oh, yes, and on the mainland of Scotland too.'

'And it was legal?'

Grizel gave a little shrug of her shoulders. 'I know nothing about the ins and outs of that.'

'But surely Mr McFadden...' Kate began.

'He was reluctant to enforce eviction, but saw that it made economic sense. Angus was all for it ... even more so after Malcolm left.'

'So Malcolm was against the policy? He fell out with his father over it and left?' said Dorothea.

'But his concern was strong enough to bring him back?' added Kate.

'Yes.' Grizel decided it was better to give Kate and Dorothea the full picture. 'You must realise that Malcolm, his sister Lavinia and Angus had close contact with some of the crofters' children, but especially with Rowena Murray who was the same age as Malcolm. I'll not disguise the fact that he and Rowena became very close. Something happened between them – I know not what – about the time he fell out with his father over the policy.'

'The bond between him and this girl must have been strong, to bring him back to Shetland to help her?' queried Kate.

The gesture Grizel made with her hands showed she wanted to make no further comment, but she did add, 'It also concerned his sister Lavinia. When Malcolm had gone, she helped the crofters during their troubles, fulfilling a request he had made of her. Angus betrayed her to his father who told her if that was where her loyalties lay, she had better go to them. And, being a principled and strong-minded girl, she did.'

Kate looked thoughtful. When she made no comment, Grizel felt she had to make a further explanation. 'You will hear all sorts of stories about the evictions so I must speak up in defence of my brother. He was harsh in enforcing the policy, it's true, but it made sense economically. I think he would have tried to make further compensation to the crofters here on the estate but Angus was clamouring to assume responsibility for the process because, after Malcolm left, Mungo told Angus he would become heir to the estate. After that, Angus saw to the clearances. He carried them out showing little consideration for crofters, but it was done when his father was absent from the estate. When Mungo returned it was too late to retrieve the situation. What had been done could not be undone. All he could do was to try to make things a little easier on the ship for his people.'

Kate nodded. 'Thank you for telling me. I appreciate your frankness.'

Dorothea endorsed this. 'I now feel I understand Malcolm a little better.'

'So do I,' agreed Kate, but didn't elaborate upon the thoughts that were going through her mind.

'I believe your appearance is a great comfort to my brother, Kate. You have brought a breath of new life to him. You see, you have brought Malcolm close again. He was always Mungo's favourite.'

'Was?' said Kate. 'Don't you mean is?'

Grizel's expression told Kate and Dorothea that Malcolm's aunt hoped Kate was right.

27

At breakfast the following morning, when Kate, Ben and Dorothea were ready to leave, Angus said, 'I need to go into Lerwick, Father. I could take the carriage and bring Kate back from the ship with me after she has collected her clothes.'

'Is that agreeable to you, Kate?' Mungo asked.

'Of course. Very convenient. I am most grateful, Angus.'

He acknowledged her gratitude with a small wave of his hand. 'Shall we say, at the harbour at four?'

'Whatever time you wish.'

'Four it is then.'

'You'll be all right at Garstan House, Kate?' queried Ben when they were settled on their way to Lerwick.

From his tone of voice she knew he felt in some way responsible for her. 'Of course, Ben. I will be among friends.'

'True,' agreed Dorothea, 'but I suspect you are hoping to find out what has happened to Malcolm.'

'I will seize on any chance that comes my way, without making it obvious that was my primary intention in accepting Mr McFadden's invitation.'

'I think you are uneasy about the situation regarding Malcolm?'

'It is very unlike him not to consider others by leaving word of his whereabouts. I cannot help but feel something is wrong.'

'Something might have happened so quickly that he had no time to do so,' said Ben.

'Even so, where is he now?'

'When we get to Lerwick, let me try and make some more enquiries before you go back to Garstan House,' her brother-in-law said.

On arrival, Ben left the sisters in the carriage while he sought out the pier-master. Twenty minutes later they saw him returning.

'He's found something out,' observed Dorothea. 'I can tell by his brisk step.'

Ben climbed into the carriage and sat down. 'I've found out when the ship that brought Malcolm here, the *Guiding Star*, arrived. It was the day we supposed. A stranger from the ship was seen ashore; we can take that to be Malcolm.

Then I got lucky. In a casual way, I mentioned sailings from Scalloway and learned that, later the same day as the *Lady Isobel* arrived here, an emigrant ship left, bound for Canada and America.'

'And it was carrying crofters from the McFadden Estate?' added Kate excitedly.

'Yes!' said Ben.

'But that still puts us no nearer to finding Malcolm,' cautioned Dorothea. 'There is no proof that he contacted the crofters.'

'No,' agreed Kate, 'nor does it prove that he didn't.'

'In either case, where is he?' said Dorothea.

'Rumours of a body?' said Ben, and almost immediately wished he could take back the words when he saw the colour drain from Kate's face. He added quickly, 'The men I spoke to knew nothing. In fact, they treated that idea as tittle-tattle.' He hoped this attempt at reassurance had been strong enough.

'Thank you for enquiring, Ben,' said Kate. 'Let us get out to the *Lady Isobel*.'

Within a few minutes of returning the hired carriage to the stableman, Ben made the prearranged signal to the ship and moments later they saw a boat leave for the quay. They were welcomed back on board by Captain Williams and Kate immediately informed him of their plans. 'I will be returning to Garstan House later today. My sister and her husband will stay aboard. They will pick me up in a week's time for the return voyage to Whitby.'

'Very good, ma'am. I hope you have a pleasant time on shore and that Mr and Mrs Crichton's honeymoon here will be all they would wish. A

319

boat is at your disposal whenever you wish to return ashore.'

'Thank you, Captain. I will need to be there for four o'clock.'

'The boat will be ready, ma'am.' He paused then added, 'Mrs McFadden, I take it you have had no word of your husband?'

'None, Captain. Maybe that will be rectified by the time I leave Garstan House.'

With the time nearing four o'clock, Kate, Dorothea and Ben came on deck to await Angus's arrival. 'You are sure you are happy about returning to Garstan House?' Dorothea asked.

'Of course. I'm looking forward to getting to know Mr McFadden and his sister better.'

'What about Angus?' Dorothea asked, noting her sister had not mentioned him.

'I'm not sure. I'm a little uneasy. There is something about him that doesn't quite ring true, but I really shouldn't judge him on the short time we've been acquainted.'

Dorothea gave a little nod and frowned as she said, 'I know what you mean, though. Reading between the lines of what his aunt told us, he seems to have been particularly harsh on the crofters. But as you say, who are we to judge?'

Their exchanges were interrupted by the appearance of a carriage on the quayside.

'He's here,' said Kate.

They made their goodbyes, and once Kate was settled in the boat it was rowed quickly to the quay. Angus could not have been more attentive in his greeting and the way he saw her safely to his carriage.

'Comfortable?' he asked as he took the reins.

'Yes, thank you.' Kate waved to the two people standing watching from the deck of the *Lady Isobel*. Angus kept the horse to a walking pace until they were clear of the waterside.

Kate noticed that curious glances were cast in their direction, no doubt from people wondering who the young lady was sitting beside Angus McFadden, to whom more than one hand was raised in greeting.

'You seem to be well known in Lerwick,' she commented. 'Do you come here often?'

Angus gave a wry smile as he answered question with question; a habit in people that irritated Kate. 'What do you mean by often?'

'Well...'

'It depends what there is to see to on the estate.'

'Is it business that brings you into Lerwick then?'

'Yes, that and pleasure. After all we are a bit isolated at Garstan.'

'Do I detect a note of ennui?'

'No, of course not. It is my home and I love the estate. It has my full interest and attention. Malcolm walked away from it. I have not.'

'If you expect to inherit, then you must assume he is dead,' said Kate coolly.

'No, of course I don't. But we have to consider the future of the estate. My brother has to all intents and purposes disappeared. It is only hearsay that he came to Shetland to help the crofters. They have gone now and nothing more has been heard of him. He certainly didn't return to Whitby. If he did indeed come to Shetland, there can be only one conclusion. This is a wild and lonely place, with many pitfalls even for one who knows it. He could lie dead somewhere and not be found for years.' Kate shuddered at the possibility. 'I don't mean to alarm you, though. I could be wrong. Please don't let my views spoil your visit, I had no intention of doing that. I know my father and aunt want you to have a pleasant time with us.'

Kate was welcomed warmly by Mungo and Grizel when she and Angus arrived at Garstan House.

'Treat this as your home,' said Mungo as he walked inside with her. 'I am delighted you chose to stay but afraid the week will pass too quickly for us.'

'I am most grateful for your hospitality,' said Kate, 'and I know that being here with his family will help bring Malcolm nearer to me.'

'It's the same room as you had last night,' said Grizel. 'I'll take you up now. I've put a maid at your disposal for the week.'

Mungo, turning to Angus who was removing his outdoor coat, said with a brusque tone in his voice, 'My study – as soon as you've shed your outer clothes.'

As his father headed across the hall, Angus, sensing conflict, put a question to him. 'More trouble with the fishing?'

As Kate and Grizel started up the stairs, Kate saw Mungo raise one hand in a gesture confirming this, and heard irritation in the snap of Angus's voice as he said, 'I've told you what to do. Why won't you do it?'

Grizel, embarrassed by the exchange, glanced

at Kate, raised an eyebrow and muttered, 'Won't he ever see eye to eye with his father?'

The evening passed off pleasantly; the fishing problem and estate matters were not raised. Angus presented an amiable side that made Kate realise he could be good company if only he would let such aspects of his character predominate, but she was never conscious in him of the endearing Mc-Fadden traits she had found in Malcolm: thoughtful consideration, gentleness and respect for others.

As she settled down comfortably in her feather bed, curtains drawn back to allow the Shetland moon to pour its soothing light into the room, Kate felt close to her husband. The overwhelming certainty that he was still alive brought a silent cry to her lips: Oh, Malcolm, where are you?

Malcolm straightened up to eye the repair he had carried out on the clinker-built boat that had been pulled up on the beach. He gave a little nod of satisfaction, yet there was a small tug of annoyance in his mind. He couldn't remember doing such work before and yet he had carried out the task automatically, without really having to think how he should go about it. He gave a little shrug of his shoulders. What did it matter? He was confident Mr McDuff, who had come to Canada from the Scottish Lowlands to seek a better life, would be satisfied with the work. Now his two fishing boats would be operational again. Mr Mc-Duff had seen the opportunity to establish an inshore fishing enterprise from the bay about a half a mile from the main community of Pictou. The entrance to the bay was protected by a small island that helped to break the waters when storms swept up the main channel from the sea.

Now, lost in thought, Malcolm gazed across the water towards tree-covered hillsides; he liked it here. He'd have no qualms about staying, would find it an appealing prospect, if only he knew what his life had been before coming here. He was content to be with Mrs Murray, Rowena and Lavinia, though; he liked them and they seemed to like him and were happy to give him a home. Often, when he heard them talking about the lives they'd left behind in Shetland, he hoped some remark might spark off recollections of his own past.

'Now, young fella, got the job finished, I see.' A pleasant voice, breaking into his thoughts, startled Malcolm.

'Oh, Mr McDuff, you surprised me. I was miles away.' He nodded at Jamie, standing beside Mr McDuff, and grinned sheepishly at them both.

'Where were you?' Mr McDuff asked.

Malcolm shrugged. 'I don't really know, but I had just been thinking how pleasant it is here.'

'Aye, it is, lad. I agree and so does Jamie.' He turned to the other young man. 'I'm away, things to see to. You can tell Malcolm your news.'

'Thanks, sir,' replied Jamie.

They watched Mr McDuff examine the repair Malcolm had made. 'Excellent job,' he praised before he straightened up and started to walk away.

'That's good, Malcolm. Mr McDuff doesn't give praise lightly. You can be sure it will mean more work coming your way, through your employer, but Mr McDuff will ask for you to do it 'specially.'

Malcolm was pleased by this but his only answer was, 'Is that what you had to tell me?'

'No, no,' replied Jamie. 'Mr McDuff is moving.'

'Moving? That surprises me. I thought he was well established here.'

'He is. But he is going to found another fishing operation further down the coast, the other side of town, and...' Jamie firmed his voice to announce proudly '...he's leaving me in charge here.'

Malcolm's eyes widened with surprise that turned to pleasure for his friend. 'Wonderful news! I'm happy for you.' He slapped Jamie on the shoulder. 'Do your parents know?'

'No. Mr McDuff just told me when we set out to see your repairs.'

'So, celebrations are in order! They'll be delighted, and so will Mrs Murray, Rowena and Lavinia. You'll be truly settled here and soon taking a wife.'

Jamie blushed. 'I don't know about that.'

'I do. I've seen the way you look at Rowena.'

Jamie reddened even more.

'I'm right,' laughed Malcolm. 'Look at your colour now.'

'She won't give me a thought,' countered the other man.

'How do you know?'

'Well ... I just do.' Jamie was almost on the point of telling him with whom Rowena's thoughts lay, but he held his tongue.

'Have you ever told her how you feel?'

Jamie shrugged.

'Well, you'll never know how she feels about you unless you tell her how you feel about her.'

Jamie was getting anxious about the direction of this conversation so ended it with, 'I'll see. Let's get home and break my news.'

Malcolm realised he should not press the matter further. They fell into step and set off for Pictou.

As they neared the Millers' home Jamie said, 'Fetch Mrs Murray and the girls. Don't tell them why. Just give me time to tell Ma and Pa first.'

Jessie was just putting the finishing touches to some baking when Malcolm walked in. 'You're home early,' she said. 'Got the job finished?'

'Aye. Mr McDuff was pleased with it.'

'Good. He'll tell your boss, Mr Stanton, and he'll be delighted. While I've been delivering my baking, I've heard tell that he's very satisfied with your work and attitude.'

'I'm pleased to hear that,' Malcolm replied, 'but now the three of you must come to Mr and Mrs Miller's. I've just left Jamie and he told me to bring you right away.'

'Why?' asked Rowena, voicing the question the others were on the point of asking.

'I'm not going to tell you.'

He resisted their pestering and they had to curb their curiosity. Impatient to satisfy it, they lost no time in leaving for the Millers' home. When they entered the house they sensed excitement in the air, and their inquisitiveness was answered immediately by good news that couldn't be held back.

Once the elation had died down a little, Jessie spoke up. 'We must celebrate Jamie's advancement. I've just finished a baking. There'll be enough for everyone so come and share it this evening.'

No one needed second bidding to partake of Jessie's wares.

As they walked home to get ready for the evening, she managed to say quietly to Rowena, 'It looks as though Jamie will settle and make a good living here.' The inference behind the observation was not lost on Rowena but she said nothing. In her mind she pleaded: Malcolm, remember who you really are. Your name isn't Swan, please remember!

As the days progressed, Jessie became more and more preoccupied by the success of her business. She was lauded for the cakes and pies she produced in her kitchen at home and the people of Pictou couldn't get enough of her bread.

One day a well-dressed gentleman called on her.

'Good day, Mrs Murray. I think we have spoken but once since your arrival,' he said, his tone light and friendly as he politely swept his hat from his head.

'Indeed you are right, Mr Stanton. It was after a church service.'

'And you have remembered my name? I am flattered.'

'I pride myself on my memory.'

'And rightly so.' His smile was warm. Jessie liked his open face and pleasant manner.

'You have not come to make a purchase, Mr Stanton. Your wife was here earlier.'

'Quite right, Mrs Murray, I have come to make

327

you a business proposal.'

'A business proposal?' She made no comment to this but could not hide her surprise. What on earth could he mean?

'Yes. Your baking is extremely popular. You manage very well from your own kitchen, but if I am not mistaken you would relish the chance to have purpose-built premises?'

Jessie gave a merry laugh. 'Then I think you had better sit down, Mr Stanton.'

He thanked her and sat on the chair she indicated while she took one opposite him.

'Before we go any further and waste each other's time, Mr Stanton, let me say there is no hope of that. I still owe money for this house. That was one of my reasons for starting the bakery.'

'And the other?' he asked.

'I thought it would help employ those who are with me, and give them a reason to stay on and live here.'

'Admirable. Though I know who you have living with you, I do not know the precise relationships between them. Malcolm Swan I employ in my shipyard, and I must say he is a skilful, hard-working and pleasant young man.'

'He is a friend from Shetland. Lavinia is also a friend from there.' Jessie thought it wisest to reveal no more about their relationship. 'Rowena is my daughter,' she went on. 'She and Lavinia help me in the bakery.'

'That sounds a good set-up. And, if I may say so, if the two young ladies are as enthusiastic about the bakery as Malcolm is about his work in the shipyard, then your enterprise should thrive.

Now, I said I had a business proposal, but first let me tell you a little about myself.

'I came to Pictou several years ago. I have helped it grow since and wish to see that growth continue. My wealth comes from a very large inheritance, and from the shipyard which I saw as essential to Pictou's future growth given its maritime position. I have a finger in several other commercial ventures, and would like to participate in making yours of further benefit to us and to the town.'

Jessie could not envisage where this might be leading.

'Mr Stanton, you have completely flummoxed me. My head is awhirl. My humble bakery interests you?'

'Yes. Will you allow me to go into a little further detail?'

'Very well.'

'Thank you. First I would pay off the loan on this house and you could pay me a token rent.'

Jessie gasped. 'But...?'

'Let me finish,' he said gently. 'And let me say now, there are no strings attached to whatever I propose.'

She nodded.

'By doing that I free you from financial worries, which will enable you to concentrate solely on the business. I will build and equip a bakery, which will be part of the assets of the company we will form, but we will share the profits on a two to one basis in my favour.'

'But I can put no money into it...'

'You don't need to worry about that. I will finance it completely. We can review the situation later. You will be in sole charge of production and staff.'

'Wait, Mr Stanton,' she interrupted. 'Let me consider what you have just proposed.'

He nodded and sat patiently awaiting what she had to say next. He was wise enough to know that any interruption of her thought processes at this juncture might ruin the whole enterprise.

'Mr Stanton,' Jessie said when she was ready, 'this is an offer of great generosity – one I would be mad to refuse. It assures me and those with me of a secure future in a place which I am sure we could grow to love.' She paused, then stood up and held out her hand to him. He rose from his chair and shook her hand to seal the bargain. 'And here's to a long and happy association,' he said.

'Do sit down again, Mr Stanton. I think we should have a little celebration, though I have nothing to offer you but tea.'

'Admirable. Along with one of your delightful cakes, it will be most appropriate to mark the founding of the Pictou Bakery.'

After he had gone, Jessie called for Rowena and Lavinia. They were curious to know the reason for Mr Stanton's visit and from the sparkle in her eyes guessed it was something exciting. Both of them enthused when she told them, Lavinia seeing it as bringing new purpose to her life in Pictou.

'Oh, Ma, this is wonderful,' said Rowena with undisguised enthusiasm. 'It means we are settled here, if only Malcolm could regain his memory...'

'Don't bank on that,' her mother warned. 'And if he does your troubles may still not be over.'

28

Her mother's words kept drifting to the forefront of Rowena's mind. It was true. Her position with Malcolm was only tenuous. She knew what they meant to each other, but he... There were some attractive girls in Pictou; what if he became attracted to one of them? Should Rowena use her wiles to entice him away from any such possibility? So far his only interest in her appeared to be as a sister; could she change that?

But even as these thoughts haunted her, her own feelings were stirred not by the steady, likeable, brotherly Malcolm who now shared their lives in Pictou, but by the Shetland Malcolm, the one with whom she had shared many adventures along the wild cliffs, and moments of tranquillity in their special bay. If only there was something she could do to bring back his memory; if only some force from outside would spark off a realisation that would draw them together again.

'Aunt Grizel, the weather looks settled, are you coming for a walk?' Kate put the question as she looked into the small room that Grizel used for letter writing and checking the household accounts.

She paused with the pen still in her hand and looked up with a smile. 'You tempt me, Kate, but there are things I must attend to. I've let them slip rather for the last three days.'

'Ever since I came,' said Kate. 'I'm sorry if I've...'

'No, don't think that. There are often times when I'm lackadaisical about keeping things up to date.' Grizel suggested, 'I'll tell you what. Why don't you take a stroll up the path to the top of the cliffs and I'll join you somewhere along there? You'll be in sight of the house for most of the way.'

'All right, I'll see you soon.'

Kate hurried to her room, tied her hair into a bunch at the nape of her neck, grabbed a shawl and fastened it at her breast with a silver clasp which Mungo had given her: 'To welcome my daughter-in-law to Garstan House.'

She tripped lightly down the stairs. These three days had given her a taste of what life must have been like here for Malcolm. She also realised that his concern for the crofters must have been very strong for him to have put his inheritance in jeopardy for their sake. She was careful in the way she made any reference to his disappearance, but realised her discretion was getting her nowhere; maybe she should be more direct.

Such thoughts were occupying her mind as she strolled along the path towards the cliff-top, pausing to admire the views across a mixed landscape of enchanting wildness and peaceful pastures of grazing sheep. There were faraway glimpses of the sea, which she knew would open out before her once she reached the cliff-top. She looked back at the house, marvelling at its wonderful position and trying to imagine how Malcolm would have seen it.

She strolled on. The path dipped into a hollow.

Here she pulled up sharp, her heart racing. A man was sitting on a rock at the bottom of the slope. He looked unkempt, his coat and trousers patched and streaked with soil. His hair had been recently shorn in a haphazard sort of way, as if he might have put a pair of scissors to it himself, and there was at least three days' growth of beard on his jaw. One of his stout boots, which looked the worse for wear, lay on the ground beside him and he was massaging the toes that protruded from his worn sock. Kate was about to turn and hurry away when the man spoke to her.

'Good day, ma'am. I hope I didn't startle you? I don't mean any harm.' The softness of his voice, delivering words that held no hostility in their gentle lilt, stopped her in her tracks.

He did not move to stand up. Kate was thankful for that; it meant that he was not in any position to attack her.

She saw his blue eyes sparkle in a way she knew signified a man younger in years than she had first judged him to be.

'Good day to you,' she returned.

'Sorry, ma'am.' He glanced at his bare toes. 'They've been hurting this last hour.'

'You've walked far?' It was an automatic enquiry.

'Pen is always walking around Shetland, ma'am. Left Scalloway yesterday.'

'Scalloway? Didn't an emigrant ship leave from there not so long ago?' she asked.

'Aye, ma'am.' She detected caution in his reply and in the following enquiry. 'I can tell from your voice you aren't from these parts, ma'am?'

'From Whitby, in Yorkshire,' she replied, and

then added, 'but I have a Shetland name now. I'm Mrs McFadden.'

She saw the light of surprise come into his eyes. He glanced in the direction of the house. 'From up there?' His tone seemed to beg more than a brief answer.

'Yes, I'm married to Malcolm McFadden.'

His eyes widened. 'Eldest son of yon laird?'

'Yes. I was away from Whitby when he came back to Shetland recently to help the crofters.'

'I heard tell he was back.'

She detected caution in his voice again. 'Is that all you heard? I came to find him here, but I've learned nothing except that some people say he is dead.'

'Is that what they believe up at the house?'

'Mr Angus does.'

'Aye, he would.'

'What do you mean by that?'

'He'll inherit if Mr Malcolm is dead.'

'You say "if". Do you know otherwise?'

The ragged man hesitated.

'Pen, do you know something?' Still he did not answer. 'If you do, please tell me. I am desperate to know the truth, and I have to return to Whitby in a few days' time.'

He nodded. 'I have no proof of what I tell you, but I hear things and I keep 'em locked away in there.' He tapped his head.

'So?' Kate prompted.

'First, you should know Malcolm was always good to me; helped me along my way without any criticism of the way I live. Mr Angus was a different matter. Never a kind word from him so maybe you'll think me biased. Second, never believe all you hear.' He gave a wry smile and added, 'Only what Pen tells you.'

Kate latched on to this quickly. 'You know something then? My husband is alive?'

'I didn't say that.' He looked thoughtful. Kate could tell he was pondering whether to continue or say no more, and reckoned it was best not to interrupt while he thought.

He broke the silence that had become charged with Kate's hopes and expectations. 'Two men, Alan and Colin Duguid, have not been seen since that ship sailed.'

'You mean, they are on board?'

'No, no. They've no desire to leave Shetland. I believe they've gone to ground; want to stay out of sight for a while.'

'Why?'

Pen shrugged his shoulders. 'Who knows? Only them ... and maybe someone they've done a job for.'

'Who would that be, and what sort of a job?'

'They do all sorts. Generally unsavoury. Some of them things they wouldn't want the authorities to know about.'

Kate nodded; she understood the implication. 'Who would employ them?'

'Anybody who could pay them. They've worked for all sorts of people, though you never hear them mention names. But I know a few ... among them Angus McFadden.'

Kate was startled. 'Are you saying...?'

'Ma'am, I can't be sure. We'd better leave it at that.'

'All right, but one more thing. Do you know anything about the body that was supposed to have been taken from the harbour when the *Hope* sailed?'

'Very little, ma'am. I believe there was someone, body or not, taken from the water then.'

'Why do you believe that?'

'Sharp eyes, ma'am.'

'You saw...'

'Not me.'

'Who?'

'I'm not at liberty to tell ... gave my word not to. But I'll say this. Only those on board that ship know who or what was taken aboard. You can link up what I've said and find two and two ... make three or five.'

'Or four, and hit on the truth?'

'Be that as it may, ma'am.' Pen was busy pulling on his boots as he spoke. He stood up. 'It has been a pleasure to speak to you. I hope you find your fine young husband. But a word of warning: when the stakes are high, be careful.'

As she watched him go, Kate's mind was running through all the inferences she had drawn from his words. She must do something about them; she would not rest unless she did. But what and how? She could not do this on her own; she would need help. After what Pen had implied, help from Angus was out of the question; even though she had seen tension between Mungo and his younger son, Mungo was hardly likely to take action against him without hearing some solid proof of wrongdoing; confiding in Aunt Grizel was a possibility, but Kate's strong feelings

336

for her prevented her from involving a gentle lady she already admired. Ben and Dorothea were her only hope now, but she could hardly curtail her visit to Garstan House without raising queries that she would not wish to answer. She would have to sit out the rest of her stay here, maybe find clues to reinforce her suspicions, and then disclose all this information to Ben and Dorothea when they arrived and hope they could be persuaded to stay longer in Shetland.

She turned to continue with her walk but was halted by Grizel's voice. 'Wait for me!' Looking back she saw Malcolm's aunt at the top of the slope behind the hollow.

'Has Pen been talking to you?' she asked on reaching Kate.

'Yes. He was taking a rest when I came upon him. You know him?'

'Most people do; he's always walking around Shetland.'

'Doesn't he have work?'

Grizel smiled. 'He takes the occasional job, but generally he avoids them.'

'How does he live then?'

'On other people's kindness.'

'He seems pleasant enough, and he was polite to me.'

'Oh, yes. He's harmless, but he's a gossip. You can't believe all he says. Gets hold of some wild stories. I reckon he embellishes what he hears.'

As Grizel was speaking Kate wondered if there was a hidden warning in these words. She was about to tell her what Pen had said, but held back. That would be better kept to herself for the time being. She nodded and said, 'Shall we continue the walk?'

They chatted pleasantly and Kate could not help but admire the wonderful scenery around them that embraced rolling hills, plunging cliffs and a sea that seemed to hold Shetland in its embrace.

'It must have tugged at Malcolm's heart to leave this place,' commented Kate.

'I'm sure it did,' said Grizel, 'but he left to up-hold a principle that had brought two stubborn men into conflict.'

'Who was right?' Kate asked.

'Only time will tell,' replied Grizel, sadness in her voice at the recollection of the dispute.

Wanting to know about Whitby and Malcolm's life there, she diverted the conversation in that direction. 'But wait,' she said when Kate was about to enlighten her, 'only tell me if it causes you no pain.'

'It won't,' Kate replied. 'I'll be sharing it with Malcolm again one day.'

Grizel made no comment and waited for her to speak about his time in Whitby.

They were about to turn back in the direction of Garstan House when Kate stopped and pointed in the direction of some ruins near the horizon. 'What are those?' she asked.

'They were the crofters' cottages,' replied Grizel. 'I don't go there ... too many sad memories of recent events.'

Kate made no observation but, feeling she would like to see the place that was so much at the centre of the dispute that had brought Malcolm into her life, marked the position of the crofts in her mind.

Kate needed to find the right moment to escape Garstan House on her own, but with her time monopolised by Mungo, wanting to get to know his daughter-in-law better, and Grizel, it was not until the day before she was due to leave that she was able to seize her chance to escape for a short while.

She was thankful for reasonable weather, but having endured the abrupt changes from sun to rain locally, she dressed herself for the worst. There was a strong wind, she had judged from the scudding clouds.

Kate assumed a brisk pace and was thankful, when the ruins came in sight, that her recollection of their direction had been right. She slowed her pace almost to a stop as she neared the place. Charred stones lay upon charred stones; blackened walls rose stark against the sky. Marred timbers had been thrown down in haphazard heaps. Browned grass had failed to regenerate, despite the rain. The atmosphere here hung heavy, as if marking a site that would be haunted for ever.

Chilled by a sense of unease, Kate shivered. The day was not cold but she pulled her shawl tightly around her, seeking reassurance from its softness. Her mind drifted, seemingly taken back into a time and place that had witnessed horror.

'This is no place for you, Kate.'

She started at the unexpected intrusion on this tragic scene. With her heart racing, she spun round, causing the shawl to slip a little. 'Angus!' He stood on the brink of the devastation, a powerful presence despite the ruin all around. 'You startled me.'

'I'm sorry, Kate. I did not mean to.' He let the words come slowly and quietly, allowing them to make an impact.

She found herself unable to respond as she realised that she was seeing a different side to him today. He was exuding a menace that made her cold, and his dark eyes were hard and intent on her, as if trying to read her mind and discover what her intention was in coming to this place.

He stepped towards her. 'I'm sure you find this scene depressing. Allow me to escort you back to the house.'

'What happened here, Angus?'

'I think you know.'

'The crofters were turned out?'

'"Had to leave" is the phrase I would use.'

'But not in this way.' Kate made a sweeping gesture with her hand, embracing all the violence of the scene.

'I am not going to try to excuse it to you, Kate. It is no concern of yours. But what you see here was done for the benefit of the estate.'

'Then it will be of concern to Malcolm, and what is of concern to him affects me as his wife.'

Angus gave a sardonic smile and said, as he slowly shook his head, 'You should not delude yourself. Malcolm is not coming back.'

'He *is* back.' Kate's voice was firm with conviction and she saw a flash of concern in Angus's eyes. 'He's here in Shetland.'

'You are living in a fool's paradise! I grant you he was seen arriving, but he has not been seen since and that, I'm afraid, means he must be dead.'

'I don't and will never believe you.' Kate wanted to put an end to this conversation. If Angus knew anything, she realised she was not going to learn it from him. 'I am going to return to Garstan House and I would rather walk there on my own.'

Angus shrugged his shoulders. 'As you wish.' He stepped aside, bowed and stood out of the way to let her pass.

Kate tossed her head and walked quickly away from the desolate scene that had moved her considerably.

The conversation with Angus dwelt in her mind afterwards. He had seemed so certain that Malcolm was dead, yet had made no offer of proof. Was there something he needed to hide? And with that question came a reminder of Pen's words.

29

'I'm so glad you were able to stay the night,' said Mungo as he shook hands with Ben, 'but it wasn't long enough for us really to get to know you. Kate has spoken very highly of you. Please look after her for me.'

'I will,' Ben assured him. 'And thank you again for your hospitality. I'm pleased Kate was able to spend some time with you while Dorothea and I were shipboard.'

'Her visit was good for my sister. Grizel will miss Kate, as will I.' Mungo glanced in the direction of his son who was having a word with Dorothea. 'Angus can be difficult at times, but not so while Kate was here. Now if ever you see the possibility of visiting Shetland again, be sure to come and stay with us.'

'Thank you, I will keep that in mind.' Ben turned to Dorothea who joined them when Angus wanted a final word with Kate.

'Goodbye, Kate. I'm sorry if your visit to Shetland did not produce the result you had expected,' her brother-in-law told her, soft-voiced.

Kate felt her skin go cold as his smooth voice, lacking all sincerity, seemed to taunt her. His dark eyes carried an expression of menace, emphasising his words. 'Remember, don't believe all you have heard. Don't pin any hopes on Malcolm ever coming back. Better to make a life for yourself free from memories of the past.'

'My choice is my prerogative,' she said, holding his gaze. 'Goodbye, Angus.' She turned away, knowing he watched her as she went over to Grizel. 'Aunt, it has been wonderful to meet you. You have brought Malcolm close to me, and I thank you for that and for your hospitality and kindness.'

There were tears in Grizel's eyes as she embraced Kate. 'I too have memories to treasure; Malcolm chose well. I only wish we knew...' She let her voice trail away, kissed Kate one final time and then helped her into the carriage where Dorothea and Ben were waiting.

In a few moments the carriage rolled away from Garstan House as goodbyes rang through the Shetland air.

342

Once they were settled, Dorothea and Ben were eager to know about Kate's stay with the McFaddens and if she had learned any more about Malcolm.

'Grizel was kindness itself. She is mystified that Malcolm returned to Shetland and did not contact any of them. Mungo was equally mystified. He's a formidable man at times but not in any way hostile towards me. In fact, I think he was delighted that Malcolm had married.'

'Does either of them believe Malcolm is dead?' asked Dorothea, feeling that she had to.

'They cling to hope, but as the days pass I believe they are thinking they must face the inevitable. Shetland, though beautiful, is desolate in many parts; a person could easily disappear, suffer an injury and never be found.'

'Is that what Angus thinks?' prompted Ben.

Kate pulled a face. 'He said he did. I could never be sure exactly where I stood with him. He would ooze kindness, and consideration one moment, but I had the distinct impression that they were only surface deep. There were times when he sent shivers down my back, and I could not distinguish the truth of his attitude to me, which sometimes I found hostile and menacing.'

'That's a bit strong,' commented Dorothea.

'You only saw him for a short period,' Kate reminded her. 'On closer acquaintance, believe me, he is so.'

'It sounds as if you had a disturbing encounter with him?'

'I did.'

'And did you draw any conclusions from it?'

343

Kate went on to tell them of meeting Angus among the ruins of the crofters' cottages and of earlier coming across Pen.

'So there is uncertainty in your mind about what has happened to Malcolm?' said Dorothea.

'Yes,' said Kate.

'And once we leave Shetland, the truth will drift further away and perhaps become lost for ever,' commented Ben thoughtfully. 'I think we should stay a while longer. Your suppositions may be along the right lines, Kate. I believe they could be worth looking into. I could try and locate the two men named by Pen, who sound most unsavoury.'

'But we can't commandeer the ship for much longer. I know what Archie said, but he is hiring her for us.'

'True. We must consider that. Let's take Captain Williams into our confidence and see what he thinks should be done. After all, he knows you came north with the hope of finding Malcolm.'

The two sisters agreed that this was probably the best course to take.

Captain Williams was at the rail to greet them when they came on board. 'Good day, ladies, sir. I trust you had a good journey. And you, Mrs McFadden – a pleasant time with your relations?'

'I did, thank you, Captain,' replied Kate.

'Any news of your husband, ma'am?'

'Sadly, no, but...' She glanced at Ben who took over.

'Captain, we'd like you to come to our cabin.' He gave a little smile. 'Well, yours really. There is something we would like to discuss with you.'

344

Once they were settled as comfortably as possible in the confined space, Ben told Captain Williams about Kate's experiences with Pen and Angus. 'It would seem, Captain, that there may be something to be learned from these two characters, Alan and Colin Duguid. If only we knew where they were and had the time to contact them... We are only too aware that it would be unfair to Mr Swan to keep the *Lady Isobel* longer than is absolutely necessary. Unless you have any suggestions, I fear we must now call a halt to our search.'

Captain Williams had listened carefully to his explanation. 'Knowing something of the schedule Mr Swan had in mind for the *Lady Isobel*, though he told me I should not be bound by it if there were developments in the search for Mr McFadden, we could afford another three days before setting sail.'

'Then, if we are to stay, let us stick by that schedule,' said Kate.

'Very good, ma'am.'

'Early tomorrow I will go ashore and start making enquiries about those two men,' said Ben.

'Sir, if you'll pardon me, I don't think that is a good idea.'

Ben showed his surprise but, before he could protest, Captain Williams continued. 'You'd stick out too much. A well-to-do Englishman enquiring about two Shetlanders with dubious reputations would raise too many questions locally and word would soon get back to the Duguid brothers, even though according to this Pen they've not been seen since the supposed incident in Scalloway.'

345

'So what can we do?' asked Kate. 'Are you implying we should give up our search now?'

'No, far from it, ma'am. I'll go ashore and take Tom Davis with me. He won't stand out the same way. I know some Shetlanders who have sailed with me ... two in particular have served with me on several voyages. They are reliable, tough, know the islands and their people inside out. If anyone can find the Duguid brothers they will, and they'll make certain they get the truth out of them. But I will only approach these two men with your approval.'

'Do so, Captain Williams,' agreed Kate.

'I would also like your permission to reveal to them all the information you have given me?'

Dorothea and Ben looked at her. It was Kate's decision. She did not hesitate.

'Tell them everything you think necessary, Captain.'

'Thank you, ma'am.' He stood up. 'I will go ashore in a few minutes. The First Mate is in charge of the ship while I am ashore.' He glanced at Ben. 'I know you would rather be with me, sir, but it's best you look after the ladies.'

Though he was reluctant to be inactive, Ben understood the reasoning behind the captain's request. He escorted the sisters to the deck where, a few minutes later, Captain Williams and Tom Davis appeared.

The captain gave a little smile. 'Excuse our appearance, ladies, but we'll be less conspicuous in working clothes. I don't want us to stand out where we are going.'

Kate came forward. 'Captain Williams, please

346

don't take any risks on my behalf. But whatever you do, I hope it leads to a speedy reunion with my husband.' She turned to Tom then. 'Bring Malcolm back to me.'

'We will, ma'am.'

Rowena strolled beside the shore. Her mother always arranged for her and Lavinia to take their breaks separately during the working day so that she was never without the help of one of them. Rowena had no complaints about life in Pictou; it was certainly better than it had been in Shetland. There were few restrictions here and everyone had a chance to better themselves, but Rowena still lacked the one thing she wanted – the Malcolm she had known and loved in Shetland. She kicked at the sand as she walked, dwelling on what had been and what she desired in vain. She was so engrossed in her thoughts that it was only at his third shout she realised someone was calling her name. She turned and saw Malcolm hurrying towards her. Her heart missed a beat.

He smiled as he stopped in front of her, panting to get his breath back.

'You've been rushing,' she said sympathetically.

'To catch up with you.'

Rowena's heart skipped another beat.

'Am I worth that?' she queried with a demure look in her eyes.

'Of course you are. You and your mother and Lavinia have been so good to me. I don't know what would have happened to me if it hadn't been for all of you.' He reached out and touched her arm. 'Thank you. I should say that more often.'

Before she could make a comment he swiftly changed the subject. 'Where were you going?'

'I was just taking a walk, it's my break time. And you?'

'I was heading in search of Jamie; wanted to make sure that he approved of some repairs I did. You can walk with me, if you like?'

Rowena's mind raced. Could this simple invitation lead to Malcolm regaining his memory of other walks they had shared together, another beach in a bay they had called their own? 'Would you like me to?' she said quietly.

'Of course I would. I always enjoy your company. And I'm sure Jamie'll be pleased to see you.'

Rowena wanted to scream. Jamie! It was always Jamie. Oh, she knew he liked her; her woman's intuition told her his feelings went deeper than that, though she knew why he still did not voice them. He knew that in her heart she still yearned for the man who stood beside her now. Dare she make the advances she wished he would make? To do so, with Malcolm's past unknown to him, might prove unpredictable. The thoughts spinning through her mind were suddenly interrupted.

'Let's go this way, Rowena.' Malcolm indicated a path that forked to the left. It led up a low incline that rose high enough to hide the coastline ahead.

'But isn't this the better way?' she asked, glancing at the path to the right. 'And it's easier.'

'Have you never been the way I've suggested?' asked Malcolm with some surprise.

'No.'

'Then come on ... you'll get a treat.'

'Why? What is there?'

'You'll see.' Malcolm laughed teasingly and quickened his pace. He reached the top of the slope ahead of her, turned and watched her. 'Come on, slowcoach!' he said good-humouredly.

She took it in good part and put on a frown of disapproval at his mock rebuke. 'It's all right for you, you've done it before.' She struggled to find a firm foothold for the final few feet.

'Here, take my hand!' he called, and reached out to her.

Rowena looked up and saw the encouragement in his eyes. Stretching out to him, she felt his hand close upon hers. His touch sent waves of joy through her; her whole being absorbed sensations she had not experienced since their parting in that special bay in now-distant Shetland. She became aware of his fingers entwining with hers, locking and strengthening his hold on her. Her mind raced. Was this a sign that his desire for the future was akin to hers? Or was she simply reading things into his innocent actions that were no longer there?

'At last!' he laughed as a final tug on her hand brought her up beside him at the top of the slope. 'And what do you think of that?'

But even before his words were finished, Rowena was spellbound. So many sensations sped through her. A tiny bay lay before her, undisturbed except by gentle waves breaking on an unmarked shore-line that ended in a low cliff similar to that on which they were standing. Our bay! The words came silently to her mind and her thoughts spanned thousands of miles of ocean and found the passing of time no barrier.

'Isn't it beautiful?' Malcolm's question brought her back to Pictou.

'Beautiful ... just beautiful.' There was a great depth of feeling in her voice. 'When did you find it?'

'A short while ago. I was walking by the shore, the way we have just come.'

'And you took the left fork instead of the right one. Have you been back since?'

'Yes.' He paused thoughtfully and she saw a distant expression come into his eyes. 'Several times. The first time I came here, I thought I had been here before. But I couldn't have; it was the first time I had been this way. I was puzzled. Why had it seemed so familiar? I returned but found no answer, and so I have kept returning, seeking the reason why it has this effect on me?'

'And still no solution?' she asked.

'None.'

'Why did you bring me here today?' Rowena asked cautiously.

He frowned. 'I don't know. It just seemed the right thing to do.'

'Why did it?'

Malcolm gave a little shake of his head. 'I don't know.' He paused. 'Unless, somewhere, there is a bay where you and I have been before?'

Rowena felt her pulse racing and her thoughts whirling in hopeful anticipation. Was Malcolm on the point of remembering? Was the moment she had longed for about to happen? She felt her eyes dampening. Was this the time to be open with Malcolm and make him understand the truth?

'But that is impossible,' he said slowly. 'You

would have remembered.'

'Oh, but I do.' Her heartfelt words were spoken in scarcely above a whisper but he caught them.

'Then why haven't you mentioned it before?'

'People thought that if what was known of your life was suddenly thrust upon you, it could upset the balance of your mind more badly and then you might never make a recovery. Now I am placed in a dilemma. You seem happy here. Maybe that should not be disturbed. If I recall the past for you, will it destroy your future?' He read in her expression that her heart and mind were torn.

'Surely that is for me to decide,' he replied gently. 'I need to know where I came from, where I belong. I can never, ever feel whole again, no matter how contented I may be, if I don't know what happened before I found myself on board the *Hope*. You seem to know something, Rowena.' He reached out and took hold of her hands. 'What is it you remember? Please help me if you can.'

She bit her lip. Moments slipped by in indecision, but then the pleading in his eyes became too strong to resist. She could not deny his desire to know. 'Do you recall anything about Shetland?' she asked.

'No. I've heard people on this ship talking about it but their words meant nothing to me.'

'Garstan House?'

He shook his head.

'The laird, Mungo McFadden?'

Malcolm looked mystified as he shook his head again.

Despair weighed heavy on Rowena. 'Do you remember playing with me when we were children?'

351

He hesitated.

Hope touched her then. Had she struck a chord, no matter how weak it was? Maybe this was the moment to go on.

'With you?' he queried doubtfully.

'Yes. You, me and Lavinia, and sometimes Angus, though he would more often go off on his own. We never really bothered what he did.'

'Angus?'

'Yes, your brother.'

'But...'

'And Lavinia is your sister.'

'The Lavinia who is with us?' asked Malcolm. 'But she is *your* sister.'

Rowena shook her head. 'No, she is yours. She came to us when she was in trouble and decided to emigrate with us to Canada.'

'If she is my sister, why don't I remember helping her when she was in trouble?'

'You couldn't because you weren't in Shetland then.'

'Where was I?'

'I don't know.'

'Why can't I remember?' Malcolm shook his head and his blank expression forced Rowena to conclude this was a path she could not follow because she knew nothing of that time; had no information about it she could use to jog his memory. Instead she returned to what was at hand.

'Something must have happened to cause you to lose your memory. Wherever you had been, you had returned to Shetland before it happened or you wouldn't have been fished out of Scalloway harbour on to the *Hope*. You were badly injured then ... maybe by your fall.'

'Damn! Why can't I remember? Why hasn't anyone talked to me about this before?'

'We thought it best to take care. Any sudden recollection might have had worse consequences,' replied Rowena gently. 'Can't you remember anything of your life in Shetland before you left?' She knew she had put a leading question, and held her breath as she watched him ponder it.

'Are you sure I used to live there?'

Rowena felt she must immediately counter the doubt that was coming into his mind. 'Yes. Certain,' she replied emphatically.

He grabbed her hand. 'If that is so, then Jamie might be able to help. Between the two of you, you should be able to restore my memory! Come on!' He started off, and Rowena, thrilled by his touch, held his hand firmly. But she wondered what she had done. Would he recall all his past? Would he remember the love they had shared in their bay in Shetland?

They ran down to the shore and crossed the bay. Rowena felt once more the carefree joy she had experienced with Malcolm many, many miles away and what seemed a lifetime ago. Would the veil obscuring his past soon be lifted and their relationship deepen in this new land far from their previous troubles? Her heart was soaring as they climbed the short rise at the far side of the bay. They paused for a moment at the top. The path they would have taken, if Malcolm hadn't chosen to show her the hidden place, swung round the rise on which they were standing and stretched from far to their right towards the shoreline ahead.

'There,' said Malcolm, pointing to two boats pulled up from the water in front of a tiny shack. 'And there's Jamie.' A figure had appeared from behind the shack. He paused and looked in their direction.

'He's seen us,' Rowena said, and waved.

There came an answering gesture of his arms.

Jamie watched them. Rowena and Malcolm. Malcolm and Rowena. Their names alternated in his mind as jealousy surged back and forth. They were holding hands. What had happened between them? What were they doing here together? He waited with dread in his heart.

Captain Williams, keeping his collar up and head down, hurried through Lerwick's streets, which were still illuminated by daylight, late though the hour was. He turned into a street lined by two rows of six cottages facing each other. Reaching the last one on the right, he wielded the brass knocker. A few moments later, on hearing a bolt being drawn back, he glanced along the street and was thankful that there was no one to observe him. The door opened.

'Cap'n!' Donald West was surprised to see the captain of the *Lady Isobel* on his doorstep. 'And Tom Davis.'

'Can we come in, Donnie?' Captain Williams asked.

Recognising the urgency in the Englishman's voice, Donnie opened the door wider and moved aside.

The captain strode over the threshold, saying,

'Is your brother in?'

'Aye, Eric's in here with Ma.' He indicated a room on the right and opened the door. 'Captain Williams and Tom Davis,' he announced.

Eric showed surprise too as he pushed himself quickly from the chair he occupied to one side of the open hearth on which a peat fire burned. 'Captain Williams, sir.'

'No formalities tonight,' said the captain, and gestured to his own borrowed sailor's clothing. 'Mrs West,' he acknowledged the widowed mother of the two men politely. When not at sea, fishing round the Shetland coast or away to the Arctic whaling on the *Lady Isobel*, they visited her every evening before going back to their own homes further along this same street.

'Good evening, Captain Williams, and you Tom Davis,' she said. 'I can tell there's something serious in the wind.'

'Indeed there is, ma'am. I need your boys' service for a few hours.' He glanced at the two powerfully built men who had served him well on several whaling voyages and who, in their forties, could still show the twenty-year-olds a thing or two if ever they dared make a challenge. 'I need to find the Duguid brothers as soon as possible.'

Donnie pulled a face. 'From what I've heard they haven't been seen for a while. Maybe they aren't even in Shetland.'

'If anyone can tell us it's Pen,' said Eric. 'And I reckon I know where we can find him.'

'Well, it's through Pen that I'm here,' Captain Williams explained, and then went on to tell them briefly about Kate's meeting with the man

355

and why they were following up on what he had told her. When he had finished, he looked at Eric. 'Lead us to him.'

'I can't, but Hamish Bulter might.' The two brothers instantly grabbed their coats and caps.

'See you later, Ma,' they said.

'Take care, you four. The Duguid brothers have bad blood in them.'

The men set off along the street, pausing only for the brothers to tell their wives to expect them when they saw them.

'Where do we find this Hamish?' asked Captain Williams as they set off again.

'He has a croft about eight miles to the north. Pen might be with him. If not, then Hamish might know if he's off on his wanderings or is at his own croft, though that's little more than a shelter.'

The door to Hamish Bulter's croft was flung open and the four men were met with a roar that deafened them. 'What d'ye think ye're doing on my land? Oh, it's you.' His voice trailed away into a soft lilt that seemed alien to the broad powerful man with a flaming red beard who barred their way. 'Who might this be?' he asked the brothers, eyes roving to the two men standing behind them.

'Captain Williams, master of the *Lady Isobel* out of Whitby, and one of his crew, Tom Davis,' explained Donald.

'Aye, I've heard tell of her. A bit out of time for berthing in Shetland now?'

'She is,' agreed Captain Williams, 'but I've brought her on a special mission.'

'And that's led you right to the door of Hamish

Bulter's croft? I'm no seafarer. What's your business with me?'

'Hamish,' said Eric, 'we're looking for Pen. We thought you might know where he is.'

'Well, that depends on whether he wants to be found or not.'

'He's in no trouble,' Captain Williams quickly reassured Bulter. 'But he might be able to tell us where we can find the Duguid brothers.'

'That pair of rogues!' Hamish's growl showed his disapproval of them. 'You'd best come in.' He turned back into the croft. The four men followed to find a slight, stooped figure holding his hands out to the warmth from the peat fire. He did not turn or straighten up but said to them over his shoulder, 'I reckon I can help.'

'Then I'd be grateful if you would,' Captain Williams told him politely.

Pen straightened up and turned slowly to face them. 'I heard what you said at the door. I take it this has something to do with the fine young lassie I met the other day?'

'Aye, it has,' Captain Williams assured him. 'We need to find the Duguids quickly.'

'There's an old tumbledown croft that they use. No one else knows about it.' He gave a little knowing grin. 'But Pen gets around.'

'Are they there now?' asked Donnie.

'Don't know for sure, but I do know they haven't been seen around Lerwick or Scalloway.'

'So where is this old croft?' pressed Donnie.

'West Burra, south of Grunasound. It looks like a heap of stones but they've made something of it that is not really noticeable but which serves as

357

a hideaway if they have to disappear, so to speak.' He gave another knowing little grin. 'They have had to use it a few times already. I've seen 'em there. Their absence this time coincides with Malcolm McFadden's disappearance. Make of that what you will.'

'We mean to find out,' said Captain Williams with resolution in his voice.

'If you plan to deal with those two scoundrels I reckon I'd better come along too,' said Hamish. He raised a hand when he saw Captain Williams about to object. 'It'll be my pleasure.' He rammed one fist against his palm. 'Gives me a chance to pay them back for wrecking my boat. Though I couldn't prove it was them, it was their type of handiwork. But,' he went on, 'it's no good us setting off now. It'd be too dark by the time we got there. Better you stay here and we start fresh in the morning.'

Anxious as he was to get things sorted out as quickly as possible, for Kate's sake, Captain Williams saw sense in Hamish's suggestion.

The following morning, when they were all ready, Pen started for the door too but Captain Williams stopped him. 'You stay here, Pen, and then you won't be connected with what we are about to do. And that's an order,' he added authoritatively.

'Aye, and you can keep an eye on this place,' said Hamish, knowing Pen liked to be trusted with some responsibility. 'I will take it as a great favour,' he added, and Pen smiled, grateful to be kept out of the confrontation with the dangerous brothers.

As they headed south from Grunasound, Donnie moved ahead of the other four. Captain Williams lengthened his stride to keep up with him but was restrained by Eric. 'He wants to feel the lie of the land when he sees the croft.' Twenty minutes later they saw Donnie drop to the ground and inch forward to peer over the top of a small rise. After a glance that told them they had reached their destination he signalled to the others to wait. A few minutes later he shuffled backwards and, when he knew he would not be seen by anyone at the old croft, rose to his feet and hurried back to the others.

'As Pen said, it looks like a heap of stones so I reckon it has been made usable on the side farthest from here. Around the croft I could see some trackmarks that look recent, so it is more than likely they are there. There's no movement so they are probably inside. There's no door visible on the back. If Eric and I come in from the left and Hamish, Captain Williams and Tom from the right, we've got them trapped.'

Once over the ridge and starting down the slope to the old croft, they split up. Captain Williams, Hamish and Tom reached the corner of the croft first. There was no visible sign of life and they began to wonder if their quarry was elsewhere. Donnie and Eric appeared at the far side of the croft. At a signal, the five men closed in quickly and quietly. Hamish pointed at a low door and then at himself. The others stepped back a stride, allowing the big man more space. He nodded at them, raised his leg and drove the flat of his foot against the door. It burst open with a loud crash. The five men rushed inside.

The crescendo of their arrival blasted the Duguid brothers out of sleep. Before they had time to realise what was happening they found themselves hauled out of their beds and pushed on to the floor, protesting. They struggled to focus bleary eyes on the five men towering menacingly over them.

'What the...?' Alan managed to gasp, but any further queries were cut short by Hamish's foot pressing him hard against the earth floor.

'Talk, and talk fast,' he growled. 'About Malcolm McFadden.'

Fear sent a chill through Colin Duguid.

'What about him?' growled Alan.

He grimaced as Hamish exerted more pressure with his foot.

'He's not been seen since he returned to Shetland at about the time you two disappeared from your usual haunts,' said Captain Williams. Though quiet, his voice was cold as he added, 'Talk or I'll turn these four loose on you.'

As if to emphasise the captain's words, Donnie slipped a dirk out of his belt and Tom thudded one fist meaningfully against his palm.

'No!' screamed Colin and tried to shuffle out of the way, to no avail as Eric stamped on his hand and kept it pressed to the floor. 'Tell them, Alan, tell them!' yelled Colin.

'Shut up, you snivelling brat!' snapped Alan. 'You'll get us...' He cut his statement short.

Donnie bent down and nicked Alan's neck with the point of his dirk. 'Talk!' he hissed, and drew blood with another nick.

'We were told to get rid of him!' Alan cringed away from the blade. 'We pitched his body into Scalloway harbour.'

'Who told you to?' asked Captain Williams.

Silence enveloped the room. The five men who wanted justice hung on the words that would tell them on whom to levy it. The two thugs knew they faced retribution too, but Alan seized the chance to seek an easy way out and prevent his snivelling brother from caving in too easily.

'If you want that information so badly, we'll give you it and swear to its truth only if you'll guarantee our immunity from prosecution, safety from the man who hired us, and passage to Norway.'

The other men all looked at Captain Williams; it had to be his decision.

He considered the situation thoughtfully for a few moments. Agreeing would save further bloodshed. 'All right. And when I have it, I want your word that you will never divulge the name to anyone else. It is up to others to decide if any further action is to be taken, but I guarantee that it won't involve any of you.' He let this statement also embrace the men who'd helped him. 'Let one word of what's happened today get out, and you'll have more than me to answer to,' he promised.

Captain Williams received agreement from each man in turn while the Duguid brothers were still under restraint. He gave a nod of satisfaction. 'All right, who was it?'

Hamish pressed his foot a little harder; Donnie moved his dirk a little closer.

'Angus McFadden!' gasped Alan.

Disbelief met his words. Malcolm's own kin?

Colin sensed it and cried out, 'It's the truth!'

'Angus McFadden paid you two to get rid of his brother?' Captain Williams queried.

'Yes!' yelled the Duguids.

Though still reeling from the implications of this information, Captain Williams nodded. The restraints were eased on the two men, who scrambled to their feet.

'Right,' said the captain, 'here's what is going to happen. You two,' he looked hard at Alan and Colin, 'will lie low until there's a ship for you. Donnie and Eric will see to that. I will arrange it with them. They will inform you when passage is available. You must have no communication with anyone in the meantime, certainly not Angus McFadden. Once you leave Shetland, you must not return or else you'll suffer the consequences. Understood?'

Relieved to be getting off so lightly, the two brothers mumbled their understanding.

As they left the old croft, Captain Williams's thoughts were mixed; it seemed that Malcolm McFadden was dead. He was not looking forward to breaking that news to Mrs McFadden. On top of that, he would have to reveal that Angus was behind his brother's murder. That would be doubly hard for the widow to take. It was not going to be a joyous voyage back to Whitby.

30

'Hello, you two,' Jamie called when Rowena and Malcolm neared the beach on which he was working on a boat. His eyes rested on Rowena maybe a moment longer than he should have allowed them to. 'It's good to see you here.'

'Jamie,' answered Malcolm, 'we've come hoping you can help me.' He paused to get his breath.

In that moment Rowena quickly took over from him before he could say any more. 'On his way to visit you, Malcolm saw me and suggested I should come too. He brought me across the tiny bay back there and it started him wondering about his past.'

'When Rowena mentioned that I used to live in Shetland it made me think that between you, you could help me,' Malcolm explained. He looked desperately at Jamie. 'I need to know. I need a complete life, Jamie. Rowena tells me people feared that telling me might have worse consequences for me.'

'That's right,' he replied tentatively.

'I am prepared to risk that,' urged Malcolm.

Jamie looked askance at Rowena whose slight nod indicated her approval. Still Jamie looked doubtful. Both of them knew there was a danger of Malcolm reacting badly to what he learned. Hoping for a few moments to think, Jamie indicated a shelf of rock beyond the boats as he said, 'Maybe we'd best sit down and between you you can tell me what you discussed about Shetland. It might be good to go over it again.'

As they finished, Jamie asked Malcolm, 'Has that jogged any more memories?'

'No. But it has given me an even greater desire to fill the void in my life.'

'I noticed Rowena did not mention your aunt,' said Jamie.

'Aunt?' Malcolm looked puzzled.

'Your Aunt Grizel,' Jamie explained.

In the few moments' silence that followed Rowena saw Malcolm was battling with his thoughts. Had the mention of his aunt stirred a memory? 'She was a very kind lady, your father's sister, who came to look after you when your mother died.'

I cried. The two words formed in Malcolm's mind but he did not speak them.

'She did not object to you playing with the crofters' children,' said Jamie. 'You played more with Rowena than with me. I always had chores to do.'

So the reminiscences went on, with Malcolm trying to grasp anything that would generate the return of a life that still eluded him.

Finally, Jamie moved on to a different tack. 'We know your name is McFadden but you are going under the name of Swan. Why? Where did you get that name?'

Malcolm's lips tightened and he blurted out in annoyance, 'Well, that's my name!'

Frustrated, Rowena cried out, 'It isn't! You were McFadden when you left Shetland. You must have heard that name somewhere else.

Where, Malcolm, where? And why Swan?'

'I don't know!' he yelled, his whole attitude filled with frustration. He jumped to his feet and strode away.

Rowena got to her feet to follow but felt a restraining touch on her arm. 'Let him go, Rowena. Don't disturb him any more now. Let him think about what we have told him in peace. He'll certainly do so and maybe, when he considers the facts, something else will slip into place and then he'll remember everything.'

She looked anxiously after the figure striding away from her. It reminded her so much of the day Malcolm had walked away for the final time in Shetland. Tears streamed down her cheeks. 'Oh, Jamie!' she cried, and sought comfort in the arms he held out to her.

He let the tears cease and then said, 'Come, Rowena, I'll walk you back.'

The names McFadden and Swan circled through Malcolm's mind, mocking him as he ran then stumbled up the incline, unaware of anything around him until he reached the top where he bent over, gasping for breath. He straightened up, his eyes focusing on the tiny bay that only a short while ago he had crossed happily with Rowena. Now this beautiful place lay clouded in confusion, like the names that had been brought to his mind in a conversation he was beginning to regret he'd ever initiated.

That feeling remained with him for the rest of the day until he tumbled into his bed. In the dark silence of his room, drowsy from physical and mental exertion, his consciousness drifted. The next morning, when he woke, he found to his intense relief that his life in Pictou was uppermost in his mind; this was his life now and it always would be. The past was relegated to a place where it would trouble him no more.

Then he saw Rowena. Even though she did not mention what had happened the previous day, seeing her brought it all rushing back, and with it came such an intense desire to know who he really was and what part this girl had played in his life that Malcolm was thrown into despair all over again. The frustrated desire haunted him throughout the day, so that, when he returned home to the Murray dwelling, he felt drained. He slumped down into a chair as soon as he stepped inside the cabin.

Startled by his unusual lassitude, Jessie eyed him with concern. 'Is something the matter, Malcolm?'

'No energy,' he replied, 'just done in.'

'You look it. Get yourself off to bed,' she ordered.

'But I have to do...'

'Nothing that can't wait. Off with you. Rowena and Lavinia can see to anything that is essential.'

He knew she was right and went to his room. By the time he was undressed and into bed the information he had gained from Rowena and Jamie was bothering him again. He tossed and turned and broke out in a sweat that drained him even more. How long this went on he never knew. Then he realised it was dark, which only added to the fog that seemed bent on clouding his mind for ever.

'For ever. Swan. McFadden. For ever.' The words kept forming in his mind. They began to take a grip on him. 'Lavinia! Sister!' She was McFadden. His name was Swan! That was the only name he knew. But where...? Then that other word again, pounding at his mind. For ever! For ever! In a half-sleep he yelled it over and over again, his voice protesting angrily against the barrier that held him back from discovering his past. He flailed his arms about wildly, trying to tear it down as the fever tightened its grip.

'Malcolm! Malcolm!' A voice came from far away. 'Malcolm!'

Another voice, this one more forceful. 'Malcolm!' Hands grasped his thrashing arms.

A third voice reached him then.

He felt his shoulders held back on the bed. Reason began to force its way through his fever and his body began to relax. He stared at the three figures by his bedside, trying to identify them in the light from their three candles.

'Kate. For ever.' His words came in a whisper. His eyes focused on each of the women leaning over him. He saw features he recognised, filled with concern. 'Mrs Miller... Lavinia... Rowena.'

The three of them felt a sense of relief and surprise flow through them. A full recovery? They'd soon know. Each of them was filled with joy, but each had caught the other word he had whispered, 'Kate,' and each, in her own way, wondered.

'For ever!' came louder from Malcolm. His eyes widened with the realisation of what that word meant to him as it brought the thought of Whitby to his mind, and that shook him to his very core. 'Oh, my God! Kate ... my wife!' The enormity of his recollection was too much for his overburdened mind. It plunged him back into unconsciousness.

When Hamish's croft came in sight they saw a figure emerge from the building and start towards them.

'Pen's eager to know if we found the Duguids,' commented Donnie.

'Well?' he urged when they were near him.

'You were right,' replied Eric. 'They were where you thought they might be.'

'And?' pressed Pen.

'Made 'em talk,' said Donnie. 'They told us they dumped Malcolm McFadden's body in Scalloway harbour.'

'Seems like it's certain,' said Captain Williams when he saw the doubt on Pen's face. 'They've confessed to us, but they'd deny it if we took them before a court. And we've no means of proving it.'

'Robbery, was it?' asked Pen.

There was hesitation among them all and then Captain Williams said, 'Pen, what I tell you now must be kept secret. They accused Angus McFadden of hiring them.' Disbelief clouded Pen's face as Captain Williams went on, 'An accusation like that against a laird's son, made by two known blaggards, wouldn't stand a chance of being believed.'

'So he and those two thugs will get away with it and leave a poor wee lass wi' a broken heart.' Pen's lips tightened in dismay.

'Angus McFadden we can do nothing about, but I've told the Duguid brothers to leave for Norway and never to come back to Shetland. If they do, they'll face dire consequences,' Captain Williams explained.

'And, Pen, you keep your eyes and ears open for the next ship bound there,' said Hamish. He turned back to Captain Williams. 'We'll see they're safely on board, sir.'

'Thanks, Hamish, and thanks for what you've done today.' Captain Williams shook hands with him and Pen, and then he and Tom accompanied Donnie and Eric back to their homes.

As they parted, Donnie said, 'Captain, I expect you'll have to tell Mrs McFadden that her husband is dead?'

Captain Williams nodded. 'I'm afraid there is nothing else I can do,' he said, sadness and regret filling his voice.

Kate and Dorothea were below deck when Ben came hurrying to fetch them from the deck where he had been keeping an anxious lookout for Captain Williams and Tom. 'They are on their way,' he announced.

Kate and Dorothea flung their capes around their shoulders and Ben escorted them into the open air. They stood by the rail, hoping that the returning men were bringing good news. Kate's first reaction had been disappointment that Malcolm was not with them, and that was not helped by the two men's serious expressions.

Captain Williams stepped on deck and touched his forehead. 'Ma'am.' Tom stood to one side.

'Captain.' Kate acknowledged his gesture. 'What news?'

He dampened his lips. 'I regret, not good, ma'am.'

'You didn't find him then?'

'No, ma'am, we did not. I think we should all go below deck.'

She stopped him. 'Tell me now, please.'

'I am sorry to say, ma'am, that I have every reason to believe that your husband is dead.'

Shock ran through the three people who had been waiting for news which they had hoped would presage a joyful future for Kate. Instead they were left with feelings of numb despair. With her face draining quickly of colour, Kate swayed and clasped her hands together in front of her throat. Ben and Dorothea stepped close to support her. They felt her stiffen, saw her draw her head up and sensed her resolve not to break down under this shattering news.

She looked at the captain. 'I think perhaps now we had better go below deck to learn what you found out.' She glanced to Tom for confirmation of the news.

'I'm sorry,' he said quietly. 'Malcolm was a good friend to me.'

A few minutes later, seated in the cabin, Captain Williams told them what had transpired from the moment they had stepped ashore. He left nothing out except for the accusation made about Angus's involvement. Better, he thought, to spare Mrs McFadden that.

Though her feelings were in turmoil, by the time he had finished Kate was sufficiently in control of them to say, 'I thank you, Captain Williams, for all you have done. You could have done no more.' The momentary pause she left seemed to strengthen her resolve. 'Captain Williams, can we set sail for Whitby?'

'Yes, ma'am.'

They were a day's sail away when Dorothea put a question to Kate. 'Will it be mourning dress for us all?'

'I've been thinking about that,' she replied. 'There is still no hard evidence that Malcolm is dead. We have only supposition, though strong I grant you; the word of Captain Williams but no real evidence, only the say-so of two scoundrels. No body, no funeral, so I am not going to go into mourning dress. And nor need anybody else.'

'But...' started Dorothea.

'No buts,' cut in Kate, 'and no mourning!'

The voyage south brought back many memories of Malcolm. How she wished they had had longer as man and wife, but Kate clung to those memories she did have with an intensity of love that she knew would last throughout the rest of her life.

In Pictou the shock of Malcolm's last words left the three women feeling numb. They exchanged glances of puzzled disbelief and then looked back at the expressionless face that now lay unconscious against the white pillows.

'Ma ...?' Rowena's voice faded away.

'Let us go downstairs,' Jessie cut in, and led the way to the door.

Once downstairs Rowena could not hold back. 'Ma, he said he was married,' she moaned, her eyes wide with desperation.

Jessie grasped Rowena's shoulders. 'He was delirious! Get that into your head. He didn't know what he was saying.'

'But, Ma, he called out a name ... Kate. That must have come from somewhere.' Rowena turned her desperate eyes on Lavinia. 'What do you think?'

'I don't know. I don't understand what is happening. Did he have a momentary recollection of something or someone from his past? He intimated that Kate was his wife, but we know he wasn't married.'

'But do we?' Rowena's voice rose. 'We don't know what happened after he left home ... not until he was dragged from the water!' Thoughts of what might lie behind Malcolm's words, which were still echoing in her mind, set the tears streaming down her cheeks. 'He said he was married!' She ran to the door, flung it open and raced out into the cold morning air.

'Rowena, stop. You'll catch your death...' Her mother's instinctive warnings were followed by her own dash to the door, where she grabbed two shawls from the nearby pegs. She ran down the path to the figure holding on to the gate and sobbing her heart out. 'Put this on, love,' she said, draping one of the shawls round Rowena's shoulders. Then Jessie swung the second one round herself and took her daughter into her arms.

Rowena buried her face in her mother's shoulder, almost muffling her plaintive cry. 'Oh, Ma.'

Jessie let her be for a few minutes then gently turned her round to face the house and led her slowly inside.

Lavinia said nothing but gave them sympathetic looks and placed two steaming cups on the table. Jessie said a quiet, 'Thank you,' for them both.

Silence filled the room but their thoughts brought none of them nearer any understanding of the words spoken in his fever by Malcolm.

'Ma, what can we do?' asked Rowena with a piteous note that tore at her mother's heart.

'We can only wait until he regains consciousness,' replied Jessie quietly. She wished there was something she could do to speed that up. She knew Malcolm's words had been a blow to her daughter and the wound would be deeper if they proved to be true, but better to get to the truth sooner rather than later. Over the previous days she had sensed her daughter's resolve to take Malcolm as he was weakening, undermining the strength of character that had once been such an asset to Rowena. She feared what might happen if it was destroyed entirely, and waiting with those words on her mind would not help.

'And when might that be?' asked her daughter.

Jessie stared at the cup she held between her hands, and shrugged her shoulders. 'Who knows? Be patient, my love. He might never remember what he said a short while ago.'

'But he must ... he must! And I must know if it is true,' cried Rowena in anguish.

Lavinia came and kneeled beside her. She put an arm round her friend's shoulders and looked earnestly into her eyes. 'Have faith, Rowena, but prepare yourself for the worst.'

Her faith was tested over the next three days, during which time Malcolm showed no sign of recovery. With each passing hour Rowena's despair intensified, in spite of her constantly trying to tell herself that Malcolm would make a full recovery. The last words he had spoken hung like an ominous pall over her expectations. With that came anger with him for what she saw as his betrayal of her.

As she left her room on the third day Rowena thought she heard a movement as she passed his door. She stopped and listened. Yes, there it was again – movement. She hurried to fetch her mother but stopped, realising that Jessie was at work and not due home for another hour when the first baking of the day would be ready for distribution. Rowena looked towards the closed door again.

She heard a weak call. 'Mrs Miller.' She stepped towards it then, with her hand on the latch, she hesitated. What would she find? What would be said? The questions brought a bitter reminder of the last time Malcolm had spoken, and Rowena felt her anger rising. She jerked the door open, strode inside and stared at the figure lying in the bed.

Malcolm turned his head. Their eyes met and she immediately knew that his last words had not been the raving of a sick man. She saw recognition in his eyes of who she really was, the Rowena he had known in Shetland. She knew her heart should have been rejoicing at his recovery, that his two lives were now one, but she felt no such joy. Mingled with that recognition of her she saw embarrassment, guilt and the desire to talk, but she did not see regret. A piercing cold gripped her.

Even though he realised the truth, Malcolm had to put the question, 'You heard?'

'"Kate, my wife". Yes, I heard!' She spat the words as if they had fouled her mouth.

He reached out, wanting to touch her hand, but she held back. 'Rowena...'

'Don't, Malcolm, don't plead for forgiveness! I don't have it to give you! How could you do this to me? You knew my reasons. You accepted them, then suggested we wait for five years. I was waiting, Malcolm. Waiting for you. And what did you do? Flew into the arms of another woman! Who is she? Who is this Kate?' Contempt filled her voice.

'I asked you to come with me and you refused.' Some strength came back to his voice in his attempt to defend his actions. 'We made no firm commitments but I still came back.'

'After you were married,' she sneered. 'What was the use of that?'

'I heard of the treatment of the crofters on my father's estate and came to try and help.'

'Too late.'

'I was attacked and thrown into the sea.'

'And it was we crofters who saved you. It would have been better if you had died!'

'Rowena, please...'

'I mean it,' she snapped, and then her voice rose in fury. 'I do! I held on to a dream!' Tears started to come in spite of her trying to hold them back. 'What a fool I was, expecting you to

375

marry a crofter's daughter. No doubt your ... your wife is of your own kind. What a fool I've been, hoping you'd recover your memory and that all would be as it was again ... or even better. We could have been happy. Now you've ruined everything. Go! Get back to your woman, wherever she may be. I never want to see you again! Never!' Rowena turned, tears streaming down her cheeks, and fled from the room.

'Rowena!' Malcolm's call was faint; the door had slammed behind her. His head sank back on to the pillow. His memory was flooded with the recollection of three children running happily on a beach in Shetland, with the sea lapping gently round their feet. Then the picture was replaced by one of two figures walking away from each other, and tears filled his eyes.

31

Rowena ran out of the door and headed for the bakery; she needed her mother's arms around her. Her tear-filled eyes saw no one but she felt hands grip her arms, stopping her headlong rush.

'Rowena, what's wrong?' Lavinia made her tone sharp, recognising the need to calm the distraught state of mind of her friend.

'Your brother! It's true ... he *is* married. Once he left Shetland, he forgot me. Me whom he'd promised...' Her voice broke. She tore herself free from Lavinia's grip and ran.

For a moment Lavinia hesitated, watching her friend go, then she turned and hurried to the house. She went quickly to her brother's room and found him in the last stages of dressing.

'You should be in bed!' she protested.

He shook his head. 'I'm all right. My mind is quite clear; my two worlds are one now. I've got to go.'

'So what Rowena just told me is true?'

'Yes, I have a wife and she will be tormented with worry for me.'

'Did you not tell her you were going to Shetland?'

'She was away at the time I heard that Father was about to implement the clearances. I left immediately, hoping to help the crofters, but found I was too late.'

'But she'll know you went to Shetland?'

'Yes, but how long ago was that? And no word from me since. She'll think I'm dead. I've got to find a ship going to England. I've got to get back to Whitby!'

'How will you do that?'

'Well, I can't stay in this house, that would be unkind to Rowena, so I'll get lodgings in Pictou and find a ship heading for a port where I may take passage for England.' As he was speaking Malcolm had started packing his clothes and few belongings. It took only a few minutes but just before he finished they heard the front door open and close. They glanced at each other and waited. As expected they heard footsteps approaching followed by a knock on his door. It opened and Jessie Murray walked in. She closed the door behind her, turned and looked at Malcolm. Her heart was filled with sadness for her daughter and for this man who had become like a son to her, but then her eyes turned to ice. 'Rowena has told me. How could you break her heart like this?'

'Mrs Murray, I'm sorry,' said Malcolm, with evident discomfort.

'Malcolm,' Jessie said quietly, holding herself straight, hands clasped in front of her, 'apologies are not enough. My daughter held on to the hope that you would make a full recovery and that you two would marry and make a life together in Pictou. This news has devastated her. Her dreams are shattered.'

'Mrs Murray,' he said, 'I am so sorry for what has happened. I cannot thank you enough for the way you have cared for me since I was pulled from the water, and given me a home here with you. You will never be forgotten by me and nor will Rowena. She meant a lot to me when we were growing up, and still does. But now I must make plans to return to England.' He went on to repeat what he had told Lavinia.

Jessie acknowledged his words with a small nod. She looked at Lavinia. 'Do you intend to return with your brother?'

'There is nothing for me in Shetland. Here I have been given a new purpose in life,' Lavinia told him.

'Then seize it,' he replied, and kissed her on the cheek. 'Be happy. I will miss you.' With that he hurried away from the house where he could no longer expect to find a welcome.

Lavinia turned to Jessie. 'If you will let me stay

and Rowena accepts that, I would like to continue to work with you and help to make your bakery an even bigger success.'

There wasn't a moment's hesitation; Jessie held out her arms and Lavinia came to them gratefully. They held each other tight and their eyes were damp when Jessie whispered, 'You are like a second daughter to me. Now go and tell Rowena. It will help her to hear that you are staying. Your brother's actions are no fault of yours. I'm sure Rowena will understand that and will count you still as a valued sister.'

'Thank you for accepting me into your family,' replied Lavinia. She gave Jessie another hug and hurried away to break her news to Rowena.

Once the *Lady Isobel* had been sighted heading towards Whitby, Archie had dispatched a messenger with the news to Rosemary. Standing together on the quay, they were disappointed not to see Malcolm on deck beside Kate.

'I wonder if they gained any knowledge of him?' Rosemary voiced their thoughts quietly.

Once the immediate greetings had been made, the inevitable question was put in one word. 'Malcolm?' Because of the sombre expressions on the faces of the new arrivals, Archie and Rosemary already feared the worst.

'We are almost certain he is dead,' replied Ben.

'Oh, my God!' Archie exclaimed.

'No!' Rosemary's cry came from the heart. She held out her arms to Kate who felt in their embrace all her sister-in-law's love and sympathy. 'Is it absolutely certain?' she asked.

Kate, knowing she would break down if she stayed surrounded by so much compassion, gently eased herself away. 'Almost,' she replied, with a catch in her voice.

'Tell us no more now. Come home with us first,' said Archie.

Nobody objected, seeing the short walk from the ship to the house as a chance to gather their thoughts. Once inside, with the panacea of a cup of tea before them, Ben explained what had happened in Shetland.

'So it seems Malcolm was the victim of a robbery that took place when he was on the point of making contact with the crofters,' he concluded.

'It would appear there is nothing more we can do,' said Archie, looking at his sister sadly.

'I have thought about the train of events as we know them,' she replied, 'and I can only reach the same conclusion.' She faltered for a moment. 'The days I had with Malcolm were idyllic. I don't want those memories to be marred by open mourning. I will mourn within myself, but all the outside conventions I will not observe. Although I will not see Malcolm in person again, I know he is still with me.'

'But what will people think?' protested Archie.

'I care not a jot,' replied Kate. 'I'll do things my way. As I said to Dorothea, we have no body, no funeral ... there's no point in observing mourning.'

Archie raised his eyebrows but knew it was no good trying to persuade her otherwise.

'And before you all make your offers, which I know will be forthcoming and for which I am

380

grateful, I am telling you that I am determined to make my life, as from this minute, in the home Malcolm and I would have shared. I will go there immediately. Archie, please see my luggage is sent there.'

Dorothea looked at Ben. This was exactly what she had expected of her sister. When she had mentioned it to Ben, he had approved her suggestion that she should accompany Kate on her first return. But Dorothea was a little surprised when her sister did not protest. As resolute as she was, Kate obviously found the prospect of going home without Malcolm a daunting one.

'Mrs McFadden! Welcome back,' cried her maid with delight when she saw the mistress on the step.

'Thank you.' Kate stepped into the hall, followed by Dorothea. Knowing her maid would not be so presumptuous as to put a question openly, Kate explained, 'Mr McFadden is not with us, but I hope to hear news of him before long.' She saw that Dorothea did not quite approve of that statement so added quickly, 'A nice cup of tea would be most acceptable.'

'Yes, ma'am,' said the maid, taking their coats and bonnets.

Once they were in the drawing room, Dorothea said, 'Did you really mean that? Do you still cling to the hope that Malcolm is alive? Wasn't what we learned in Shetland good enough for you?'

Kate held up her hands to stem any further questions then she sat down and smoothed her dress. She looked up at Dorothea who was still standing. 'Do sit down, dear sister. I have something to tell you.'

Curiosity filled Dorothea's eyes as she did as she was bidden. 'Well?' she prompted, with a little irritation in her voice.

Kate looked her directly in the eyes and said quietly, 'I believe I am with child!'

For one moment Dorothea was stunned. Then, with her whole face wreathed in smiles, she jumped from her chair, dropped on to her knees beside Kate and hugged her with joy. 'This is wonderful, Kate, wonderful! I'm so happy for you. And of course I understand why you cling to the hope that Malcolm is alive.'

'I've got to in order to see me through this. Though, between you and me, that hope is becoming very very slim.'

Dorothea gave a little grimace.

'Not a word to anyone, not even Ben, until I have this confirmed by the doctor. I will see him soon, so curb your excitement for a while.'

An appointment was made for a week later.

During that time Kate visited her mother whom she was pleased to find in much better form, but who informed her sadly that there had been no softening in her father's heart towards his elder daughter, even when Archie had informed him that Kate's husband might be dead.

Evelyn Jordan, of course, took a very sympathetic attitude. 'After what you have told me, whether you are right or not to cling on to hope I do not know, but if it satisfies a need in you then do so. And remember, I am always here if you want to talk. The young lady who took your place is very amenable and considerate, but she is not you.'

'Those are kind words, Mrs Jordan. I will always remember how much I loved the time I spent with you.'

As they left the doctor's premises in Skinner Street, Dorothea gripped Kate's hand. 'I'm so pleased it's good news! Now, whatever you do, take care of yourself. This baby must be good and strong.'

'Don't worry, I will. This is something of Malcolm that I will always have.'

'Keep that attitude. We must have a family celebration. I'll organise it with Rosemary for a week today.'

'Thank you. Pretend it's a homecoming celebration and I'll announce my news then. Ask all the family including Father, and please include Mrs Jordan. She was like a second mother to me.'

'I know. I wouldn't have left her out.'

With everyone who was present in a good mood after a resplendent meal, Kate rose to her feet and silenced the joviality around the table. 'I am so very pleased to find you all here. You have made my return to Whitby truly special. Thank you for keeping any reference to my visit to Shetland out of the conversation, exactly as I requested. I am only sorry Papa is not with us too to hear that he is going to be a grandfather.'

For one moment there was stunned silence then joy and excitement filled the room.

After an uneasy week, impatient to be on his way

383

to England and back to Kate, Malcolm was leaning on the rail of a ship which was leaving in half an hour for St John's, where he hoped to find another for the Atlantic crossing. His thoughts drifted back over his six months in Pictou. In spite of the ever-present desire to regain his past, he had been happy during his time there. But once his life became whole again, a burning desire to be with Kate had dominated his mind.

Then he saw Lavinia hurrying along the quay and other thoughts were driven from his mind. He was down the gangway in a flash to hug his sister and say, 'Thank you for coming. I will miss you, Lavinia. You have been a wonderful sister to me. I hope the revelation of my marriage did not...'

'Say no more about that. It was your choice. I do not know the circumstances and I don't want to know them. I want no rift between us, only for you to lead a happy life. If ever you go to Shetland, give my love to Father and tell him I bear no grudge. Life has turned out happily for me,' said Lavinia, holding her brother's hand as if she would never let him go.

'I will, if I go there,' Malcolm said, and hugged her to him as if he would never let go.

She felt him stiffen and pull away. She glanced round and saw the reason: Rowena was walking towards them.

Malcolm stepped briskly over to her, wondering what her reaction would be. He stopped a few yards from her so as to try and read her mood, but her expression was impassive. She stopped in front of him, eyes searching his.

'Rowena,' he said gently, and held out a hand to

her. He let it drop when she did not respond.

As if Lavinia were not there she fixed her eyes on him. 'You betrayed me,' she said. 'I hadn't intended to come today, but thoughts of you kept intruding on my memory. I knew then that I could not let you go without saying a final farewell, to cleanse my mind for ever of the past I shared with you. So here I am, Malcolm. And, as angry and as hurt as I am, I wish you well.' But still she managed to fill her words with anger and scorn.

With a smooth action, she drew some papers from the bag she was carrying and for a moment held them so he could see the drawings he had once given her, the ones she had treasured and saved from the burning croft. Then she screwed them up and flung them contemptuously into the water. They meant nothing to her now, were no longer worth keeping.

Seeing his reaction and sensing his feelings, she was glad she had come to the quay. She had ensured that his guilt would remain alive within Malcolm McFadden for a long time.

Rowena turned and walked away, dismissing him from her thoughts and vowing never to let him enter them again.

Maybe her mother had been right years ago in Shetland. Maybe she could grow to love another young man she had known since childhood and had always liked and respected. A man she knew held deep, unspoken feelings for her – Jamie Miller.

She left the quay without waiting to see the ship sail.

Lavinia glanced at her brother. 'I'm sorry I

witnessed that,' she said, sadness in her voice.

'Rowena's attitude is understandable,' he replied. 'Don't hold it against her. Don't let it mar your friendship.'

A movement at the far end of the quay caught his eye then. Jamie Miller! Malcolm felt some relief. The other man cared for Rowena and could bring her happiness if she would let him.

Orders were being shouted on board ship.

'Sailing time,' said Malcolm, taking his sister into his arms. There were tears in their eyes when, after one final hug and kiss, he strode on to the deck, which he did not leave until Lavinia had passed from his sight.

Malcolm eyed the land ahead through the drizzle that swept across St John's. The miserable weather did nothing to raise his hopes. As the ship was manoeuvred in towards the wooden jetties that stretched along the shoreline, he studied the town with disappointment. It looked dull and depressing under the leaden sky. Wooden storage sheds, shacks and undistinguished buildings were set adjacent to the wharves. There was no mistaking that this was a working port, though. The majority of the craft at the quayside were fishing vessels, but maybe one of the bigger ships was bound for England.

Once his own had docked he lost no time in getting ashore. With collar turned up against the drizzle, he slung one bag over his shoulder, grasped the other tightly in his hand and headed for the ships he had surmised were large enough for ocean voyages.

His enquiries dashed his hopes; the ships were all bound for New York. Despondent, he turned away from the quays and headed into a nearby section of streets where he reckoned he might find lodgings. His first enquiry was successful.

Terms were swiftly arranged. In the next two days he let it be known among the shipping companies based in St John's that he needed a passage to England, and also found a temporary job in a shipyard.

The days passed into weeks and the weeks moved towards the end of his second month in St John's. Beginning to despair of ever finding a passage to England from there, he was contemplating moving to one of the ports on the American seaboard, wishing he had done it sooner. Surely a ship bound for England must come soon.

One evening, pondering his options on his way back from work to his lodgings, he found he had wandered unthinkingly along the quays. Surprised that his mind had drifted, he heard footsteps quicken behind him and half turned to see who was in such a hurry. A burly man, bundled up against the inclement weather, slowed his pace and fell into step beside him.

'You looking for a ship?' the man asked him in a no-nonsense voice that carried authority with it and betrayed his origins on the eastern seaboard of America.

'Aye, I want a passage to England, one way or another,' replied Malcolm.

'You aren't from these parts,' commented the man.

Malcolm grinned. 'Accent gives me away. I'm

from Shetland originally.'

'Can't offer you England but I can offer you New York. You're more likely to find a ship sailing to England from there. Worked a ship before?'

'Fishing around Shetland.'

'Nothing bigger?'

'Once. A whaler short on crew for the journey home.'

The seaman looked thoughtful for a moment then said, 'Yonder's the *Silver Star*. She sails in two hours. Two of her crew have jumped ship. Captain sent me ashore to try and find at least one replacement. If you'll work your passage, you can sign on.'

'I will,' replied Malcolm without hesitation.

'Good. I'm Daniel Porter, First Mate on the *Silver Star*. I'll clear you with the captain; he won't make any trouble, he's anxious to be away on time.'

'I'm thankful we met,' Malcolm told him.

'Get your belongings; be on board within the hour.'

An hour after boarding the *Silver Star* Malcolm was hauling the mooring ropes on board and seeing the Newfoundland coast slip away. At first he was eyed with suspicion and doubt by the crew, but once they saw he did not shirk a job, no matter how unfamiliar, they accepted him. The voyage to New York was uneventful, and once he was released into the teeming masses of this fast-growing metropolis he could not wait to be on board another ship and crossing the Atlantic this time. He had little trouble in finding a berth and wished he had come here sooner, but that was no longer of any consequence – he was finally on his way home to Kate.

32

Nagging doubts began to push their insidious way into Malcolm's mind as Whitby drew closer and closer. Had he been away too long? If Kate had presumed he was never coming back or thought him dead, her whole life might have changed; she could have moved on, making a new life for herself in which he would play no part.

And what of Whitby and Shetland? Which meant the most to him? Shetland was his ancestral home but he had left it on bad terms with his father. Could this ever be amended if the pull of Shetland proved too much for him? He had made a new home for himself in Whitby and his marriage and involvement in Archie's ship-building business had promised him a good, stable future, but that had been shattered by his concern for the crofters and its consequences. Could the future in Whitby for him ever be the same? So much depended on what he found at the house in Prince's Place. He threw off all the doubts and hopes that churned in his mind and, as the ship slipped between the piers into the calm waters of the river, went to speak to the captain.

'Thank you for this voyage, and for signing me off as soon as that gangway is run out.'

The captain gave a small smile. 'I know nothing about you, McFadden, except that you worked well on this old collier. I reckon you have someone you are eager to see in Whitby. So best of luck to you.'

'Thank you, sir. Have a good run to Newcastle.'

Malcolm had his two bags in his hands. As soon as the gangway touched the quay on the West Bank, he was on his way.

Not wanting to be recognised and delayed, he kept his head down and took no notice of anyone. He only allowed his steps to falter when his home came in sight, an automatic reaction as doubts assailed him again. Then he was at the front door, placing his bags on the ground and rapping the knocker.

The door opened. The maid paled at the sight of him, eyes widening with a mixture of disbelief and fright. Malcolm was quick to react. He did not want her calling out. He put one hand to her mouth and raised his forefinger to his lips, to tell her to keep silent. 'Mrs McFadden? Drawing room?' The girl nodded. He stepped past her towards the drawing-room door.

Opening it quietly, he saw his wife sitting with her back to him, writing at her mahogany secretaire. He stepped softly towards her.

When she received no response from her maid, Kate started to turn and say, 'Who is calling...?' The words faded as she fixed her eyes on this person who could not be real.

The ghost before her spoke one word, 'Kate!' and reality flooded over her. She jumped to her feet and flung her arms round him, gaining extra reassurance from the contact. Tears brimmed in her eyes as she looked up at him. 'Malcolm, Malcolm! What...? How...?'

He stopped the torrent of words with the pressure of his lips on hers. She relaxed in the embrace that she had remembered throughout their separation. Now it was real. So many thoughts, so many questions, stormed her mind. She wanted to know so much, but for the moment was content to stay as she was, locked in the arms of the man she loved, drawing from his lips the reassurance that wherever he had been, whatever he had done, his love for her had never waned.

She eased herself from his arms finally and looked up at him. 'Come with me.' She took his hand and led him from the room. He looked at her with surprised but eager anticipation when she led him to the stairs. Kate laughed but said nothing. On the landing, she opened a door and let him enter first. As he stepped inside his eyes swept the room. It had all changed. The plain olive-coloured curtains he remembered had gone and plaited cords now held back thin blue curtains no longer than the window pane. There was only one picture on the white walls whereas he recalled there had been several before. On a marble-topped table stood a fancy-edged wash bowl and matching ewer. He was aware of it all in the same moment that his eyes rested on the crib standing close to the single bed. Bewilderment widened them yet more as he stared in disbelief and wonderment at the babe innocently sleeping in the crib. He felt Kate's arms slide round his waist from the back. She snuggled close and whispered, 'Malcolm, meet your son Malcolm.'

He twisted round and took her in his arms. 'I love you, Kate McFadden.'

When she'd twisted out of his hold again she picked the babe up, turned to her husband and said, 'Hold your son.' Malcolm hesitated. 'Go on,' she laughed, 'he won't hurt you and I'm sure you won't hurt him.'

Malcolm cradled him in his arms. The child snuggled closer, looked at him with bright blue eyes and smiled.

'That's a true welcome home for you,' Kate whispered.

They had so much to tell each other that the rest of the day was full, and they kept to themselves by ordering the servants to tell no one of Malcolm's return. 'We will make it known ourselves tomorrow,' they announced.

They let their stories flow in tandem, making the full picture comprehensible at last, but inevitably some questions remained to be answered. These surfaced the following morning while they lay in each other's arms.

'When you were suffering your loss of memory, had you no recollection of me or of your time in Whitby?'

'None,' replied Malcolm.

'Then there may be a girl back in Pictou...?'

'There isn't,' he cut in, rather more quickly than she would have expected but Kate decided to probe no further. Malcolm was here and Pictou was a long, long way away. But she did ask, 'Do you think your sister will return?'

'No. She told me there was nothing to bring her back to Shetland. She has settled so easily into life in Pictou.'

'I wish I had met her. From all the accounts I heard in Shetland, Lavinia is a wonderful person.'

'She is. I will miss her,' replied Malcolm, making no attempt to disguise the regret in his voice, but he went on to ask quickly, 'You stayed at Garstan House, so how did you get on with my family?'

'I loved your aunt, we got on very well. What a wonderful woman, to step into your mother's shoes like that. Your father I found very hospitable after some initial doubts. Angus?' Kate gave a little shake of her head. 'No, I can't say I took to him. I can't really put my finger on why. He is very different from you. It disturbed me how strongly he believed you were dead.'

'Did he?' asked Malcolm thoughtfully. 'Well, he was wrong there, but what does it matter? When I walked out, Father said he would make him his heir.'

'But he didn't. Apparently the necessary papers were never signed,' said Kate.

Malcolm sat up in surprise, sending the bedclothes flying. He looked down at her, his eyes searching her face. 'How do you know?'

'Aunt Grizel told me. Your father confided in her. Maybe she told me because she thought there might be a child even though we were married but a short time before you disappeared.'

Malcolm gave a brief smile. 'And she was right, but Whitby is our home. Angus can have the estate.' He kissed his wife. 'Now, let's give Archie a surprise and I'll get back to work ... if he still

393

wants to employ me. I expect Mrs Jordan's ship is completed?'

'Yes, it is, and she is delighted with it. And I know she will be more than overjoyed at your return. She has been a staunch friend to me when we did not know what had happened to you.' Malcolm started to get out of the bed but she held him back and looked earnestly at him. 'Archie? Well, I know he was going to make you a partner and I suppose he will still want to...'

'That would really cement my homecoming,' Malcolm said, with a note of satisfaction in his voice. 'It gives us a great chance to build a wonderful future here for our son.'

'But, Malcolm,' Kate looked at him intently as she asked, 'do you truly want to deny him his rightful inheritance?'

He took her hand in his. 'My dearest Kate, the important thing is, wherever we are, we will always be together and he will always have our love. We'll let him choose his own road to travel.'

EPILOGUE

Rowena walked happily towards the top of the low incline. Every Thursday, if the weather was fine, she carried up a basket of food to share with her husband at midday. She paused at the top, and for a few moments let her eyes rest on the waves lapping at the shore before taking the final step that brought the hut and the two fishing boats into view.

Jamie straightened from the boat he was tending, saw her and waved.

In his gesture she sensed his love flow across the distance between them. She started down the slope and saw him come to meet her. A new joy surged through her. Today she had some special news to tell him; something she knew he had been hoping would happen, something that would bring joy to them both.

Their steps quickened as they drew closer. Rowena let the basket drop gently on to the sand and opened her arms wide to the man with whom she had found true love and contentment. She was doubly blessed since she had never for one moment doubted his love for her.

ACKNOWLEDGEMENTS

To come to fruition a book needs the input of many people besides the author. I have been extremely fortunate in this respect.

Advice and criticism have come from my twin daughters; Judith throughout the writing, and Geraldine after reading the manuscript as a whole. Anne and Duncan have also been there with their interest and support.

Donna Condon of Piatkus has always given me her wholehearted encouragement and advice, and for that I give her special thanks.

There are many more behind the scenes at Piatkus without whom this book would never have appeared. To them my thanks, especially Lucy Icke who has readily answered my queries.

This page would not be complete if I did not, once again, acknowledge the expert editing of Lynn Curtis who has worked on all the Jessica Blair books. Thank you, Lynn.

Information was readily given by: Rosie Atkinson of the Yorkshire Dales National Park Authority; Matthew Woolfenden, of the Lake District National Park Authority; Nick Thorne, the Access and Rights of Way Officer of the Lake District National Park Authority. My thanks to them all.

Last, but by no means least, thank you to all my readers who make writing for them such a pleasure.

The publishers hope that this book has given you enjoyable reading. Large Print Books are especially designed to be as easy to see and hold as possible. If you wish a complete list of our books please ask at your local library or write directly to:

Magna Large Print Books
Magna House, Long Preston,
Skipton, North Yorkshire.
BD23 4ND

This Large Print Book for the partially sighted, who cannot read normal print, is published under the auspices of

THE ULVERSCROFT FOUNDATION